LONG AGO AND FAR AWAY

LONG AGO AND FAR AWAY

John O'Sullivan

Book Guild Publishing
Sussex, England

First published in Great Britain in 2007 by
The Book Guild Ltd
Pavilion View
19 New Road
Brighton, BN1 1UF

Typesetting in Times by
SetSystems Ltd, Saffron Walden, Essex

Printed in Great Britain by
Athenaeum Press Ltd, Gateshead

A catalogue record for this book is
available from the British Library

ISBN 978 1 84624 131 4

CONTENTS

Dedication and Acknowledgements

To the memory of my parents, my grandmother and the extended circle of family and friends who were the fascination and delight of my childhood. But most of all to Elsie, my suffragette aunt, whose recollections, photographs, letters and souvenirs of the past have made this book possible.

For all those others whose memories I have plundered, and for my wife for her patience in losing me for so long to those far away years.

With acknowledgements to the Times Digital Archive, the Imperial War Museum and the East London Postcard Co for permission to use the quotations and images included in this book.

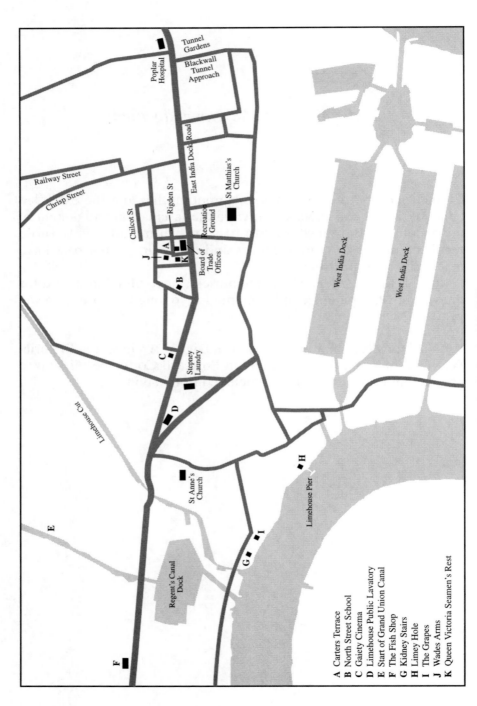

The Family Patch 1932–1940

A Carters Terrace
B North Street School
C Gaiety Cinema
D Limehouse Public Lavatory
E Start of Grand Union Canal
F The Fish Shop
G Kidney Stairs
H Limey Hole
I The Grapes
J Wades Arms
K Queen Victoria Seamen's Rest

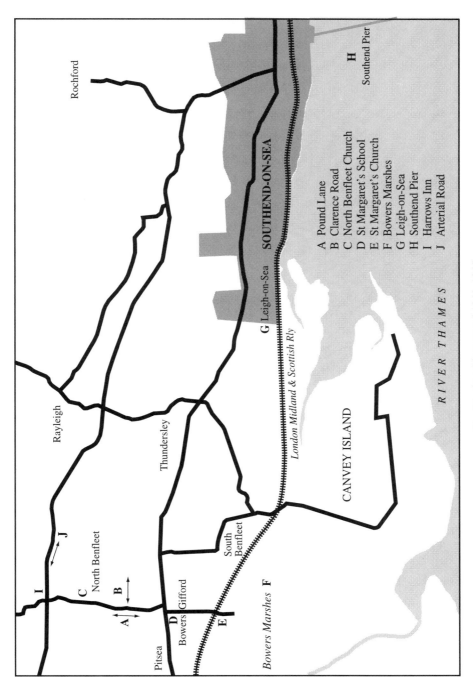

A Pound Lane
B Clarence Road
C North Benfleet Church
D St Margaret's School
E St Margaret's Church
F Bowers Marshes
G Leigh-on-Sea
H Southend Pier
I Harrows Inn
J Arterial Road

The Wartime Playground 1940–1945

PART ONE

PART ONE

1

Arrivals

'No sign of her yet?'

Impatient to enjoy the next juicy instalment in the Stiffkey scandal, Elsie directed the question to her sister sitting by the window dreamily stirring a cup of tea that was fast growing cold. Long familiar with the querulous note in the voice, Kath looked towards the terrace, shook her head and returned to her dreaming.

It was a fine summer morning in the heart of Dockland in the days when Canary Wharf meant bananas not newsprint. A Saturday, when most of the working world was already hard at work, as it generally would be for six long days a week or more, and bloody glad to get it too, but for the two sisters it was a rare day of ease. The sash window was raised, cool morning air drifted into the room, and above the whitewashed wall of the small front yard and garden the upper windows of the Seamen's Rest gleamed in the June sunlight. In the background, half-lost behind the racketing of the parrot on the bars of his cage, a programme of popular music from Hilversum played softly or faded almost to silence as the signal waxed or waned from the long aerial sagging across the backyard. The infant BBC, patronisingly indifferent to the wishes of its audience for a little light relief to start the day, would have nothing to offer for an hour or more.

Stifling her irritation at the delay Elsie topped up the pot, fed a tea-soaked, sugar-dipped crust to the parrot to quieten him down, and resigned herself to wait for Clara's return. Daughter in residence or not, at thirty-eight as junior sister Clara still did the fetching and carrying and had slipped out to collect the morning paper with the concluding stages of the story that for almost six months had kept the sisters and the nation engrossed.

It wasn't often that the family got the chance to be together. For much of the year the two older sisters worked and lived away, and on their few days at home they made the most of it. Breakfast had been a relaxed, unhurried affair of family chat and gossip, but with the plates cleared away they lingered longer than usual waiting for the paper with the latest report on the Stiffkey affair.

As scandals go there would be better, even royal ones, to come but it was the country's first real sex scandal, and the content and timing were right for the story to flourish. The year 1932 was perhaps the worst of the Great Depression. Unemployment, poverty and hunger were rife, and the papers a daily diet of political, economic and social gloom.

Against that dark and desolate backdrop the lascivious exploits of the naughty vicar of Stiffkey blazed like a comet to the delight and entertainment of the reading public. It was the established church washing its dirty linen in public, and before it had run its course even the august pages of *The Times* had given it hundreds of column inches. On the misty February Sunday after the affair first broke in the *Daily Herald* hundreds travelled to the little Norfolk church of Stiffkey to hear its rector preach and get a look at him. Special coaches were chartered, and it was standing room only at the back of the nave to hear 'Little Jimmy' preaching to a congregation that spilled out through the door of the church and into the graveyard beyond.

Mysterious allegations of bribery, corruption and blackmail had whetted appetites, and when the trial began on 30th March the daily reports were followed avidly. The charges were of immoral conduct, the details such as to satisfy the most pernickety of scandal devotees, and the protagonist as choice as they come. Harold Francis Davidson was an undischarged bankrupt, a congenital liar, an inveterate self-publicist and a born performer. Indeed in his early years he earned his living on the stage as the music-hall padre, and after ordination it was only a short step from this to his subsequent career as the prostitutes' padre.

For ten years or more prior to the trial the parishioners of Stiffkey had seen precious little of their rector. Apart from a day or so at the weekend most of his time was spent in London associating with his young ladies: 'bringing comfort to the unfortunate,' as Davidson preferred to describe his benevolent activities. It was purely coincidental and entirely innocent, he would have explained, that those activities found him in Paris, and in bed, with an attractive prostitute; in non-parochial attendance on actresses,

4

always the young and pretty ones, to forgive them their sins; an enthusiastic voyeur at one young lady's nightgown-clad gymnastics; and comforting another between the sheets wearing nothing but his pyjama top. Barefaced in his approach and utterly unabashed by any rebuff he propositioned perfectly respectable young women in public with a banal routine straight from the halls where he had learned his acting skills. 'Are you Miss X the film actress?' was his opening gambit, and astonishingly it worked. Perhaps it was the clerical collar that did the trick. To suspicious landladies he was his young girls' Uncle Harold – a role that came quite naturally to him after his youthful theatrical successes as Charley's Aunt.

With occasional time out for both sides the case ran from 30th March to 7th June and included the final sensational disclosure that on Easter Monday, the day before the trial began, Uncle Harold had featured in 'artistic' photographs with a near-naked fourteen-year-old. The affair was reported in intimate detail in every paper and read with relish across the nation. Only *The Times*, having indulged itself with the rest, was po-faced enough to write, 'Most newspapers are not particularly eager to fill their columns with the kind of evidence voluminously supplied by this case.' The truth was that the newspapers were falling over themselves to satisfy their readers, and most of their readers couldn't get enough.

The guilty verdict on 9th July was inevitable and Davidson faded from view until interest was revived on 5th September when side by side with an act of performing fleas he appeared in a barrel at an open-air exhibition on Blackpool promenade to raise money for his special defence fund. From 10 a.m. to midnight (with breaks for lunch and tea) he was to be on display in the barrel, busily preparing his defence for an appeal. Within two days the show had been stopped. Crowds in excess of a thousand had been blocking the street and charges of causing an obstruction were brought.

His appeals dismissed, sentence of deprivation was formally announced in the solemn surroundings of Norwich cathedral on 22nd October. But Davidson was not a man to pass unnoticed from the world's stage. In August and November of 1935 his star again flickered briefly when he was charged with appearing in a Blackpool exhibition, admission 2d, with intent feloniously to kill himself by starving himself to death unless he was restored to his former position in the ranks of the clergy. Found not guilty, he followed up this one success in the courts with characteristic chutzpah by suing Blackpool Corporation for damages for false imprisonment.

His last appearances were a sad affair played out in 1937 in a Skegness sideshow. Back once again as the music-hall padre, he now shared his stage with a lion and lioness and from inside their cage played out the role of a latter-day Daniel. Preaching from the Bible, and continuing his crusade against conviction to the last, he passionately proclaimed his innocence of all wrongdoing to the enthusiastic public who flocked to see him. And before that public, on 28th July, his final exit was as dramatic and sensational as all that had gone before. Carried away by the fervour and intensity of his own performance Davidson made a false move and the lion attacked. Rescued from the cage but savagely mauled, he died two days later mourned by his public, and even at the last making headlines in the press.

The sound of Clara's footsteps wandering slowly, or stopping altogether as she buried her head in the paper, marked a return that was all too leisurely for Elsie.

'Come on, Clara. You've taken your time.'

'Well you know the answer to that, Else – get off your backside and fetch it yourself next time,' came the answer through the window. Clara wasn't as acquiescent as Kath when it came to strictures from her older sister.

They heard the front door slam and Clara in the passage softly singing the old trenches song.

> *Whiter than the whitewash on the wall,*
> *Whiter than the whitewash on the wall . . .*

'Fat chance he's got if that's what he's saying, the filthy beast.'

Elsie's opinion was the general one. The case had already produced enough disclosures for them to have made up their minds about Davidson. They were broad-minded and free-thinking enough to laugh off and enjoy his sexual shenanigans. 'If a vicar wants to chase the ladies, well good luck to him,' had originally been their view, but later disclosures that he featured in indecent photographs of a young girl had been more than they could stomach.

Clara spread the paper neatly on the table before her, Louisa joined them from the kitchen, and as they sipped their last cups of tea Clara read out the report of the latest court proceedings. It contained no further sensational disclosures, but Clara made the most of the landlady's evidence. Mr Davidson was a big-hearted man, she told the court. His Christian charity embraced mankind at large not just the ladies. He regularly made a fuss of her, called her queen of his heart, and kissed her many times, especially when he wanted anything extra. He didn't just kiss her, she said, he kissed everyone, her, her husband, and even the milkman.

'He should try that with our man from United Dairies,' said Elsie, 'He'd get something extra all right.'

They were still laughing when their brother-in-law looked in through the door.

'Well if you've finished today's instalment and want to see them, they're both fed, watered and waiting.'

This was why Elsie and Kath were home for the weekend: a son for their sister Phoebe and the first boy born into the house since they had moved in at the beginning of the century. They had arrived home late on the Friday and this was their first chance for an inspection. The rest of the family would be gathering in the evening to wet the baby's head.

It hadn't been an easy confinement for Phoebe. There had been complications and a rush to hospital. An exceptionally extended labour had been a close call for the child and the struggles showed on both of them. Phoebe was still in bed, stitched and pale, but had recovered her spirits.

'Never again,' she said as they walked in. 'Not bloody likely.'

They laughed, gave her a kiss, handed her the morning paper open at the Stiffkey report, and turned their attention to the boy. Scratched, scabby and bruised, with skin flaking from flesh the colour of beetroot, it was a sullen and resentful conscript to the family that gazed up through swollen, unfocused eyes at the three aunts who would be surrogate mothers to him on those not infrequent occasions over the years when his mother's maternal instincts faltered.

They stood gazing down at him reflectively until Elsie broke their silence.

'Blimey, Phoebe, he certainly isn't a thing of beauty.'

'Takes after his aunt then, doesn't he, Else?'

Phoebe was clearly back on form and was out of bed for the evening do to wet the baby's head, but by family standards the get-together was a modest affair. There would be no christening. Religion played no part in a family ethos which was at least robustly sceptical, at most enthusiastically atheistic. His first name came by default – John, as it had been for the first son in each generation.

It had been his weight and size, together with an obstinate reluctance to assume the responsibility of living for himself that bred the initial confrontation with his mother and a relationship that was uneasy from the start. There was resentment on both sides which a tentative and uncertain bonding process did little to improve, and that punishing birthday tussle with his mother was to be only the first in the long, long line of skirmishes that defined their relationship over the years.

His birth in a small side-ward of Poplar hospital had been a chance, accidental affair. Built primarily to deal with the steady flow of industrial accidents from the surrounding docks, factories and shipyards, the hospital had been chosen when Phoebe's condition suddenly worsened and was recognised as sufficiently critical for her to be taken there as the nearest place where the necessary help was to hand.

For a couple of days they remained together in the seclusion of the ward, licking their wounds while Phoebe recovered from her labours. Then, cradled in his father's arms, he passed out to join the press of people passing by, and there on the grimy pavements of East India Dock Road where the traffic slowed and bunched to turn into the docks, or drop past the gardens and recreation ground into the long sloping approach to Blackwall Tunnel, the sights, smells and sounds of the East End world enveloped him as they turned for home.

When, a lifetime later, he called up memories of those pre-war years of childhood he found it impossible to reconcile his immediate world with the long catalogue of depressing reports describing the deprivation, degradation and misery of life in the tenement slums and squalid housing of the East End in the 1930s. True as they were of so many areas, there was nothing in the descriptions that he recognised in his own home surroundings. There was no doubt that poverty existed all around him. He had seen what it did to people, but he never felt that he had at any time endured it. If he was wrong that was perhaps a measure of the success of the efforts of the extended family on to whose bosom he fell. That bosom was expansive, protective, and almost exclusively female. There was Phoebe his mother; Moira his older sister; Louisa his grandmother, a few years widowed; three maiden aunts who came and went in the household according to the demands of their work, and a younger aunt who later married and joined the fold with her husband. Jack, his father, was generally more absent than present, either at work or pursuing the political and other interests that absorbed him.

It was a short and mongrel pedigree he inherited, known for a couple of generations only and then petering out in the mists beyond the Baltic Sea or the soggy bogs of Ireland. Far enough, however, to show that Latvian revolutionary fervour and Irish radicalism, with a heavy dash of Celtic melancholy, distinguished the male line. On the female side a blend of English, Jewish and Scottish blood was spiced with a little French – a connection which may have given to the women of the family their lively extrovert natures and love of company.

By 1932 his grandmother (Louisa or Lou to her friends, but Ma within the family) was already a grey-haired old lady whose appearance changed little during her remaining years. After marriage at nineteen her life had been typical of the period and her social class. Years of hard work and constant pregnancies ground away at body and spirit to take a final toll of many like her early on in life. Others, blessed with the right constitution and luck, survived past the years of childbearing to enjoy a vigorous and lively old age. Lou was one of the lucky ones. A slight figure, even when young, she survived nine successful pregnancies, the loss in childbirth of two sets of twins, and the ensuing years of child rearing and unremitting hard work with a toughness and resilience that belied her appearance. As she aged she bent, twisted and wrinkled, but even in her final years, less than five feet tall, she remained a bright-eyed, wiry, energetic little figure with a chirpy bird-like face topped to the last with a good head of hair.

Her education had been thorough, but in the old style, and even in her final years she could recall those pieces learned by rote in the classroom over half a century earlier. She was proud of her memory, and needed little prompting to provide an impromptu recitation. Scott had been her teacher's favourite, and Lou had his lines by the hundred. It took no more than a smile from her grandchildren, a reference to the *Lay of the Last Minstrel*, and she

9

was off. As her audience stretched on the carpet before her, chins cupped in their hands and all attention, Lou was carried back down the long years to the little school in Blackheath.

She gave her performances in character: a little girl embarrassed at being called to the front of the class for a test. Head up, back straight, and hands clasped behind her she began:

> *The way was long the wind was cold,*
> *The minstrel was infirm and old . . .*

As the words stirred memories of those early years her voice faltered briefly, but then she was off again until such time as her young audience had had enough.

Her husband had died in 1930. He was a Latvian, born in a village close to Riga where his parents ran an inn and lived a comfortable middle-class life. Educated and well read, he spoke German and Russian fluently, and English well, or not so well, depending on who reported the matter. Christened Wilhelm Gottard, he was Pappy to all who knew him.

For more than a hundred years Latvia had endured oppression from a duality of German nobility and Russian bureaucracy, but things were changing and radical groups were stirring. Pappy joined them and was embroiled in the ensuing political turmoil. When a repressive and brutal response from the Russians put his life at risk he fled the country. Beyond those few facts he chose to say little of the years before he left Latvia, but by the time he met Louisa his beliefs were uncompromisingly socialist, revolutionary and atheistic.

Homeless, he worked for a few years as a deckhand on ships running between the ports of Europe and America, and it was on board ship that he had his first vicarious encounter with Louisa. A few days out of London on the way home Pappy and his mates were off watch swapping tales and family stories. Photographs were exchanged, and one of the hands passed to Pappy a few pictures of his family: parents stiff-backed in formal studio poses, sisters gazing hopefully from romantic rural backdrops. Possibly Pappy was seen as a potential beau, but the photos were returned with polite but unenthusiastic comments.

Then, in a move that would alter both their lives, his shipmate produced a portrait of the young lady from Blackheath with whom he would be walking out when the ship berthed in London. Whatever Pappy's response he gave nothing away, and in the final days of the voyage home, as they worked their way up the Channel, he not only learned more, but somehow prised the young lady's address from his shipmate.

Whatever duplicity he employed when he made his first call there seems to have been no doubt about the final outcome. Pappy was handsome and dashing, the shipmate less so, and woman is fickle. When the ship left port the shipmate sailed with it, a sadder but a wiser man. Pappy abandoned the sea and moved on to a happy, joyful union and a singularly relaxed married life with a family that grew and grew.

The earliest image of Louisa is a studio portrait of a young lady of sixteen or seventeen in which the fine lace and satin trimmings on her handsome front-buttoned dress testify to a comfortable home background. Her features are open and pleasant, but serious, reserved and unsmiling, and the sepia-tinted photograph shows nothing of the rich auburn colouring of her hair which so impressed her young admirers. If the shipmate's portrait was a companion piece then Pappy showed more than a little discernment in looking beyond the stiff formality it displayed.

By contrast the portrait of young Pappy might have been that of a good-looking young gentleman of leisure were it not for hands that showed strong, stubby fingers and nails short and broken by hard physical work. Handsome, well-built and dressed in his best for a studio photograph, he stands relaxed and at ease, one arm resting casually on a plinth. Hair carefully parted, moustache and beard neatly trimmed, with fine broadcloth jacket over shirt, tie, waistcoat and watch chain, he looks out at the world with a questioning air, as though inviting the viewer to solve the mystery of a double portrait carefully trimmed to show only the young man. Of the other party there remains only a trace; the top of a shoulder at a height and clothed in a material which suggests that it may have been a woman, but who, when and where are unknown. Pappy offered no explanation.

In the years after leaving the sea he learned his trade as a steel erector. A skilful and conscientious worker he was seldom out of work at a time when so many men were idle. If he was laid off when one job finished, he was always back in work within a day or so; which was just as well, for it was much the same with Louisa –

one lying-in over, and she was pretty soon back in business with the next one.

'You talk of the British Empire on which the sun never sets; well I was born in a London alley on which the sun never rose,' was a contemporary reference to the squalid slums of the East End, and from the fresh airs of Blackheath, it was to a two-roomed tenement in just such a Canning Town slum that Louisa moved to start her married life.

Pappy's regular employment spared them the worst of the poverty that blighted the lives of so many, but babies came thick and fast, and money was always tight. In Canning Town three children were born, Elsie, Kathleen and William, and one set of twins died in infancy. With yet another child on the way a move was made to a roomier cottage in Chilcot Street, Poplar. No longer to be found on the maps, it was one of the many streets lost from the face of London. Blasted and burned by the Luftwaffe, it was then razed completely in the redevelopments of the post-war years.

Buried now under the maisonettes and houses of the Lansbury Estate, the Chilcot Street that Pappy knew belonged to a different world. Small, scattered pockets of the cattle and sheep pastures that had once covered the area were still to be found tucked into corners of Poplar. It was not unusual for cattle to be seen moving through the streets from one patch to another and children, jug in hand, carrying home the family milk fresh from the cow.

The cottage had a garden big enough to grow a few vegetables, and there were hutches housing two or three rabbits kept for the table. Inside, the facilities were primitive and insanitary: just one cold tap, gas lighting and cramped, damp little rooms – two down and two up. But it was an improvement on Canning Town, and in Chilcot Street, in increasingly cramped and testing conditions, three more children, Clara, Albert and Charlie, were born, and another set of twins lost.

The usual offices consisted of a privy at the end of the garden, basic but capacious enough to provide space for storage of tools and other items. There was no outside lighting, and if nature called by night then a piss-pot by candlelight was usually favoured by the family over an uncertain journey through the blackness of the garden to an unlit privy. But as William grew older he became increasingly embarrassed at having to use a pot so close to his sisters and with sturdy independence of mind decided that he could quite well make his way to the privy if the need arose. When the call came the night was cloudy, moonless and dark. Groping his way down the stairs he slipped quietly out, felt his way cautiously down the garden path, and pulled open the door. Within the privy the blackness was absolute. Lifting his nightshirt he backed confidently into the darkness and crouched towards the broad expanse of the bench seat.

His account of what followed was understandably confused and emotional. Instead of the familiar touch of well-scrubbed wood on his buttocks they settled on to something warm, soft and yielding. As the something moved, so did William, at speed and noisily, towards the cottage, while the tramp who had chosen the privy as a refuge from the chill of the night took off into the darkness. A lesser boy might have been deterred by the experience and abashed by the derision of his sisters, all roused by the noise, but William was made of sterner stuff. When next the summons came he went noisily along the path and carried a big stick.

After a couple of years the prospect of yet another happy event for Lou coincided with a better job and pay for Pappy, and brought about the move to 4 Carters Terrace, his home for the rest of his life. By then Elsie was old enough to give her mother a hand in the running of the house and care of the younger children. This was common enough in all large families, but the relaxed regime operated by Pappy extended to Elsie an influence over and above the normal.

She was a voracious reader, consuming anything and everything that came to hand, but her preference was for romantic fiction. As the younger daughters arrived Lou had more than enough to keep her occupied, and as Pappy's atheism precluded any christenings names for the babies were never a matter of immediate concern to anyone other than Elsie. She found them for the younger daughters in the heroines of her book of the month, and so Phoebe Rosalie and Irene Olga joined the growing family.

Whatever the nature of Pappy's involvement in Latvia's political turmoil he must have been a reluctant activist driven to it by force of circumstance, for he assumed his new domestic role with single-minded enthusiasm, and the revolutionary became, almost, the personification of the family working man at home. Content to earn his living, and rear and educate the children, his one indulgence was his reading. When not at work or occupied about the house he settled in his chair by the range reading, or trying to, and complaining that home was nothing but an endless sequence of interruptions from his family.

If pressed he would reluctantly leave his books to tackle any jobs about the house that the women could not cope with, but generally, after a long and hard day's work he was content to leave domestic matters to Lou and, as they grew old enough to lend a hand, the children. The one regular household chore he enjoyed was his snobbing on the children's boots and shoes. Using the sawn-off leg of an old table as a base for his hobbing foot he cobbled away to admiring and concerned glances from the youngsters at his ability to hold a reserve of tacks between closed lips without swallowing any.

A thorough education in church schools had left him on intimate terms with the Bible, but growing political awareness and the dead, reactionary hand of the Church in Latvia led him eventually to atheism and his radical left-wing views. As a Russian foreign subject who never sought naturalisation, however, he thought it wise to forgo any active involvement in British politics, although he retained his political interests and continued to attend meetings.

For a late-Victorian father he exercised a well-directed but benign and broad-minded influence. He saw to it that the children were well educated and had the encouragement and means for further self-education around them. Only in matters of religion did a firm edict run: he permitted no christenings and no church attendance.

As the children matured he was satisfied with their general good sense, and his daughters when young ladies were allowed to do pretty much as they liked. Such a relaxed attitude bred independence of mind and action, however, and Elsie, who most took after him, was not slow to exercise it. Leaving school at fourteen she entered immediately into domestic service and moved quickly through a couple of places until at seventeen she settled with a Mr and Mrs Marshall. They were a pleasant couple with no children of their own, and as Elsie was their only servant seem to have been rather more kind and attentive to her than might otherwise have been the case. They were also regular churchgoers, however, and within a short space of time, and no doubt with a little gentle pressure on Elsie, now beyond Pappy's influence and moral support, had persuaded her to join them at the Sunday services.

Whether it was loyalty to her employers, the novelty of the affair, or simply the theatricality of the High Church service that appealed, Elsie never said, but one thing led to another. In no time at all Elsie had been christened, the Marshalls acting as godparents, and in due course was confirmed as a fully paid-up, card-carrying member of the Church of England. Pappy, of course, was not informed that Elsie had crossed the floor in this way, and as long as she was with the Marshalls her occasional trips back home produced no conflict of interest or conscience.

Her time with the Marshalls over, however, she returned to employment and home in Poplar. There she eased Lou's burden of work by taking responsibility for the youngsters and once again embarked on a demonstration of her own firm independence of mind. In something akin to a fit of religious fervour, and seeing herself in loco parentis, she surreptitiously set about having the youngsters christened. For the toddlers this was nothing special, just a little trip out with big sister and her friends. They returned from the experience with no outward or visible sign that they were damaged goods, and Pappy remained unaware of the viper he was nursing in his bosom.

For Elsie, however, religion was a little like measles, and once beyond contact with the Marshalls and their influence it weakened rapidly and she was soon fully recovered. Her eventual confession to Pappy was heard out in all seriousness, but answered with a grin and a shrug of indifference.

As the sons and daughters grew up, married and moved into their own homes the large ground-floor rooms came into use more and more frequently for family celebrations and gatherings. Although Pappy enjoyed and often funded these he was content to let the youngsters get on with the partying and stay with a book in his own corner of the lower living room. From there he controlled and dispensed little drops of the special tiddly that he bought for the occasion from the family's favoured off-licence.

L. Frumkin & Co (Wine and Spirit Dealers) of 162 Commercial Road East was a retail institution providing a service which gave meaning and substance to the phrase 'the good old days'. In much the same way as cheese shops provide thin slivers of their provisions to sample, Frumkins dispensed 'tasters' to those whose regular custom they valued. This special dispensation included the Lagsdings, and so a few days before a party was to be held Elsie and one or two others would call in at Frumkin's to taste and select two or three specials for the coming celebration. Lou's 'girls' didn't drink a lot, but they knew what they liked and when the occasion arose they had a taste for the right stuff. Kümmel, kirsch, Cherry Heering, Frumkin's special Tokay, chartreuse green and yellow, advocaat – always Warnink's, crème de menthe and Grand Marnier with perhaps a schnapps or aquavit added for Pappy and the men: they had a run at them all at one time or another before settling on their favourites.

Pappy would be told of their choices, arrange the purchases to which he added one or two of his own and on the night of the celebrations sit with his few special bottles in the cupboard by his side. As the songs and sounds of the gathering drifted down the stairs, or the ceiling above his head gently oscillated to the tread of young feet he would sit quietly reading and sipping his own particular fancy. Every so often a couple of the young ladies would detach themselves from the crush and slip downstairs for a word or two with 'poor old Pappy' – who was all alone by himself. Pappy received a greeting kiss, a bottle emerged from the cupboard, and the ladies returned to the fray refreshed, flushed and perhaps a little less steady on their feet.

For Pappy the celebrations ended on his seventy-third birthday, just three years after retirement, when he died suddenly after the briefest of illnesses. In matters of death most people, especially in the East End, were then firm traditionalists: for all but the smallest percentage burial was the only option to be considered, with a good 'send-off', often at crippling expense, considered obligatory by most. Pappy, in accordance with his known wishes, was cremated following the simplest of ceremonies. His coffin, covered in the red flag, was carried from the house by his sons and sons-in-law. There were no flowers, no religious service; just an address to the mourners before the cremation.

At a time when the cremation process was still viewed by many with distaste, even suspicion, there were none of today's soothing, hushed arrangements and well-oiled mechanisms that divert the mind from the final reality of the procedure. There were still relatively few cremations, and regulations were relaxed. When the rest of the family dispersed the sons stayed behind. They saw the coffin into the furnace chamber and through its sight holes watched

16

the start of the process. Pappy would have commended their scientific curiosity.

If Pappy was the spirit of the house and the main provider, Lou was the guts, flesh and sinews driving all the domestic operations. By those who knew her when she was young she was thought to be a pretty woman. Eighteen years old, and almost ten years younger than Pappy when they met, she was a slight little thing with curly auburn hair and a lively personality that all the years of child rearing and family management did little to diminish.

Nor at the time had she been short of other admirers. A few days before Pappy appeared on the doorstep one of her followers, with an eye to his own advancement, made her the gift of a fancy hat piped round with golden cord. Pappy, arriving newly paid off with a few pounds stuffing his pocket, swept her off her feet, showed her the town dolled up in his rival's hat much to her delight, and rounded their evening off with a box at the Queen's Theatre.

Those days soon ended and thirty years of childrearing and housekeeping began. The wages coming in may have been regular, but it wasn't easy to keep pace with outgoings, and she had quickly to learn the domestic arts and crafts to manage on the money. Dresses and clothes were made from scratch or altered from second-hand items bought in, but even as the daughters grew up she made no real attempt to teach them either hand needlework or how to operate the old treadle sewing machine. For whatever reasons she was content to soldier on by herself. 'She was a proper old slave in a way,' said Elsie.

Food was never short in the household and if meals were basic there was always a hot dinner, even if it was little more than potato and a baked pudding, and as the children grew up and moved out to work their contributions to the household budget made life much easier.

Unlike Pappy, Louisa was not a non-believer. Her background was that of a conventional Church of England family, and she retained whatever religious belief she had, but there were never any arguments about religion. Pappy went his way, she went hers, but it did not extend to church attendance, and her Mothers' Meetings were the closest she came to any sort of religious gathering.

17

Home was a large four-storeyed, terraced house standing at the centre of a small quadrangle of land just a short walk from the gates of the West India Docks. To the south, fronting East India Dock Road, lay the long range of the offices of the Board of Trade. Formerly a sailors' home, it was a handsome property standing within grounds closed off to the front and sides by low walls topped with wrought-iron railings and at the back by a longer, higher wall. The stone facade, shaded by five or six tall London plane trees, was dirty and discoloured, but a central portico of Doric columns flanked by two wings of solid conservative architecture still sought to preserve a measure of Establishment authority in the heart of a radical, working-class borough. It was the buildings of the Board of Trade that released the few houses built behind them from the depressing pattern imposed on the rows and rows of identical terraced houses nearby, where doors from front living rooms opened directly on to the pavement, and cramped little yards backed on to those of the houses in the neighbouring street.

Rigden Street marked the northern side of the quadrangle. At its western end stood a few two-storey houses with well-tended gardens running down to the rear boundary wall of the Board of Trade. The family home was the last of four houses in Carters Terrace, a short cul-de-sac cut into the heart of the land.

Along the terrace the ground fell away slightly, with entry to each of the houses made up steps that gradually increased in number. By number four the fall in the land was such that the house incorporated a half-basement and, with three floors above, was larger than any other house in the area. By estate agents it might have been described as enjoying extensive grounds and a superior outlook. In relative terms, and by most East End comparisons, that would have been true. As the last house in the terrace the area at the front, instead of serving as a common access way, was closed off by a low wicket fence. Broken and rickety, all traces of paint had long since been scoured off by sun and weather, but it served to mark off a small garden area in front of the house that distinguished it from the others in the terrace. In one corner an ancient pear tree leaned for support against the wall and optimistically burst into leaf and blossom each spring, but as summer progressed seemed to be overwhelmed by the futility of it all and cast off such hard, malformed fruits as it carried. It held its leaves, however, and so survived from year to year to provide a welcome patch of shade in summer. At the foot of garden walls whitewashed each spring narrow footing beds were carefully tended and weeded by Louisa. She popped in a few slips from neighbouring gardens, sprinkled them round with cottage-garden seeds saved from the previous year, and by June or July it looked almost rural. Flowers that brought some perfume into the garden were her favourites: sweet williams or wallflowers, but in particular tobacco plants and night-scented stocks that would sweeten the evening air in the little courtyard.

The upper windows of the house overlooked the gardens of the Rigden Street houses where city gardeners, many of whom had never seen a real country garden, made the best of well-worked but exhausted London soil, and competed strongly for the piles of steaming manure dropped by the horses that were still a common sight pulling their delivery carts around the back streets. Beyond the gardens, in Jeremiah Street, stood the Queen Victoria Home for Seamen, and to its doors the transient, floating population of the docks brought an air of mystery and romance with the customs, dress and languages of the nations of the world.

When, a few years after the war, the boy returned as a young man to the site of his childhood home the line of the terrace could still be seen, but the houses that survived the war had disappeared in the clearances of peace. Of the pear tree and the little garden there was no trace. Nothing remained but two walls to which the whitewash still clung in a flaking, dirty, grey coat except where the thin, black ghost of a trunk marked the line where the pear tree, leaning hard against the bricks, had frustrated the best efforts of the painters. The Board of Trade building survived, but in later years its handsome portico was lost in the process of conversion to flats, and within its walls systems analysts and computer programmers, home from their high-rise offices in the City, rubbed shoulders with the ghosts of greasers, stokers and seacooks from the nations of the world, and gazed out across the fragmentary remains of the old Docklands to the new commercial visions of Canary Wharf.

To the south of the house, through the gardens of the recreation ground, stood the old Poplar workhouse building, a Dickensian relic still flourishing under a workhouse master described as a dictator by the few recalcitrant inmates who had the temerity to refuse to obey his directions and got twenty-one days hard labour from the local magistrate to give the matter second thoughts.

Beyond the workhouse a tangle of railway sidings looped like a noose across the neck of the Isle of Dogs, bounded to the south by the river and the perimeter road that ran in a great sweep around the West India and Millwall docks. Despite the high walls that guarded the wealth of the warehouses and stores, it was still possible through open gates to catch glimpses of the life hidden within: of barrels, crates and sacks piled high by the dockside, of the swing and dip of cranes and the chaotic bustle of dockers, carts and trains. From the perimeter road narrow byways and lanes ran down towards the riverside where the casual passer-by could wander on to the foreshore, stroll the embankments with views of the wharves, jetties and piers, and the river traffic sweeping up and down the Thames, or idle away a quarter-hour while a couple of terrier tugs snapped and nudged at the heels of a freighter being warped and hauled into the corseting constraints of a river lock.

Down the centre of East India Dock Road double lines of tram tracks, polished and gleaming, receded into a haze of industrial pollution and dust from passing traffic: one way to Blackwall, the East India Docks and the country, the other to the City and the West End. It was an area the family knew well. Twenty years earlier Jack's father had been part of its daily traffic, travelling the main roads and into the back streets, alleys, workshops and warehouses of Limehouse, Poplar and Millwall, loading and delivering from his horse-van wherever the trade took him. Once a week he travelled beyond the docks into the growing suburbs, and on through open country. Finally, in a Dagenham that was little more than a country village, he delivered goods from the docks and London warehouses to the inns and shops, and loaded fruit and vegetables from Dagenham's market gardens for delivery back to the East End. At weekends and school holidays Jack was there too, a young boy assisting with his father's work; getting to know a London that still held much of its Victorian past, and travelling through the last of its rural fringes before the suburbs swamped them for ever.

Despite all the commercial and industrial activity that surrounded the docks there were still little oases of calm: secluded courts and alleys where life could be lived in relative peace and

20

tranquillity. Carters Terrace was one of these. Although close to the press of traffic on the East India Dock Road it was screened from much of the noise by the long bulk of the Board of Trade. Throughout the day, above the low hum of motor traffic as it rose and fell, the clack of hooves, the clanking passage of a tram or the rumble of steel-shod cartwheels played out their own interweaving counterpoint and variations. Even on the main roads there were relatively few private cars. In the minor side streets around the terrace there were none, and when new flats were planned for Vesey Street it wasn't garages that were proposed but barrow sheds for costermongers. For most of the day the streets were empty; a safe, convenient and interesting playground for children except for an occasional visit from horse and cart – a milkman, coalman or rag-and-bone man making the rounds, or a brewer's dray on its way to the corner pub.

And so the young boy's early memories were of quiet, sunny times playing within the safety of the wicket fence, with just a few reminders of the world outside drifting in from beyond the walls of the garden, and one of the women in his life keeping an eye on him from an open window and singing (they were great singers all of them) snatches from *Maytime*, *Rose Marie* or one of the many operettas that entertained the theatregoers of the West End.

For those around him prospects looked less sunny. In Poplar more than 20 per cent of families still lived in poverty, and unemployment stood at one in five. The Missions for Seamen solicited cast-off clothing and boots for the down-and-out mariners who tramped the streets looking for work. Appeals were made for contributions to feed the hungry poor, for five shillings to send a Dockland mother for a day by the sea, or for old clothes, toys or books regardless of condition. Those were matters enough to occupy most people for the foreseeable future and beyond such domestic issues no threat was perceived.

Even for those who had the inclination to look further than the tribulations of the Stiffkey vicar or the first-ever test match against India, the political turmoil reported from Germany seemed remote and of little concern. Although the inner columns of their dailies showed fascism firmly entrenched in Italy and on the march and flourishing in Germany, Herr Hitler, Dr Goebbels and Captain Goering (as yet languishing in the middle ranks) would be accorded the courtesy of their titles for many years to come. But between them and an SA army of 400,000 brown-shirted Storm Troopers they were already orchestrating a reign of terror, violence, disorder and political murders that within twelve months would see Hitler Chancellor, democracy abandoned, the Nazis with absolute dictatorial powers, and the first steps taken on the relentless descent into six long years of war.

2

Rescue the Perishing

In East London at the turn of the nineteenth-century contraception had yet to come into its own and large families were still the norm. Jack was one of seven children, Phoebe one of nine, and after their wedding it was to her childhood home that they returned to start married life. Those members of her family who had already married and set up home for themselves lived nearby, as did most of their friends. When occasions arose for joint celebrations, and they frequently did, the size and character of the family house made it ideal.

From the terrace a flight of seven or eight stone steps edged with wrought-iron railings led up to a balcony, the front door, and a narrow passage through the house. Reserved exclusively for formal and festive occasions, the steps were a public declaration of Lou's domestic efficiency and pride. Once a week, on her knees, she scoured them with hearthstone, vigour and liberal quantities of soapy water. Beneath the glaze of autumn rain they glowed. In the midday sun of summer they shimmered and dazzled. 'Not for public use,' was the message, and traders, hawkers and itinerants needed no notice to direct them to the common entrance through the wicket gate into the front yard. There, beneath the balcony, a few steps led down to the door of the half-basement, and just along the passage, into a good-sized room with a wide sash window, its sill at garden level.

This was the heart of the house where Pappy had sat with his books and dispensed his liquid favours. Nominally Lou's own living room, it was in practice in common use: the place where visitors or family settled down most comfortably. In the chimney space on the far wall the gleaming black-iron range was a buffed, polished and black-leaded showpiece. In the early days it had handled all the cooking of the house, but in later years a gas cooker in the scullery

23

took over. The fire was now used only to heat the room, and the ovens to warm plates, dishes and, just once, a kitten that had slipped in while a door was open, but emerged little the worse for its gentle roasting when the source of its mewings was finally located. Cupboards and shelves filled the recesses on either side of the chimney breast.

A long, lace-fringed mantelpiece over the range carried vases, a clock and small pieces of brass and copper ware, test pieces of work by Lou's sons during craft training after school. At each end the decorated brass brackets and sconces of gaslight fittings were retained and kept polished, although electricity had long been installed. Above the mantelpiece the last photograph of Pappy looked down after death with the same good-hearted tolerance of his family's idiosyncrasies that he had shown in life. It showed him in his late sixties, casually dressed in comfortable, well-worn clothes. The thick head of hair was untouched by any signs of grey, but the beard had gone, and the neatly trimmed upper-lip hair of the youthful picture had thickened to a luxuriant walrus moustache. The same questioning, slightly challenging, expression of the earlier portrait remained, and he looked in all respects a man entirely at ease with himself and his values.

Against the wall opposite the window, on a sideboard overhung by two prints of scenes from old Amsterdam, Lou displayed a couple of treasured blue meat dishes, two or three large Staffordshire figures, a heavy green-glass paperweight flecked with a whirling pattern of bubbles, and a varied collection of photographs, mostly her daughters as young women before and during the First World War. A broad chenille-covered dining table stood beneath the window and a mixed collection of dining and easy chairs completed the furnishings. Close to the warmth of the range, and handy for the fire-irons, Lou had her old American-style spring rocking chair, its double rockers a painful trap for any young fingers that played with it carelessly in defiance of cautions and warnings. For all her visiting grandchildren that room was the most comfortable, cosy and secure refuge in the house.

The passage led on to Phoebe's smaller living room with gate-legged table and dining chairs, a couple of low-backed easy chairs before the fireplace, a small sideboard against the wall, and behind the door Jack's home-made bookcase stuffed with books, pamphlets and papers. The furniture was plain and simple apart from a

24

pretty display cabinet that had been bought second-hand as a wedding present. Shallow, glass-fronted and elegant, it stood on slender legs and displayed the small collection of knick-knacks built up over the years. Jack had an eye for pieces of quality and picked up for very little a few china or porcelain items that came in time to be well regarded for their value as well as their looks. They stood between the family photographs: wedding groups, serious, formal and proper; supplemented as the years passed by Moira in her dancing years poised in arabesque and tutu; and John as a young boy shoulder to shoulder with a senior and very serious chimpanzee following a London Zoo chimps' tea party.

Outside, a little beyond the narrow sash windows, and to one side of the stone-paved backyard, stood the family bathhouse, a domestic amenity of rarity and distinction in an area where few, if any, bathrooms existed. Solidly constructed in timber by the men of the family it looked to be no more than a garden shed, but what it lacked in elegance it made up for in convenience. The bath itself was the pride of the household. Shining in white vitreous enamel, substantial, luxuriously deep and finished with two gleaming brass taps, it stood on elegantly cast clawed feet – a sanitary jewel lost in the unlovely ad hoc arrangements that surrounded it: the roughly whitewashed timbers and boarding, the thick battered lead piping bringing in the cold water and draining the bath to a sump in the yard, and the looping cable across the roof timbers extending the lighting from the house. A gas boiler, all copper tubing, brass taps and galvanised tanks, provided constant hot water.

Water, steam, gas and electricity – it was potentially a lethal combination installed when planning constraints and building regulations were non-existent, but they suffered no casualties. Unheated, apart from the boiler, the bathhouse could be a bracing, misty experience in winter, but the privacy it provided was greatly valued, and its popularity extended beyond the immediate family to friends who called by appointment and made their sixpenny contribution to the cost of gas when they left.

It was not entirely without its problems. The gas boiler was temperamental; prone to spectacularly noisy but otherwise harmless blow-outs, and occasional extended failures that forced a return to the public baths. Close by on the East India Dock Road they were housed in one of Poplar's many fine municipal buildings. Recently built and christened East India Hall, their cost had occasioned some criticism. 'Baths deluxe for navvies and dockers' was just one of the snide comments, but the tens of thousands still living in slums devoid of any such facilities had no complaints.

Upstairs in the hall the cost of the slipper baths was much the same as visitors paid to use the family bathhouse, and would have included towel and soap, but where personal hygiene was concerned Phoebe had an inbuilt antipathy to the use of any public facility. When boiler failure left no option but the public baths she took her family there reluctantly armed with personal soap, towel and the wherewithal to scour out the bath before it was used despite the fact that it would already have been cleaned.

'I'm not having my kids getting into a bath following some lousy old scruff from God knows what fleapit,' was her response to others who were less fastidious. She felt the same about public lavatories and was blessed with a bladder that was the envy and admiration of her sisters. On family outings when they were regularly seeking relief, Phoebe would sail through a twelve-hour day without turning a hair, and then be in no rush about the matter when they returned home.

If the public baths were an inconvenience for the family they proved a novel and fascinating experience that was the young boy's delight. Warm, steamy and odorous, they were visited by family groups almost as a day out, and echoed with the shouts of children, loud, unflattering comments on the temperature of the water, and the conversations of the regulars over the walls of their individual cubicles. Emboldened by the cloistered anonymity these were conducted noisily and in surprisingly intimate detail: a running background entertainment to the noise, steam and water. They were potentially embarrassing, too: it was not unknown for a reproving cry to sound out from a cubicle nearby. 'Oi! You keep you gutter gossip about your neighbours to yourself, and don't take bloody liberties.' That was enough to quieten things down and it never came to blows.

Views from Poplar back windows were seldom a life-enhancing experience, and from Phoebe's living-room window the outlook was no exception: an expanse of sky criss-crossed by a tangle of aerial wires; the chimneys, slates and upper windows of the houses at the back; three whitewashed brick walls strung with clothes lines and hung with the two galvanised baths used on washdays; a large

26

mangle; and at the back of the yard a brick-built lavatory in one corner and the dog kennel in the other.

Terry, its resident, was an Airedale with a temperament that led many visitors to wonder that he continued to be given yard-room, but in truth he had a generosity of spirit, nobility of character and a touch of the eccentricity that ran in the family at large. His thought processes, which had the clarity and elegance that distinguish the minds of the best of dogs, had determined that the centre of the yard, covering the shortest route from back door to lavatory, was his. He recognised the restraining limits of his chain, however, and so an unchallenged right of passage to the lavatory existed by an L-shaped route along two walls and skirting the bathhouse. Everyone in the family knew the standard procedure for crossing the yard, and visitors were briefed on it, but there were times when the call was urgent and yard rules forgotten, and thereby Terry achieved his remarkably high strike rate.

Never openly confrontational or vicious, and looking only to establish his territorial rights, he came quietly but swiftly in a flanking attack and was in general content to apply a gentle pressure to calf or ankle before retreating to his kennel. If occasionally he went a touch too far, it was a forgiving household and so he ruled his little domain for many years, only to be finally bested by the Nazis in the chaos that followed the first great air raid on 7th September 1940. After the rest of the family had left the house Jack returned there regularly for some weeks, and in a letter written shortly after the confusion that followed the raid one sentence marked poor Terry's passing: 'I fed the parrot, the bird, the cat and the goldfish – all are still alive and well. I took Terry to be destroyed last week so he is gone.'

It was an indulgent family, and as soon as he was able the young boy had the run of the house to explore where he would. Beyond the living room an extension scullery/kitchen with one small room above projected into the yard, and ill-lit stairs led up to join the passage into the house from the upper door. On this floor the large front room, the best in the house, was in general and constant use. The family met there on a regular basis for a cup of tea and a chat, and the children used it as a playroom. It faced west and from noon on a fine day was bright with sunlight streaming through the broad sash window which overlooked the gardens below Rigden

27

Street, the grounds behind the Board of Trade, and the entrance to the Seamen's Rest in Jeremiah Street.

Throughout the East End unemployment, poverty and the squalor of the slums bred resentment and a determination to seek improvement. Any protest meetings to express discontent were inevitably met by a strong force of police, on foot and mounted, and all too often their heavy-handed interventions led to violent confrontation. In general these affairs took place far away and the even tenor of life in the terrace was unaffected, but in the same month that the Stiffkey vicar faded from the papers Lou and Phoebe watched from the front windows of the house as events taking place in their normally tranquil surroundings carried the Seamen's Rest and Jeremiah Street into the headlines. Prince George, showing the Royal Standard in the slums as members of the family occasionally did to keep the proletarian peckers up, arrived for the opening of a new extension to the Rest to be greeted with cries of protest calling for bread and an abolition of the means test. The police moved in on foot to arrest the protesters; the crowd resisted; mounted police followed those on foot to disperse the crowd, and disorder ensued. Arrests were made and the scene was repeated the following day with further mounted baton charges to disperse the crowds outside the police court where those arrested were appearing.

When the affair was reported in the paper the family were more than a little surprised to learn from the magistrate's comments that the prince was performing a ceremony which he regarded as his duty for the benefit of their particular class.

'Our particular class!' said Charlie. 'Privileged from birth to grave, what the bloody hell would he know of our class and the way some of them have to live?'

'At least he didn't tell the poor sods to eat cake,' said Elsie.

From the front room large sliding doors opened into the back room where Clara shared with her mother the double bed in which she had been born. Changing circumstances following Pappy's death and Phoebe's growing family had forced the arrangement which continued, periods of illness apart, until Lou died many years after the war. A bedroom for most of the year, at Christmas, weddings and other family celebrations it was cleared for party use. The bed was struck and moved to the side with other furniture, the sliding doors were thrown back, and one large space was created that would accommodate most of the family when they came together, as they often did.

On the first floor were two more bedrooms: Phoebe's at the front, and at the back overlooking the yard the smaller one shared by the two children. From the passage narrow, twisting stairs led to the top floor where two small, sparsely furnished rooms, tucked in under the eaves, were in occasional use by Elsie and Kath who were seldom home for more than a night or two at a time. There, at the top of the house, was the young boy's secret place, his eyrie and outlook on the Dockland world that stretched away around him. As he climbed the stairs the noise and activity from below faded away to isolation and silence in the two upper rooms closed away under the tiles behind their narrow dormer windows.

From the back-room window on winter nights, he looked out to the dim outlines of the neighbouring houses receding row on row in the faint illumination thrown by the few lamps in the shadowy streets below. Here and there diffuse lights shone through drawn curtains and smoke from the many chimneys swirled, merged and added its own contribution to the occasional 'London peculiar', when traffic on the main road slowed to a cautious crawl, and the air was full of the coughs and curses of those trying to cut their way through the fog.

Beyond the houses the lamps of the stalls and shops in Chrisp Street market burned late into the night, illuminating the mist that drifted in from the river and hung over the street, a pale Milky Way of light. If the tide was right and the night clear, the topmast lights of vessels navigating the sweeping bends of the river could be seen blinking on and off between factories and warehouses as the ships moved slowly towards the docks, or out along Bugsby's Reach towards Coldharbour Point, the Essex marshes and the open sea beyond.

In daylight he looked out over slates and gutters to the roofs and chimney pots of the Duff Street houses, the familiar slender spire of All Saints' Church and along the line of East India Dock Road towards his birthplace at the hospital and the tops of the cranes dipping and rising in the distant docks. Below, closer to the house, through a gap in the buildings the movement of pedestrians and traffic on the main road could just be seen, and from the warehouses, factories and shunting yards of the Isle of Dogs the faint hum of industry drifted in at the window.

29

In the spring of '33 the family shared the same window late into the night watching the great fire in the warehouse at Rum Quay. Burning spirit bursting from more than six thousand barrels had set the water of the dock ablaze, and the flames that lit up the night sky could be seen from miles away. As the warehouse flared and collapsed, firemen reeled drunkenly from the fumes given off by the burning spirits, and in the days that followed men in the pubs of Dockland mourned the passing of half a million gallons of rum. It was an eerie precursor of the scene just a few years later when the same window would command a grandstand view of the inferno that raged throughout Docklands as its warehouses and factories were consumed in the raids of the Blitz.

In early summer the scene at the front of the house was almost rustic: pear tree blossom in the corner of the yard and Lou's plantings in the beds at the foot of the walls, lilac and a few flowering shrubs in the gardens beyond, and flower boxes hung high up on two or three windows of the Seamen's Rest. To all of this the screeches, clicks and babblings of Mick, the family parrot, brought a touch of the tropics. In fine weather his cage was hung outside on the garden wall where the pear tree provided both shade and his favourite delicacy, a freshly cut length of branch to chew. He was a friendly, affable old chap who responded to a gentle tickle with a gruff and salty chuckle which marked him out as a bird who had known something of the low life.

In Jeremiah Street beyond the garden wall the Queen Victoria Home for Seamen was a handsome four-storeyed building in red brick, banded and ornamented with white stone. A taller tower topped with a cupola incorporated at its base an arched entrance porch with recessed steps leading into the large mission hall that occupied much of the ground floor.

In the mission hall of the home the wishes of the founders were honoured, and it was an emotional Sunday afternoon encounter with their Wesleyan traditions that formed the youngster's earliest memory of those Poplar days. John was an amenable and placid child who fell in without objection to his mother's practice of putting him down in the afternoon for a rest: whether hers or his the family could never establish. And so in the upstairs front room, in the centre of the huge double bed, remote from the sounds of the house below him, and alone apart from the gollywog beside

30

him, he was left for an hour or so. It was high summer, the curtains were drawn against the heat of the afternoon sun, and the soft murmurs of a rest-day afternoon filtered in through the open window overlooking the garden. As he drifted into a half-sleep the faint hum of Sunday traffic, a conversation in the neighbouring gardens and Mick burbling in his cage below were a familiar, soothing background.

The intrusion, when it came, was at first vague and indistinct: a tune rising and falling, then the sound of distant voices singing. Not the familiar melodious warblings of his aunts, but harsh, uncertain and discordant.

He was an emotional and imaginative child, easily moved to tears by the sentimental, and with more than his fair share of the Celtic melancholy that ran in the family. As he lay alone, alert now to every word that drifted over the gardens that summer afternoon it seemed to him that they embodied all that was mournful and forlorn:

> *Rescue the perishing, care for the dying,*
> *Snatch them in pity from sin and the grave . . .*

As he listened the sun went in and his world darkened. The pressure round his heart and the swelling in his throat, always a preliminary to tears, was already stirring and the singers had his full attention. With increasing fervour and intensity of feeling they raised their hearts and voices until from the open windows of the mission meeting hall the sound rolled out across the gardens in a flood:

> *Down in the human heart, crushed by the tempter,*
> *Feelings lie buried that grace can restore;*
> *Touched by a loving heart, wakened by kindness,*
> *Chords that were broken will vibrate once more.*

That was too much! Swept up already on a tide of emotion it needed only a return to the refrain 'Rescue the perishing, care for the dying' to overwhelm him. Howling and weeping he stumbled down the stairs and into the arms of his grandmother having tea with his aunts in the front room. Sobbing out his complaints against the perishers he was comforted with hugs, sweet tea and biscuits. The incident marked his transition from babyhood to childhood: there were no more afternoon naps.

It was Jack who started each day in the house. Late to bed and an early riser, he was up and busy for an hour or more before he called the children. In summer their routine was a relaxed and leisurely affair in a room already bright and warmed by the sun: a shout to the dog in the yard, a glance through the window at the familiar scene, and then a tumble down two flights of stairs to wash in the scullery before returning to dress in the bedroom.

In the depth of winter their mornings were a brisker, more invigorating experience. Beyond the comfort of blankets and eiderdown the bedroom was hostile, the passages and stairways freezing, and the scullery, so often open to the yard, arctic. Only the fire in the living room two floors below offered warmth, and to that, still wrapped in their dressing gowns, they fled. In front of the blazing fire, draped over the polished brass top-rail of the fireguard, their underclothes were waiting for them, warm and comforting when they slipped into them. On the coldest days, chilled by the dash from the bedroom, John lifted his nightshirt, pressed a naked backside against the wire of the guard, and for a few ecstatic moments toasted the protruding triangles of flesh in front of the glowing coals before his mother intervened.

'All right, that's enough. You know what I've told you about chilblains. Do you want them on your bum as well now?'

Before dressing for the day, they washed in bowls of hot water brought in from the scullery. Reluctant to rely on her son's attention to the finer points of personal hygiene Phoebe conducted her own rigorous inspection, guaranteed to send him off for the day in a presentable state. Ears, hands, fingers and, in particular, bum were subjected to minute and critical scrutiny. It was the bum that most frequently was judged to offend and require remedial treatment. 'Getting rid of all the clinkers' she called it as she relathered, scoured and dried the offending orifice.

Sending him out neatly and tidily dressed was a matter of family pride. Phoebe was more than capable with knitting or crochet needles, and Lou, with many years of practice behind her, was skilled on her old treadle sewing machine. Together they made much of his clothing when he was young. Having no older brothers or cousins, hand-me-down trousers, jackets or coats never came his way, but in those early years enough money could usually be put together for new hard-wearing and serviceable replacements to be bought from the shops or stalls of Chrisp Street.

That should have been as much a matter of happiness and pride to him, as to his family, but it was not. The material advantages they enjoyed over their neighbours weren't great, but they were enough for most of his friends to sport a patch or two on their clothes. Elbows and trousers' seats in particular were favoured with patches of contrasting shades and eccentric design that he saw as badges of social communion of which he was deprived. He resented the unsought distinction of going unpatched and the amused rejection of his requests for decorative, if not functional, patches on his trousers.

Their weekday breakfasts were soon over: a little cereal, with bread, marmalade and hot sweet tea to follow, or in winter, the lumpy, glutinous porridge in which his mother specialised. A good and inventive cook in most other respects, she seemed contemptuous of the minimum skills that porridge preparation demanded, and the porridge showed its resentment at her negligence. On Sundays there was something hot: a piece of smoked haddock, a kipper or a little bacon and egg.

Although they ate well enough, housekeeping money was always tight, and Phoebe had formulated a number of mysterious rules that were embedded in her standing orders and household economy. If there was bacon for breakfast the bread was served without butter; not a scrape, despite his pleadings.

'You don't have butter on your bread when there's bacon – bacon is a relish.'

She had a wealth of such gnomic utterances to baffle and frustrate what seemed to her children to be eminently reasonable requests.

The two maiden aunts, Elsie and Kath, lived and worked away from home for most of their lives, but once in every six or eight weeks they finished on the Friday evening and were back together for a weekend with the rest of the family. Then the normal routine of the house was transformed. The days were busy, visitors came and went, the front room was in constant use, and John's financial expectations were unbounded.

Pocket money was a never-ending problem. There were small weekly contributions from his father and gran which never went far enough, and he learned early on that his mother, in anything but the sunniest of moods, was proof against the subtlest of financial propositions. When mastery of the lower times tables enabled him to convert six pence to twenty-four farthings in pursuit of a jigsaw that had caught his eye, she was singularly unimpressed and invited him, as she so frequently did, to consider whether she was made of money. As the years emboldened him he responded with a little light-hearted speculation on that theme, only to learn that although not particularly quick on her feet, she had a very, very long memory and a firm hand.

The aunts' morning routines at home were relaxed and leisurely affairs, and Phoebe would be out and on her way to the market before breakfast was laid for them in Lou's living room. Left in their care, he idled backwards and forwards in the rocking chair watching and listening to a domestic routine that remained largely unchanged for the rest of their lives, until one after another they rose and left the table for the last time.

The heavy chenille cloth was covered with one of plain white linen. Plates, dishes and cutlery were drawn from a general household set, but their cups and saucers were individually patterned, of fine china, and always set at the same place on the table. A cooked breakfast of egg and bacon was standard, and although perfectly adequately fed, he scavenged on the rind trimmings cut from their bacon, and with a thickly buttered sandwich enjoyed a second breakfast as they proceeded with their first.

Deep in their newspapers they lingered over the final stages of toast, marmalade and second cups of tea. Kath took her news slowly and in depth. She read the paper from cover to cover, and at breakfast was still in the thick of the news of the preceding day. Elsie, with a quicker eye and sharper mind, took all she wanted from the current paper in half an hour. It looked a comfortable domestic scene: Elsie and Kath relaxing with their papers while their mother and Clara fussed around the table with more tea and toast. But they did so with an air of anticipation. They had only a short wait before Kath opened up the ritual breakfast exchange they were expecting.

'Here, Else, listen to this.'

Elsie kept her head down, responding only with a curt, 'Oh yes.'
With a wink at Clara, her mother poured more tea.

'What do you think of this, Else?'

'I don't.'

They read on silently for a while.

'Did you see this in yesterday's, Else?'

With a resigned look of despair to Lou and Clara, Elsie replied
slowly and deliberately,

'Yes I did. I read it – yesterday.'

A longer pause and then,

'I don't know, Else, do you suppose . . .'

'No I don't and I don't want to. Can't you just get on with your
paper and leave me to mine for once.'

'Well don't get shirty – I thought you might be interested.'

'Well I'm not and that's that.'

Their huffing and puffing was soon smoothed over. On the
following morning Sunday breakfast would be peaceful, but by the
next time they were home Kath would be off again.

Noisy witness to every breakfast was Mick, whose cage sat on
the sideboard opposite the window. From the moment the cloth
was laid his bright grey-green eyes followed proceedings, and the
morning table talk was punctuated by his interjections. As the meal
proceeded his agitated racketing around the bars of the cage
increased, until with the toast and marmalade he burst into his
closest approach to coherent speech. 'Would he like a lovely . . .
would he like a . . . would he . . . would he . . . would he . . .' – a
sentence that he never completed. A thick crust cut from one of
the slices of toast, dipped into the tea, sprinkled with sugar and
passed through the bars silenced him until the last soggy fragment
dropped to the bottom of the cage.

After breakfast there was a slack time of half an hour or so
when they went off to prepare themselves for the rest of the
morning. Employed in manual work, Clara a laundry supervisor,
Elsie and Kath cooks in LCC establishments, they earned only the
depressed wages then paid to women. But they were unmarried,
with no responsibilities beyond their contributions to Lou for the
upkeep and running of the family home, and they made their little
go a long way. When they returned, ready to enjoy the rest of their
day, they were always well turned out. 'Dressed up to the nines'

was the phrase. Three handbags clicked open, and a couple of coppers were pressed into John's hands from each of them.

'Well, thank your aunts then. I suppose that will burn a hole in your pocket as usual, and you won't be satisfied until it's all gone. And don't forget to keep something for your comic.' He needed no reminder to give thanks for the financial blessings that came his way. A kiss and a smile to each of them came naturally, and he was astute enough to realise that good manners went a long way towards guaranteeing future solvency.

After a few words with their mother, and a final hug and kiss for John, they were off, and from the window he watched them sweep away up the terrace, heading perhaps for the tram stop, and the first stage to a day out 'up West' or a visit to friends nearby. Behind them, in the passages and rooms of the house, the fragrance of their perfumes lingered, but fought a losing battle with the odour of carbolic soap and disinfectant as Lou embarked on her Saturday-morning purge of the domestic facilities.

Six copper coins of the realm received two by two from the aunts had been added to his exchequer. He was a man of substance again. How weighty and reassuring those old pennies felt in the pocket! What possibilities and vistas of delight they opened up. He ran them through his fingers, some fresh and clean-cut, others smooth with age and wear: on one the strong, sharp image of the new king or the old queen, mother of the nation; on another worn thin with fingering, nothing but a shadowy wraith of the young Victoria. It wasn't gold that paved the streets of London, but copper from coins that over forty years of handling sloughed off half their weight on to the pavements of the city.

In Lou's living room the family dining table, broad, solid and extensible to cope with any number from two to a dozen or more, stood alongside the window. Beneath the table there were ledges on the woodwork deep enough to hold a few toys and personal treasures, and there, in the dim light that filtered through a darkly patterned chenille cloth hanging almost to the floor, the youngster hid and played or, secure from discovery as he thought, curled quietly on the floor all ears to the talk around him.

Much of this meant little or nothing but he was an avid listener and looker-on, and the current of discussions and arguments that floated around him continued the radical tradition established by his dead grandfather. Two of his aunts had been suffragettes active

36

in the movement at the beginning of the century, and then following Sylvia Pankhurst in her anti-war movement during the First
World War. Although that was many years behind them their
friends from the old days were frequent visitors, and the talk and
argument swung from past campaigns to current concerns on social
issues, and pay and working conditions for women.

His father, like so many of the men who survived the trench
slaughter of the war, looked to a radical reform of society, and for
almost twenty years was actively involved in politics as a founder
member of the British Communist Party. Disagreement with developments and policy in the thirties led him to leave the movement,
but colleagues and friends still came to the house for meetings and
discussions where John's presence, tucked into a corner, seemed to
be forgotten.

Close friends of the family, working deep-sea on the ships that
came to and from the docks just across the road, appeared briefly
on shore leave with reports of their experiences abroad and a few
mementoes of their travels, before once again they were gone for
the next few months.

Add to this a leaven of social chat about the latest concert or
production at the rebuilt People's Palace, film at the Poplar Hippodrome or gossip from one of the large houses in which the aunts
had worked in service and it fermented into heady brew for a
young mind. Month after month, and year after year, as he lay
curled up beneath the table or tucked into a corner of the room, a
tide of people, places and events washed over him. Haile Selassie,
Valentino, Mosley, Ethiopia, Pankhurst, Guernica, Valparaiso, Hitler, *Maytime*, Stalin, 'Indian Love Call' – they passed before him
like a kaleidoscopic peepshow, and if their passage was transitory
and his comprehension limited, they did not pass without some
naive and basic understanding being formed. The tone of voice and
manner of expression often spoke more eloquently to him than the
words and he drifted through the seedtime years, his attitudes and
beliefs gradually being formed not only by words but by events
that foreshadowed the war that was to come.

The radical tradition of Poplar Borough and the East End
generally was one of action as well as words, and the same was
true of the family. They were in Cable Street in 1936 when
Mosley's fascist march was challenged and stopped, and in the
years immediately before the war they were part of the groundswell

of opposition and protests at German intervention and atrocities in Spain.

For Cable Street he was too young to be a witness, but on his uncle's shoulders, tucked away safely on the fringes of the crowds, he was one of the thousands at Hyde Park and Trafalgar Square rallies for Spain in which his father was taking part. It was a confusing, exciting, sometimes frightening experience. Mornings of marching masses, swirling crowds, waving banners, cries and counter-cries, passionate but good-natured until the appearance of swastika banners provoked fights and the police moved in. Well before the meeting ended he was carried away into quiet streets and a tram ride home with the cries of the meeting ringing in his ears: 'Down with the Fascists!' 'Read the Facts about Spain!'

Long before the Spanish affair had run its course it was the names and places from Germany and Central Europe that he heard around him. There were many, many ordinary people who like Churchill were quick enough to recognise the Nazi threat and the dangers implicit in appeasement.

3

A Palace on the Plots

The Children's Country Holiday Fund earnestly appeals for donations. £1 enables a poor, delicate London child to enjoy a fortnight's holiday in the country during the summer.

Factory Girls' Country Holiday Fund – Funds Urgently Needed. Hundreds of poorest working girls hoping for a week by the sea during the next few months. Contributions gratefully acknowledged.

£1 sends one East End child from the dirt and squalor of Dockland to the sea for 2 weeks. Good food and fresh air works wonders. Contributions to . . .

The 1930s: every year in the early summer the charitable appeals began to appear in the newspapers alongside the advertisements of a certain peeress 'entertaining now in London' who could include one or two (not factory girls presumably) in her parties 'until the end of the season'.

There would have been few working and living in the dirt and pollution of Dockland who did not long for the chance to escape however briefly to the fresh air and sunshine of seaside or country. Poverty or unemployment put paid to the dreams of most, but in summer every year some thousands of children and poor factory girls did make that escape and journey to countryside or coast, if only for a week, thanks to the work of those charities. They appealed for funds on the wireless and sought contributions from the Dominions. Eton College collected for them at the end of the summer half, and winter charity balls devoted their proceeds to them. But despite their best efforts, for each one of the many who made an escape there were hundreds condemned to serve out their time in the slums and sweatshops of the East End without relief.

For those that charity did not reach there was 'going hopping', a halfway house between holiday and work where a really good picker could earn perhaps six to eight shillings a day. Hopping was a family affair with its regulars who went year after year to the same locations: gran, mum, the children and any of the men who were out of work. The hop fields gave them fresh air and sunshine as they worked, and they earned a little for their beer and entertainment in the evenings. Apart from hopping there remained for a very lucky few a cheap boarding-house holiday or the 'plots'.

The plots had their beginnings in the agricultural depression in the second half of the nineteenth century which left scores of farms lying derelict and unworked. In Essex in particular the intractable soil made life more than usually difficult, and many farmers left the land in despair. By the 1870s estates of a thousand acres or more were being sold off, giving speculative developers the opportunity to buy up large tracts of land adjacent to the London to Southend railway line. These were subsequently auctioned off in smaller plots close enough to the railway stations at Laindon and Pitsea to offer the prospect of clean air and a country break to those Londoners who could afford to buy at prices that ran to ten or eleven pounds a plot.

To call the speculators 'developers' is to flatter them, they were simply get-rich-quick charlatans who took the money and ran. Their advertising was enticing and cunningly designed to appeal to the city dweller with a little cash to spare and a longing for the country. It promised tree-lined roads, gravity-fed spring water, shops and refreshment houses, and was well larded with descriptions and artistic impressions of the idyllic life on offer. In reality it was a plot, and nothing but a plot, plus years of hard graft and all too often heartache, that was purchased.

Communities developed in three areas: in the countryside around Laindon and Pitsea railway stations, and to the north of the little hamlet of Bowers Gifford, a couple of miles from Pitsea, but the pattern was the same in each of them. In the absence of any building controls or regulations the nature and quality of the early accommodation erected on the plots was variable and eccentric. At one end, simple, basic, but well-constructed bungalows were built in which a decent but hard life could be lived. At the other there were shacks fit for little more than a fine-weather weekend if people were prepared to rough it, but which, if clustered together and lived in permanently, degenerated quickly into the worst sort of rural slum, and as late as 1948 the Ordnance Survey map described one development on the outskirts of Vange as 'hovels'. The promise of services to be provided was a hollow one from the outset, and for decades there was no water, no lighting, no drainage and no roads, just grassy unmetalled lanes where in winter the Essex clays quickly degenerated into a sea of mud.

By the 1930s many of the original shacks had been replaced by more substantial buildings, but in general life on the plots improved very little. A few homes had a piped water supply, and most of the main roads had been metalled, but off those roads the side lanes remained grassy, or in winter boggy, tracks. There was little main drainage; few homes had electricity; many were still without a gas supply, but it was never without excitement and expectation that Louisa and her family made their summer escapes to the family plot in the parish of Bowers Gifford.

Bayhurst, the little bungalow they owned there, had been a joint purchase by Lou and her three unmarried daughters. Each of them had been working for many years, and they had the habit of saving, however little, throughout their lives. With those nest eggs, and a few pounds of insurance money received when Pappy died, they put together most of the cost and paid off the balance over a few years. It was a crudely built affair with four small rooms and a lean-to scullery/kitchen tagged on as an afterthought. Provided with the most basic of facilities, it was intended and used in the early years as a weekend and summer holiday retreat for family and friends, but when war arrived Bayhurst was to prove a welcome refuge and lifesaver.

Preparations for a summer weekend visit were soon made. With a couple of small suitcases carrying all they needed Lou, Phoebe and the children travelled on the Friday afternoon. Clara and Jack followed as work allowed on the Saturday. The tram from outside the Board of Trade took them first through familiar ground: Chrisp Street still crowded with stalls and shoppers, All Saints' Church, the Blackwall Tunnel gateway, and finally Bow Creek, busy with tugs and lighters if the tide was full. From then on they were off their home patch with the docks and river behind them and bound for Barking station on the London to Southend line.

41

They travelled mid-afternoon, third class of course at one penny a mile, and before the homeward bound rush from the City began, when with luck they would have a compartment to themselves. A journey on the old LMS line was never an exhilarating experience even in the 1930s. Timekeeping may have been good, but afternoon travel meant stopping trains, and although it was only twenty miles or so from Barking to Pitsea a timetable that was leisurely to the point of lethargy meant that the journey took the best part of an hour.

After the noise and bustle of the District Line terminus at Upminster came the rural somnolence of the Horndons where they waited at deserted platforms, still and silent apart from the slow breathing of the engine or the distant bulling of a cow yearning for a mate. The first signs of higgledy-piggledy plot development marked the approaches to Laindon and then the journey was soon over: a mile or so along the flanks of the Langdon Hills, the brick buttresses of a steep embankment, and then on their right the wastes of the Bowers, Vange and Fobbing marshes, an intricate and confusing web of creeks and fleets, stretching featureless to the horizon and the Thames. With a good southerly blowing, it was there, through the open windows of the carriage, that they first caught the unique, characteristic smell of the estuary, a dark, mysterious blend of salt, mud and slowly decaying vegetation, touched, when the wind turned a little to the west, by the stench from the dumps where a daily stream of barges dropped the City of Westminster's rubbish. From the distant reaches of Hole Haven, Scarhouses and Deadman's Point it rolled in over a Dickensian landscape of isolated wind pumps, salt flats and concealed fleet crossings.

The area had been well known to the family long before Bayhurst was purchased. Lou's older sister, Tot, had married a local man, and every summer for many years Lou and her younger daughters paid a visit to Tot's for a breath of country air. In those early days, once they left the train, the only transport was on or behind a horse, and Tot would be waiting for them at the station with pony and trap for a leisurely drive through the country lanes. In later years however the main road had been improved, a bus service was in operation, and Tot was too old and nervous to venture as far as the station with the trap.

But the buses covered only part of their journey, and from

42

Pitsea station the legwork started. The nearest stop was at Pitsea Broadway, an extravagantly imposing name for the ragged cluster of buildings, mock-Tudor mixed with jerry-built commercial properties, that had sprung up around the market where the station lane joined the main road. It was not much more than a quarter of a mile from the station to the Broadway, but economy dictated that they walk a little further and catch the bus at the next stop along the road, where a new fare stage started and the cost was a penny less.

From the lane a short cut led up the hill towards St Michael's Church through yet more plotland development: a few bungalows mixed with buildings that were little more than two-roomed huts with a tacked-on lean-to for the kitchen. They were well kept and brightly painted, but for Louisa the gardens were the attraction, and a reason other than economy why the walk was chosen. Liberated from the constraints of their sterile little backyards in the East End the settlers on the hill seemed to have taken a collective decision to turn their plots into one great garden of roses: wild roses, shrub roses, standards, weeping standards, ramblers and climbers hanging from sidewalls and trellises, and immaculate beds of hybrid teas all waxing fat on the heavy clay soil. Over the years Lou had got to know one of the women who like herself had spent her childhood in Blackheath, and she lingered there talking over old times while the rest of the family walked on to the south side of the church.

On a seat in the graveyard, on the very brow of the hill and high above the surrounding countryside, they sat waiting for her. Beyond the railway line below them the wide expanse of the marshes stretched away, and beyond on a clear day the Thames could be seen and the smoke of the ships running to and from the Docklands they had just left. The church itself was a relic of the days when Pitsea was an isolated settlement of farmers and water-fowlers. They never went inside or learned its history, but after the noise and restlessness of their East End world they felt soothed and eased by the peace of its tumbling gravestones, grey lichen-covered walls and battlemented tower. From the church it was a short downhill walk to the main road, and an uncertain wait for the bus to Southend that would take them the mile or so to Bowers Gifford.

Those years in Essex were over long before the blight of Dutch elm disease arrived, and the countryside through which they passed was still dominated by the great, craggy trees that had distinguished it for centuries. From the hedgerows beside the road they towered above the footpaths and lightly brushed the upper windows of the passing bus where Louisa and her family sat looking out across features that had become so familiar to them over the years: farmhouses and barns, a couple of country pubs, open fields and patches of woodland, one rambling, ancient house and a scattering of modern development.

As the bus pulled away up the hill towards Southend they turned for the final leg of their journey on foot. Behind them level cornfields stretched into the distance before dropping out of sight as the land fell away down the hill to the railway line, the Bowers Marshes and the isolated, ancient church of St Margaret's. Ahead Pound Lane ran for almost two miles to join a more recent intrusion into the landscape, the new arterial road running east from London to the coast.

The first impression was one of bucolic tranquillity untouched by the passing centuries: the long, rough-gravelled lane stretching ahead, a field of wheat to one side and to the other tall elms hanging over the deep, broad ditch that drained the hill rising to the east. But it was no longer virgin countryside. A little further on, speculative 30s development had eaten into the meadows on either side of the lane. An improvement on the plots, it had at least provided surfaced roads, drains, electricity and other services, but it remained an ill-planned and poorly executed enterprise. Just one or two houses broke the long line of characterless, four-roomed, semi-detached, pebble-dashed bungalows that stretched ahead of them, and already, after just a few years of wear and weather, the pebble-dash was flaking and the concrete roads were fractured and potholed. At the first junction the few local shops were clustered: a post office and paper shop, a dairy, and a grocer, and then there were open fields once again until they reached the start of the plots and turned up Clarence Road, a rough and rutted grass lane, on the final hundred yards or so to Bayhurst.

The front door was bolted and seldom used. Through arches of rose-covered trellis they walked to the back, and turned the key with as much uncertainty as expectation. As the shifting Essex clays shrank and expanded with the drought and rain of the changing seasons they played havoc with the timber-framed, almost foundation-less building. On one visit the door moved freely at a touch. On another it needed the full weight of the bulkiest of the party to prise it from the twisted frame.

Apart from the school holidays and occasional weekends there were always gaps in occupation, and when at last they tumbled in it was the reek of abandonment that filled the nose. Compounded of the redolence of old oilcloth, damp fabrics, dry rot, wet clay, and country-life living, dying and corrupting below the floorboards, it was not the warmest of welcomes, and it took hard work to make the place comfortable.

In high summer, if the late afternoon was dry and warm, sheets and blankets were stripped from the beds and hung in the garden to air. At other seasons a fire was lit in the old-fashioned, cast-iron range, and from the bedding draped in front of it the smell that had welcomed them was further enriched by the musty vapours drifting from toasting blankets. Until the following day the feather beds had to be taken as they found them. Generally that meant damp, and the first night could be a dispiriting experience. Apart from attending to the bedding there was other general tidying up to be done, a rushed meal of sorts to be prepared and eaten as best they could and finally, an hour or so before a very late bedtime, the room was cleared and the beds made up.

In the fading twilight Lou turned to the gas lamp with a lighted match, and their world was transformed as the mantle ignited with a muted 'pop'. Inside the globe it sighed softly as it burned: a long, unceasing, subdued exhalation of breath. As the gauze brightened, the light strengthened, investing the room in the warmth of a mellow glow that was a world away from the stark, electric glare of home. Gentle and welcoming, it softened the edges of the shadows and lay easily on the eyes. Slowly the scene beyond the window dimmed and faded, and the curtains were drawn against the night.

With only two bedrooms children had to be settled down as and where space could be found, and they revelled in the novelty. In one of the front rooms convertible armchairs were transformed into narrow beds, or if the house was really full, mattresses of cushions laid on the floor, and there they were tucked away for the night. In their Poplar bedroom, two flights of stairs above all the activity, few sounds reached them; snug in their country nests they drifted to sleep to the murmur of conversation and laughter from the room next door.

Most plots were relatively small, perhaps a quarter of an acre or less, but in Pound Lane they had been sold in varying sizes up to the half-acre. With a frontage of thirty yards and a depth of eighty or more, Bayhurst stood on one of the largest. The building had been a few years old when Lou and her daughters bought it, and if not exactly ramshackle, its construction was simple and basic and the facilities it offered limited. There were no drains and no electricity, but it had at least its own gas and water supply. A little further up the road the houses either relied on well water or the occupants had a daily trudge to a standpipe at the junction with the green lane running through to the next line of plots.

Originally timber-framed and weatherboarded, the bungalow had eventually been pebble-dashed in the fashion of the time. The frame and floors rested more than a foot above ground on uncertain foundations concealed by concrete rendering, and providing a secret haven for whatever could burrow, bore or otherwise penetrate the void beneath the floorboards.

Basically it was just a square box, with a narrow corridor and two rooms off to each side. At the rear an extension, partly lean-to partly pitched, provided space for an entrance lobby and kitchen/ scullery. There was no inside lavatory. At the front the two rooms had twin bay windows with pitched roofs, and outside a simple porch sheltered the little-used front door. It was roofed overall with corrugated-iron sheeting painted red. Inconvenient, cramped and damp, it was nevertheless considered more than adequate for quiet country breaks, and coming from the streets of Poplar it was paradise.

When the family took it over, the land had lain neglected for years and was deep in weeds and brambles. From then on all the men, Lou's sons and sons-in-law, if they had not contributed cash, invested time and labour. Weekend visits were spent hacking into the invading scrub at the back, cutting out and turning over flower and vegetable beds, fixing trellis and rustic fencing, or mixing concrete by hand for the paths and crazy paving into the garden. By the mid-thirties the land was already more than half-beaten into submission, with flower beds and shrubs laid out around and behind the bungalow in roughly grassed areas that their irregular visits left them struggling to maintain as lawns. Further back there were vegetable beds and recently planted trees or bushes of hard and soft fruit. Beyond the cultivated area uncleared scrub ran to the end of the land. From the back door a path led to the lavatory, coal store and shed at the side of the plot, some thirty or more feet away. Apart from one mature hornbeam behind the bungalow there had been no trees worth keeping, and one of the earliest plantings had been a long line of Lombardy poplars. These had thrived and could already be seen from the lane marking out the upper boundary of the plot.

Trellis work was the gardening obsession of the time, and the gardeners at Bayhurst were slaves to the fashion. Ornamental arches of trellis broke the line of the path from the gate to the back of the house. It was fixed to the walls in large and small panels, and it screened lavatory, shed and coal store from sight. Around the bungalow, climbing and rambling roses clung to it, and by the outbuildings it was clothed in honeysuckle and Russian vine. There was trellis everywhere and always something to clamber up it.

At the back of the cultivated area, just behind the apple trees, Jack planted the garden swing. No flimsy, six-foot-high toy for toddlers that would be here today and gone tomorrow, it was a serious stout-roped affair, with a seat wide enough for lovers to cuddle together, and more than capable of carrying the heaviest adult. Two thick uprights of timber rose nine feet or more to a substantial crosspiece, and planted deep in concrete they stood unshaken and unmoved for more than thirty years.

A Bayhurst day started early for all visitors including children, and before breakfast John had time for a swing and an exploration of old hideouts and dens deep in the thickets at the end of the garden. Then there were the two Heard boys to visit. Mickey was about his age, Denny a couple of years older. They lived just across the road with their mother, Nora, widowed a few years earlier. Their father, Albert, a farm labourer from youth, had died when his children were young, and before he had the chance to know anything other than the hard graft and tribulations of rural life at the bottom of the heap. In his final year his employer, following guidelines from the Agricultural Wages Board, was rewarding him with a handsome £1.12s for a 50.6-hour week. It was a nice, precise, administrative touch, that 0.6. Not quite a pound of flesh, but in the same unforgiving, uncharitable spirit.

Home for Mickey and Denny was a long narrow cottage of three rooms opening one into the other. At the back a smaller room served as scullery and workroom. The floors were bare boards, the tables, chairs and cupboards basic and rough, and the lingering odour of cooked pigswill was all pervasive. The walls were stark and undecorated: rough plaster barely covered with a thin wash of distemper. There was no comfort, no books, no ornaments – nothing to soften or redeem the meanness of the place.

Both before and after Albert died the Heards' life was one of abject rural poverty. Nora, hardworking but struggling daily to find food to put into their mouths, eked out their meals with scrag-end cuts of meat and anything else that was cheap and bulky enough to fill their stomachs, and a gourmet treat for Mickey was a thick slice of fresh bread spread with lard and condensed milk.

Even as a child John was conscious that life was very different at the Heards, but it would be many years before he appreciated the extent of the gulf between the deprivation that they endured year in and year out, and his own relatively comfortable background. Only when continuing and increasing ill health prevented his own father from working did he come to hear of Public Assistance Committees and their Relieving Officers. An administrative and equally calculating cousin of the Wages Board, the PAC was the source of what little regular money Nora received after Albert died.

The Heards' plot was a long, narrow strip of land, virtually uncultivated apart from the patch where Nora tried, but failed, to produce a few vegetables for their table. At the end, well away from the house, the boys kept the sow that was their responsibility and pride. She had her sty in a closed-off corner of a barn with access to a boarded run outside. A huge, handsome beast, red-bristled and gleaming, she farrowed with indecent rural fecundity and was seldom to be seen without a litter of piglets. When they were very young she was aggressively defensive, but once that phase had passed she enjoyed a good back scratching as much as the boys who provided it.

Mickey and Denny were her protectors and providers. They

mucked her out, collected and prepared her food, looked as much to her well-being as they did to their own, and with the relish of young boys on such topics, took delight in giving John a basic but graphic and robust account of proceedings during her regular assignations with the local boar. There was no traditional country pig sticking at the Heards. As soon as the piglets were weaned and sufficiently mature they were sold on for cash, and little if any pork or bacon ever found a place on Nora's table. Denny looked after the pigswill preparation and cooking. Mickey was responsible for collecting whatever scraps and leftovers he could and had worked up a regular daily round in the area. Whenever possible John accompanied him.

On either side of Clarence Road the hedgerows and scrub grew so vigorously that few of the buildings could be seen from any distance away. A footpath of broken brick, gravel and cinders had been built up along one side, but in summer the road was thick with grasses and weeds flattened only by the wheels of the occasional horse and cart, or the lorry delivering coal.

With a bucket each in hand they started the round at the cottage next to Bayhurst occupied by a widower always referred to as 'the German'. It would be some time yet before that distinction was to have significance for him and his neighbours, however. Many years earlier he had moved there with his English wife, and after she died he stayed on alone, part of and quite accepted by the community. He had a few words of greeting for Mickey when they made their first collection of scraps, and then they passed on up the hill, pushing their way through the gates and being as nosy as they could on each visit. At the top, where the land levelled off, the cornfields began again, the last stretch of country before Tarpots and the start of the ribbon development that stretched along the Southend road. Here they collected from two or three larger houses that were a cut or two above the usual plotland properties. In the course of their wartime wanderings Jack and his family were to get to know one of them much better.

From Clarence Road they turned next into the green lane that ran through to the next line of plotland development. Just beyond the junction another house and large barn, also owned by the German, stood empty. Beyond that there were no houses, and they passed on between small orchards of apple trees and open patches of undeveloped plots reverting to hawthorn scrub and blackberry bushes, prime targets at the right time of year for scrumping or blackberrying. The collection of scraps towards the sow's evening meal built up in the next two roads, and as they walked back was completed with waste from the greengrocer and stale bread from the grocer.

Mickey had built up his legitimate round with diligence, but was not beyond helping himself from vegetable crops in field or garden if he thought he could get away with it: a casual attitude to property that explained the few cottages and farmhouses that they discreetly avoided. Back at the cottage later in the afternoon Denny boiled the whole revolting mess together with the pig meal that Nora's hoarded proceeds from piglet sales had purchased. For an hour or more the vapours rose and the sickly smell of swill seeped through from room to room.

At Bayhurst the demands of personal hygiene and bodily functions could present problems for the unduly fastidious. In the scullery there was one cold water tap over a stone sink, and a chipped enamel bowl used for all kitchen purposes. The water was complimented for its flavour by those used only to the flat, insipid London supply, but even in high summer it ran uncomfortably cold for washing. If hot water was wanted a kettle had to be boiled on the basic gas cooker that stood alongside the sink. The adults had bedroom sets of bowl and jug, and last thing at night carried in a jugful of water for their morning ablutions. Children had to make do with soap and flannel under the scullery tap, but at least Phoebe relaxed her rigorous oversight of their personal cleanliness.

On the use of the outdoor privy there was just one standing order which had to be clearly explained to any visitors unfamiliar with the rustic arrangements, and expecting it to be freely available for what were euphemistically called 'Number ones'. Its use for 'Number Twos' was, of course, unrestricted. Non-flushing and chemically based it had a capacious pan but inevitably it had to be emptied from time to time. Volunteers for the job were understandably hard to come by, and so its frequent use for frivolous purposes was frowned upon. John was not privy to the ladies' secrets, but knew that for 'Number Ones' gentlemen and little boys were expected to make their own discreet arrangements in the hedgerow or scrub at the end of the garden. Any visiting men ignorant of local custom and asking where they should go were led by Jack to the back door where throwing it open, he waved his arm expansively and told them, 'Anywhere between here and the Isle of Dogs.'

Chemical toilets have been unfortunate in acquiring the worst of reputations and are unreasonably viewed by the uninitiated with apprehension and distaste, which is a pity. Properly maintained and in the right environment (the latter is most important), they are a satisfactory, if not life-enhancing, experience. At Bayhurst smell was never a problem. The chemical properties of the mixture with which the bucket was charged were such that the exhalations of the combined whole, quite unlike the odours of the constituent parts, were never less than perfectly acceptable.

Compared with the sterile, purely functional environment of the average water closet, the little wooden hut at Bayhurst had a romantic, rustic, dreamy charm. On summer afternoons dust motes danced in the rays of sunlight bursting through the knot holes to spotlight here and there the antique scenes on calendar tops pinned by Elsie to the walls. Woodlice crept in and out of the timbers, and in the web-hung corners spiders lay in ambush. Between roof and walls Russian vine thrust slender tendrils twisting and searching for support, and beyond the gap over the door racemes of honeysuckle dropped from the trellis above, adding their own sweet perfume to the heady mix. Bees laden with pollen turned from the flowers and disoriented for a moment droned heavily around the ceiling timbers before escaping, and from the garden and fields beyond the drowsy sounds of a country afternoon brought contentment and relaxation. 'Eat well, sleep well and shit well every day' was the old rural recipe for a healthy life. Nowhere was better suited to satisfying the last commendation of this honest rustic maxim than the Bayhurst privy in the warmth of an English summer afternoon.

For the early years of the thirties those Bayhurst days were an easy-going rural idyll for visitors untroubled by anything beyond their own local horizons. By and large it was a time when the family was spared the blight of unemployment. Cheap rail fares made regular visits affordable, and from spring to autumn during school holidays and at weekends whenever that was possible the bungalow was visited by family or friends. The flower, fruit and vegetable gardens flourished and were extended. The Lombardy poplars thickened and soared, and a new generation that as yet knew nothing of war had its first encounter with green lanes, hedgerows and life away from the dusty streets of Poplar. Only as they moved into the second half of the decade did the news from Europe begin to throw a shadow that would lengthen and darken with each succeeding summer.

May 1935 was amongst the last of those unclouded visits. It saw the bungalow bulging at the seams with family and friends on a weekend that smacked more of winter than summer: cold, windy and with unusually heavy night frosts. There would normally have been no thought of making a visit in such weather, certainly not in the numbers that set off, but the occasion was unique, and all who were free to go were more than ready to muck in and rough it for the two nights.

As one of King George's Silver Jubilee events the Home Fleet was visiting the Thames with six of the capital ships moored in the estuary off Southend for almost a week. Open to shore visitors for the length of their stay, they were also to be lit overall on the Saturday evening, with the event culminating in a grand searchlight display. Add to that the promise of spectacular cliff and seafront illuminations to celebrate both the Jubilee and the impending centenary of the pier and it was an attraction that would bring the Londoners flocking.

They travelled late on the Friday, and light was fading when they turned from the bus stop into the teeth of a mean, unchari-table north wind that teased them the length of the lane. Bayhurst when they reached it looked dark and unwelcoming in the half-light, and the back door, on one of its seasonal migrations within the frame, was unyielding until Charlie had shouldered it several times. Inside it smelt chill and damp, and Elsie, ever the pessimist, was already expressing doubts whether it was all going to be worthwhile, but with the gas lamps glowing, fires lit in each room, and hot sweet tea on hand spirits rose a little. Spare sheets, blankets and pillows were dragged out from wardrobes and from under beds and a half-hearted attempt made to air them before the younger children were tucked away in the little front room on beds of cushions. The fires were banked up, a final pot of tea brewed, and then by ones and twos they followed the children to sleep in beds (the lucky ones), on the floor, or stretched out in the two or three easy chairs as age and sex dictated.

Nobody except the children slept well and the kettle was on and the men having their first cigarette of the day in the chill of the garden not long after sunrise. Washing, shaving and lavatory facilities, basic at the best of times, were all put under more than usual pressure by the numbers with the ladies lurking in the vicinity of the privy to stake their claim to a sitting, and Jack seen stealing off to the scrub at the end of the garden with a few torn-up sheets of the *Herald* in his hand.

Mid-afternoon saw them in the lane once again but this time with the wind at their backs, the sun in their faces and high hopes for the excursion ahead. A long hour or more later from a bus crammed to capacity and beyond by an understanding conductor they fought their way into a town heaving with visitors. The unseasonable weather had deterred no one. Hotels and boarding houses were full and train after train disgorged yet more day trippers from London to join in the crush. Swept down the High Street willy-nilly by crowds all moving in the one direction they thrust their way out of the flow into Royal Parade and looked at the scene below them.

From the city by river on launch or steamer, from the suburbs by train and coach, and from the towns and villages of Essex on excursion by bus and charabanc, the masses had descended for their day by the sea with the navy. The beaches were black with them. Deckchairs and park benches were full of them. Along the Promenade dolled up in their Sunday best they paraded slowly from east to west and back again. On Marine Parade it was altogether more animated and the Golden Mile was doing what it did best: raking in the money from those on their way to bigger and better things at the Kursaal. Far out in the estuary the big ships of the fleet were anchored, dwarfing the launches that moved between them and the pier head with fresh consignments of visitors.

By the time they had queued for the tram and rumbled their way over the mile and a quarter of mudflats to the pier head and open water it was clear from the queues waiting for the launches that Clara, the only one really keen, was not going to get her trip to a ship. The telescopes on the upper pier deck would have to do, and one by one they put in their pennies and turned the glass to the biggest and best of the armoured might of the British Home Fleet lying peacefully at anchor and dressed overall in bunting and flags. Furthest off were *Courageous* and *Furious*, two ungainly carriers with all the elegance of floating shoeboxes. Conversions from cruisers of the Great War, their flight decks were ugly, slab-sided intrusions on their original fighting trim. Next, as the glass swung round, came a destroyer and then the battlecruiser *Hood*. Long, low and sleek, invincible against anything then afloat, she bristled with guns and menace, and headed the visiting flotilla of battleships *Valiant*, *Nelson* and *Rodney*.

Around the pier head the waters of the estuary were in a ferment with the river craft drawn to the celebration or just passing through. From the deep-water channel, tankers, tramp steamers, freighters and liners blasted out a greeting on their way to or from the docks upriver. Steamers returning from day trips to Margate, Ramsgate or further afield nudged their way cautiously through the throng to their moorings and then swept away upriver with a complement of passengers all wishing they could stay on for the evening celebrations. Around the capital ships, but mostly around *Hood*, a host of small craft bobbed and dodged on the waters: yachts spick and span from the local clubs; motor boats, ketches and yawls stuffed to the gunnels with day trippers from the shore; and here and there a stately Thames barge whose skipper saw the chance to earn a little on the side from those with the money to indulge themselves.

Around the upper and lower pier decks they wandered watching the bustle and activity on the water until the last of the cutters were returning with the remaining visitors from the fleet, but there still remained a long wait until sunset, the illuminations and the searchlight display. From the tearooms the ladies turned to deck-chairs sheltered from the wind while Jack and Charlie took the children back to the shore with the promise of candyfloss, fairground rides and Punch and Judy. When they met again by the shore-end Pavilion light was fading. The faint glimmering of lights on the cliffs drew them first to the shrubbery, mysterious and shadowy in the soft glow of concealed illuminations, and then up the hill to the terrace outside the Palace Hotel where crowds were already gathering for the evening display.

Only Phoebe had the sense to mention the matter of buses home, but when the lights were switched on that was forgotten. From parapet to basement the façade of the hotel was a blaze of light. Below them along the Esplanade and Parade long swags of multicoloured lamps swung between decorated standards, fixed decorative displays dazzled and confused the eye with a maze of flickering, flashing movement, and from pavilion to pier head, both glowing with a thousand points of light, the lamps along the tramway flickered and glimmered over the swirling waters. The sky was clear, the moon at the full, but seawards out on the dimly lit estuary the fleet was barely visible until the ships as one burst into light in line astern with *Hood* at their head. All shone brightly but none more brightly than *Hood*, an illuminated tapestry of horizontals and verticals from waterline to topmast tip extending even to a brightly glowing standard at her masthead.

The grand finale of the evening was yet to come but slowly the visitors were turning from the sea and along with others they wandered back up the hill to the furthest point from which they could still catch a view of the scene below them. And then as the general onboard illuminations briefly dimmed, the searchlights of the fleet burst into the night sky and in swathes of blinding light swept out across the dark waters catching and illuminating the craft that still ran to and from the shore. For a few minutes they stood and watched and then turned to hurry for the bus they hoped would still be there for them. It wasn't. Phoebe had been right. They were stuck with a bus that took them only as far as Tarpots before turning off the main road, and so late at night, under a cold moon, carrying the younger children in their arms or over their shoulders by turns, they slogged the extra half-mile or more from Tarpots to the top of the lane and turned at last for home.

Within a month of this celebratory display of naval and imperial splendour Britain had put its signature to the Anglo-German Naval Agreement, effectively acquiescing in Hitler's repudiation of the arms limitations imposed at Versailles, and from then on the German fleet assumed a new title: Kriegsmarine, or 'War Navy'.

The next searchlight display to be seen over the town would be in earnest not celebration. *Courageous* with almost half her crew was lost within a fortnight of the outbreak of war. And little more than six years from that Jubilee celebration, following the brief but violent exchange with the more advanced *Bismarck*, saw *Hood*, the pride of the British fleet, at the bottom of the Denmark Strait, and her sister ship, *Rodney*, exacting revenge in the sinking of *Bismarck* just three days later.

4

Fag Ends and Fleapits

Poplar a radical centre of infection eating away at the heart of London, the LCC organised as a Soviet, and the capital city of the Empire a socialist state: that, declared the treasurer of the Conservative Party and his supporters, was the prospect facing the country if the electors of London faltered at the coming election, but Londoners thought otherwise, and March of 1934 saw Labour in control of the LCC for the first time.

If the commissars of the Poplar 'Soviet' were emboldened by this success they had a strange way of demonstrating their revolutionary credentials. Nowhere can the Silver Jubilee of 1935 have been more enthusiastically celebrated. Streets were decorated with flags and bunting, the Mayor of Poplar was received by Their Majesties at Limehouse Town Hall, and 30,000 schoolchildren, entertained in honour of the event, each carried home with them a Jubilee beaker and portraits of the King and Queen. In 1937 the coronation of the new king was celebrated with street decorations, coloured lights and medallions for the children, and from the annual New Year's parties given to all of Poplar's schoolchildren telegrams of loyal greetings and good wishes were sent to Their Majesties and graciously acknowledged.

Such exuberant displays of patriotic flag-waving did nothing to divert Poplar or the LCC from their radical and enlightened social and educational policies, however. By 1935 pre-school centres for children were in place in Poplar and as soon as he was three years old Phoebe was able to shuffle her son off to nursery school.

They called her 'The Cuckoo Mother' in the family – always more than ready to enrol her mother or sisters as babysitters while she pursued her own interests. But in 1935 her motives were economic not personal: times were getting harder and the nursery

56

school gave her the opportunity to find work and add a little to the family income.

An outgoing, gregarious child, he chatted happily and without apprehension with his mother as they left the terrace, collected a few sweets at the corner shop and passed through the two narrow passages that led to the school in North Street. The family association with the school was a long one. His sister was in one of the senior classes, and his younger aunts had been there twenty years earlier in circumstances that tragically foreshadowed the events to come in 1940.

After her brief flirtation with religion, Elsie found her true home in the suffragette movement, and by 1917 had for more than three years been cook and general assistant at a welfare centre and restaurant set up by Sylvia Pankhurst in Railway Street, Poplar. It was a fine June day, and she had as usual taken her two younger sisters the short distance from home to school before setting off for the centre. By late morning she had been hard at work in the kitchens for several hours. The day was hot and the kitchens stifling, and for relief from the heat Elsie was working with her stockings undone and hanging slack around her ankles.

Aircraft were not a common sight in 1917, and when the noise of engines was heard from the direction of the docks she walked over to the door where one of the nurses was already standing looking up at a cluster of aircraft moving slowly across the sky. In the street there was the same interest, everyone had stopped to watch the aircraft as they passed towards the west. There was much excited talk, but no immediate show of concern when the word went round that they were German planes. The sound of a distant explosion meant little to Elsie as she returned to her work in the kitchen, but it was not many minutes before the cry was heard along the street: 'North Street School's been bombed.'

The work that she had in hand fell to the floor, and panic seized her as she thought of the two younger sisters she had left at the school earlier in the day. Still in her apron, her stockings flapping round her ankles, she rushed from the canteen. It was a long, hot run of more than half a mile: over the footbridge that spanned the railway lines from the docks; through the gaping crowds around the shops and stalls in Chrisp Street market; and on past Ricardo Street School (itself to be destroyed in the Blitz of 1940), its windows lined with children and teachers all looking to the west.

As she approached North Street the pavements were crowded with people all hurrying in the same direction, many for the same reason as Elsie, others with the interest of the morbidly curious.

Finally she stopped, breathless and uncertain whether to go first to the school or to home. Then from the passageway that led to North Street she saw a cluster of adults and children emerging. Louisa was with them, holding the two young children by the hand, and leading them back home. Their faces were white and tear-stained. They were dishevelled and dusty, but otherwise they were unharmed. A message was sent to Railway Street that Elsie would not be back for the rest of the day.

It was not until late in the afternoon that they heard for certain that other children had not been so lucky. The bomb had passed through the roof and two floors of the building before exploding on the ground floor used by the infants. Eighteen five-year-olds were killed and many more seriously injured. Three days later Lou, Elsie and the children were among the many who attended the service for the victims at All Saints' Church. When it was over, through silent crowds that lined the length of the streets, the horse-drawn hearses piled high with wreaths and flowers processed along East India Dock Road. Behind them came private carriages, motor cars and the hundreds of mourners who followed on foot. Shops were shut, curtains drawn and flags flown at half-mast along the route. Finally the procession turned back to the East London cemetery where the children were buried, most of them in a communal grave.

It was London's first experience of terror bombing. The tragedy became known as 'The Poplar Outrage', and anti-German feeling was subsequently intense throughout the East End. It was a portent of the wholesale destruction that followed a generation later when thousands died, many to be left buried in the rubble where they fell, and there was little time or opportunity to mourn them.

Close as she had been to the tragedy, Elsie remembered it not only with sadness for the children, but with compassion for those who bore the brunt of local anger and reprisals. Writing of it in the closing years of her life she said:

I used to feel awful when it happened but didn't dare say anything. There was a German bakers round by us that had been there since I was a child. We got all our bread there for

58

years. He was a decent man with a wife and two daughters and a really good neighbour. I nearly cried to see his things being thrown out of the window and his shop smashed up. I said it was a blooming shame but somebody turned on me at once and told me to shut my mouth. It was too risky to sympathise with them. The sad thing was that it was the local people, people who must have known them well and dealt with them for many years.

No thought of those events troubled John's mind as he was led into the playground and gazed up at the building before him. Typical of most London schools of the time the architecture was institutional and forbidding. Above two large double doors, row upon row of windows rose through three floors of plain functional brickwork. Around the building a bleak tarmac playground was hemmed in by walls and a wire fence.

Beyond the doors, however, teaching had progressed from the strict, uncompromising discipline of the earlier decades of the century to a more relaxed regime. Learning by rote, especially of the times tables, still had its place, but there were informal activities, and the teachers were friendly and welcoming. That was particularly true of the babies' class where after lunch and playtime the children were put down to rest for a while in little truckle beds. He found it easy to slip off to sleep there, secure and snug under the light cover. From the rest of the school a faint drone of voices drifted in through the windows, dust motes danced in the narrow rays of sunlight where the curtains gaped a little, and swimming around in his head the thoughts and dreams engendered by the novelty of it all slowly blended and merged into nothingness. Until he was five his time at school was a relaxed affair – a mixture of a very little learning by rote, story times, painting or crayoning and other informal activities.

Of those early days he remembered little apart from story time which followed the afternoon sleep, and lasted until his mother called again to take him home. All and any stories held his attention absolutely. He wasn't blessed with his gran's memory, but more than sixty years later fragments of half-remembered tales, one-liners, snatches of songs and illustrations from a rag-bag collection of North Street memories still flashed unbidden into his mind.

When, at the age of five, the business of education had to start in earnest he was less than enthusiastic and did little that pleased his teachers or parents. But if growing up brought the burden of school it also brought the freedom of the streets, and it was for the evenings, weekends and holidays that he lived, when he could be out with his friends, or paying his pennies for entry to the children's cinema show at the weekend.

For weekday entertainment the children of Poplar had only to move out into the streets where trades and activities that had their origins in Victorian times or earlier still clung precariously to life and were able to play out their farewell performances in the few years that were left to them before war arrived to ring down the final curtain.

Horse-drawn carts and wagons were one of the main attractions in a world which had not yet been entirely surrendered to motor traffic. In and around the docks horses were still used extensively to move cargo, and along East India Dock Road they plodded their way indifferent to the trams and buses that hemmed them in or the cars and lorries lined up behind them on the long, sloping approaches to Blackwall Tunnel. Not until just before the war was there any restriction on its use by horse-drawn traffic or even costermongers' hand-barrows, and even then the restraints applied only during rush hours.

Carts or wagons passing through the side streets were all fair game for any of the boys to slip up behind, hang on to the rear flap and find a foothold or even a narrow ledge for a seat and a free ride. On the main roads it was a more dangerous enterprise, but even there some bold spirits would chance their arm, find a comfortable niche and disappear into the distance thumbing their noses at the mates they left behind. But the game wasn't enjoyed without risk.

'Whip behind, Mister.' At the warning shout from a passer-by the choice was a simple one: drop off and risk losing face, or hang on and chance a touch of the lash. Most carmen when they heard the call just went through the motions of raising and flourishing their whip, but there were a few mean-spirited, vicious men who took a delight in trying to hurt, and if a boy was unlucky, a well-directed cut from the whip would leave a stinging red weal across face or arm and send him scurrying away to hide his tears.

For a brief period in the nineteenth century the Wades Arms on the corner of Jeremiah Street enjoyed celebrity as Ben Tillett's headquarters during the Great Dock Strike of 1889, and it was from the central committee rooms above the bar parlour that the delegates issued their manifesto to the workers of all trades throughout London. Within little more than five weeks with world-wide support and widespread approval their main objectives had been achieved.

There was no blue plaque on the wall to mark that watershed in the life and conditions of working men, although for many years a framed copy of the manifesto hung in the bar parlour, and the memory and radicalism of those days lived on throughout the borough. But by the time Pappy and his family moved to the area the Wades Arms was once again just one of hundreds of East End corner pubs.

For the local lads, however, its glories were revived on delivery days when the brewer's dray arrived. Pulled by a couple of monu-mental Clydesdales or shires, the steel-rimmed wheels sounded a low, rumbling warning of its approach, and street entertainment at its best. The boys were the audience, the towering horses the main attraction. With the brake applied, and the wheels chocked up for good measure, the horses were fitted with their bags of chaff before delivery could begin. Then with their noses buried deep in the bags they stood snuffling contentedly, occasionally hammering out a metallic note from the road with their shoes as they changed weight from one leg to another, and almost always fulfilling expec-tations and relieving themselves in a sparkling torrent of amber urine that shimmered on the road and streamed in the gutters. Their young audience watched the performance with admiration, even envy, while the older boys whispered their crude jokes behind cupped hands.

Occasionally their expectations were exceeded and one, perhaps two, steaming mounds of chestnutty, straw-flecked dung would be deposited between the shuffling hoofs. Then there would be a rush for a bucket and, if possible, a shovel, but if not they weren't fussy – hands would do just as well to scoop up what the horses left behind when they moved on. Competition was keen, and there was always a little pushing and shoving, for the gardeners of Rigden Street were willing to pay a ha'penny or two for a good bucket of horse manure.

With the dray secured, the hatch doors in the pavement were thrown back, and from the dark, cavernous depths of the cellar the heavy and sickening odour of stale beer and damp cellar brickwork swelled into the air, to mingle with the acrid stench of urine or the darker, richer scent of dung. One by one the steel-rimmed barrels dropped from the dray onto the stuffed sack that broke their fall, were roped down the slide into the bowels of the cellar, and rumbled across the brick floor onto their racks. With the delivery done there was a half-pint and a fag for the draymen, and then they were on their way, either indulgent or intolerant, according to their mood, of the boys who sought to cling on behind.

Milkman, coalman, baker, rag-and-bone man all made regular rounds with horse-drawn carts. None of them offered the entertainment of the brewer's dray, but there was always the prospect of a bucket or two of dung. There were other less frequent visitors of which the saddest were the occasional horse-drawn hearses, especially when they were for children. Life in Poplar had improved from the earliest years of the twentieth century when infant mortality ran at more than 80 per cent, but it was still a tough environment for youngsters, and they were not unfamiliar with the slow progress of a black-draped hearse through silent streets, and the little, flower-covered white coffin behind the glass.

Despite the changing times there were still a few itinerant traders who, with handcart or without, eked out a living in the community on foot. Some were regulars; others came and went as they made, or failed to make, enough to live on. Hawkers and muffin men shouted their wares down the terrace. The sweep called by appointment. The cats' meat man on his rounds was dogged by every moggy on the loose. The tallymen knocked their way along the doors, but not at number four: neither Lou nor anyone in the family entertained buying on tick. Nor did she buy from the shrimp and winkle barrow at the weekends: for anything fishy she had her own family connection. Bread, basic fruit and veg, and the sweepings of the street cleaner, all made their way through the streets on open carts or boxcarts, and regularly on Sundays, in good time for afternoon tea, the watercress and celery man knocked on Lou's basement door. Haggard and unshaven he was of all the callers the saddest sight and most poorly dressed. He handed over the order and collected his money in hands from which the fingers hung swollen, knotted and twisted from his occupation, or arthritis or both, and as he drank his cup of tea he listened to Lou's chat with unblinking, watery-blue eyes and slow nods of his head. He was a regular until the summer of the Phoney War when abruptly his visits ceased.

Men from the Pru and other insurers did their rounds every four weeks or so but Phoebe favoured the Royal London and Mutual, and just two days after his birth, with a proper sense of the realities of infancy and cost of funerals in the thirties, the boy's life had been insured. Phoebe's one old penny a week (a halfpenny for half the cover if that was all you could afford) was collected four-weekly by Mr French who knocked his way around the doors of the borough looking as wan and threadbare as the policyholders who paid their few coppers into his collecting bag. For that modest weekly contribution there would be a return of six pounds – perhaps a third of the cost of the most basic funeral – if the child died under the age of three, more if it survived longer.

It was illegal for any greater cover to be given either by one company or more than one in combination. With infant mortality still at around 6 per cent in Poplar, a progressive borough with an enlightened policy on public health, and worse elsewhere, there seems to have been more than commercial prudence in the provision. At a time when the use and effectiveness of contraception was patchy, when babies died for all and no reason, and yet one more addition to a family already destitute would be one too many, the temptation of even a six-pound return for a few pennies laid out may have been difficult to resist as a desperate but temporary respite from poverty.

Conscientiously kept up through peace and war, sickness and health, Blitz and blessings, Phoebe's total premiums of £12 8s converted into a paid-up policy for £88.41p when she died fifty-seven years later.

The entrance to the Queen Victoria Mission offered quite different attractions. The doorway faced east, and in fine weather small groups of resident seamen met in the arched entrance way, sunning themselves as they smoked and chatted. Fascinated by the strangeness of dress, skin colour or general appearance, the younger boys gathered at the steps below them listening uncomprehendingly to the strange sounds of the conversation, or the comments that were jokingly directed at them in a broken English too thick for them to understand.

It was a time when the pleasures of smoking were unclouded by any threat of lung cancer, and by men it was almost universally enjoyed. For the boys longing to emulate them smoking was one of the marks of being a man: they were fascinated by it, and John was no exception. Time and time again he stood alongside his father watching with admiration as he teased out a pinch of sweet-smelling tobacco into the centre of a thin Rizla cigarette paper, and rolled and shaped it skilfully between thumbs and fingers. He noted the delicate licking of the gummed edge, the flare and crackle of the match, and the expression of satisfaction as the first cloud of grey smoke was sucked down. When his uncles called it was just the same – out came the Weights or Woodbines to be offered round and lit before they could sit back and relax in their haze of blue-grey smoke. All around him the ritual was being played out by the men that he knew, and the same message was signalled by them all – this is good, this is enjoyable.

The boys had gathered as usual at the foot of the steps leading up to the mission doors when three or four seamen who had been lounging and smoking above them were called inside. As they went the short dog-ends of their cigarettes were flipped towards the steps where they fell still alight and glowing. It was a fine morning. The smoke drifted and swirled enticingly into the sunlight, and the butts lay temptingly close to the boys. They sniffed at the smoke and made up their minds as one.

John looked quickly about him, reached out and picked up one of the dog-ends. Even as he put the butt to his lips his mother rounded the corner and their eyes met. His attempted act of concealment was too crude, too late and, as retribution bore down on him, quite hopeless. His gran, who was with his mother, hadn't witnessed the crime and was astonished when Phoebe rushed from her, dragged John from his group of friends and proceeded to give him a good pasting.

'What on earth's the matter, Phoebe? Why are you hitting the boy? What has he done?'

'Didn't you see the little bugger? He was smoking those filthy dog-ends.'

In attempting to mould his behaviour his mother's arguments were invariably physical, and as they were never excessive he received them with a resigned acceptance. It was left to his father to attempt the subtler approach of explanation and reasoning. He had little to say of the habit of smoking itself, not then seen for the evil it was, but described in graphic terms the possible implications of putting into the mouth the wet and soggy butt-end of a cigarette just taken from the spittle-laden lips of a stranger.

The Saturday-morning picture show took place at The Gaiety Picture House on the corner of Pekin Street and East India Dock Road. For the local children it was the major event of the week, and those with parents who could afford to give them the few coppers that opened its magic doors were the cocks of the walk. Those without did all they could during the week to make the money: a penny, a ha'penny, even a farthing at a time scrounging old jam jars or newspapers to sell on for a coin or two, lending a hand with the Chrisp Street traders clearing up at the end of the day, or scouring the streets for the horse dung prized by the local gardeners.

A stately pleasure dome and palace of delights to the children, The Gaiety was just one of the many fleapit cinemas that peppered the East End feeding an increasing appetite in the population for an escape from the depressing reality of the world about them. Comforting, welcoming and maternal she wrapped her children in forgetfulness and offered them a world of dreams.

Closed and in daylight her dingy exterior promised little. Slab-sided brick walls, grimed with the dirt thrown up from the road, were pierced here and there with blank exit doors. At the corner, where the two roads met, the foyer was a dark, uninviting recess closed off by strong and rusty metal grills. She could have been just another Dockland warehouse had it not been for the images on large poster-boards trumpeting the delights she had to offer.

But when John first met her The Gaiety was all dolled up in party dress, and she bowled the young boy over. On a late return home from a family visit, the tram clanked to a standstill alongside the cinema. It was a depressing winter evening, dark and drizzling. Fidgeting unhappily on the wooden tram seat, cold and uncomfortable, he gazed out of the window into the night. The bulk of The Gaiety could be seen only in vague outline, but high up on the walls, on illuminated poster-boards, details of the coming attractions shone out in a blaze of lights. At the foyer entrance the rusting grills were drawn back out of sight. Coloured bulbs flickered around selected stills of dramatic or tender moments from the night's main feature. Concealed lighting threw a soft, gentle glow over entrance steps, foyer and cash booth, promising warmth and comfort within. From the top of the steps a commissionaire, resplendent in uniform and gold-braided cap, marshalled two queues of customers as they pressed forward, anxious to be inside and out of the rain. Lost in wonder he gazed out at the scene until the tram moved off.

Within a few months of that brief encounter his sister was bribed and cajoled to accompany him on an introductory visit to The Gaiety's Saturday-morning performance. For Moira it was a wasted and potentially embarrassing couple of hours, and the arrangement was short-lived. They got on well enough together, but differences of character and an age gap of six years meant that they had few interests in common. Fastidious, bookish and reserved she was home-loving and home-centred. She had a small circle of like-minded friends with whom she met from time to time, but otherwise was happy to pass the day with her books or in the company of the adults. By contrast, careless of appearance, content with comics and eager at all times to be out and roaming the streets, he was a sore burden to her whenever they were out together, and for him the limited benefit of her company was offset by the restrictions it imposed. Never happier than wandering the streets with a doorstep of bread and jam in his hand, he resented the pre-departure frisking he received and her embargo on any form of consumption. Eating in public was common and bad manners, she said. Bread or cakes were beyond the pale, ice cream was forbidden, and even sweets were kept for the dark of the cinema.

Her reluctant participation was eventually brought to an end by his response to the entertainment. Cries of excitement or shouts of warning she endured with patience. She even smiled indulgently when, fraught with tension and fearful delight at the simple horrors of a ghost story, he buried his head in her lap. But at the sound of the fluting notes that introduced *Laurel and Hardy*, or the first flickering images of the *Keystone Cops*, she sighed and gritted her teeth for the ordeal to come. His response to comedy was not merely vocal; it was physically all-consuming and unrestrained. In full spate, tears mingled with laughter, and in an ecstasy of delight she had actually seen him slip from his seat to the floor. Even in the twilight of the cinema she found it mortifying beyond belief to be associated in any way with such behaviour.

Following her withdrawal he was for a while escorted by his mother, an aunt or whoever could conveniently find the time to take him, and then return to bring him back. The streets of Poplar presented no serious threat to a sensible youngster, however, and it wasn't long before he went unescorted and unbridled by any constraints on his eating habits or behaviour. Given the opportunity he would have watched anything, at any time, in any picture house he could get to, but his solo cinema attendances while still young were restricted to Saturday morning at The Gaiety.

Long before opening time the surrounding streets were thronged with children streaming excitedly towards the cinema. On and around the entrance steps they clustered, jostling for a forward spot to be sure of getting one of the favoured seats. Sulking on the fringes were the few envious unfortunates who had been unable to earn, beg or perhaps steal the money they needed. A few may have harboured thoughts of slipping through in the rush, or getting a friend to nudge open the emergency doors so close to the lavatories, but the management were generally more than a match for any of those dodges.

At the end of each week's programme came an episode from the long-running serial, concluding always with a moment of high dramatic tension, excitement and physical danger for hero or heroine. This was the tease to lure the young audience back week after week, and as they waited impatiently to be inside they speculated feverishly on the outcome of the climax that had left them on the edges of their seats when the previous showing ended. Would the wagon train survive the savages' attacks? Would the cavalry be in time? Would the screaming circular saw roll remorselessly forward, chewing its way through flesh and bone, or would there be a last-minute rescue? Opinion was always polarised between the hopes of those of mild and timid disposition, mainly girls, who longed for the happy ending, and the anarchic wishes of those made of sterner stuff, mainly boys, aching for the blood-and-guts climax that never came.

Finally, at a sound from within, the noise subsided. The inner doors were thrown open, and the grills were drawn back. One by one the children slipped their pennies into the waiting hand, and passed through from reality into their Saturday never-never land.

The Gaiety was a poor relation indeed compared with The Hippodrome just along the road, where plush fittings, ornate decorations and an electric organ added to the pleasures, and to the cost, but the children slipped into her shabby intimacy as into an old and familiar coat. On the side walls painted images and scenes of exotic, far-away places showed dimly through a patina of nicotine and slow-dried condensation laid down over the years by a million exhalations. In the aisles the carpets were thin, worn and pockmarked by cigarette ends stubbed out underfoot. Seats and armrests shone from the polishings of a thousand backsides and elbows, lights were broken or unshaded, and at the front a shabby, flimsy curtain hung apologetically before the screen. The ventilation system, like the rest of the fixtures and fittings, was in terminal decline, and on the Saturday morning the stale, pungent odour of the Friday-night audience and their cigarettes still pervaded the interior.

On such matters the children were an indulgent and forgiving audience. Broken seats, torn fabric and dirty walls were not their concern. It was for the satisfaction and nourishment of their young souls that they were assembled, waiting expectantly for the dimming of the house lights at eleven sharp. Then the background music faded, the curtains moved, hesitated, jerked again and finally drew back. From the back of the hall a brilliant beam of light cut through the thin haze of cigarette smoke still hanging in the air, and for the next ninety minutes they were embraced by the world of adventure and excitement that burst into life before them.

Political correctness was not even a passing thought in the censor's mind. Stereotyping was not only the rule of the day, but as far as the young Saturday-morning audience was concerned it was an essential part of their viewing. Dress, accent, colour and, of course, general appearance were clear and immediate markers for their cheers and boos, and so heavily underscored that they left no scope for confusion.

Cowboys and Tarzan adventures featured heavily, most of them from Hollywood. From home studios came Blake of Scotland Yard, Old Mother Riley, Will Hay and friends, and stirring tales from the far-flung Empire. The commitment and belief of the audience in the people and events that unfolded before them was total and absolute. They were the sources on which their imaginations drew to shape the games and adventures of the week to come, transforming the dull and shabby streets, alleys and courtyards into the prairies of the West, or the tree-shaded garden of the Board of Trade into the steaming jungles of Africa. To the bark of the six-gun and a cry of 'Hi-Yo Silver' the Lone Ranger carried law and order into the badlands of Jeremiah Street. Police cars raced through Rigden Street as Blake of the Yard hunted down the sinister Scorpion in the dens of Chinatown – in reality only a few streets away and well known to most of the audience. And as Carters Terrace echoed to the chilling call of Tarzan, the throbbing drums of the pygmies stopped the milkman in his tracks.

The comedies they laughed over and talked about, but there was a quality to the anarchy of St Michael's, that infamous seat of learning and misrule, the knockabout antics of Mother Riley, and the deceptively simple idiocies of Laurel and Hardy that did not lend itself to their games.

The enthusiasms of those Saturday morning cinema days were a transient childhood affair for John, as for all of them. The villains reviled then, the heroes and heroines he loved, and the bold adventurers upon whose every exploit he hung, almost without exception faded, and were forgotten. Just two, like Everyman, remained by his side – a light in his darkness, and a very present help in trouble.

Stanley – simple, naive, honest and devastatingly helpful. Oliver – respectable, substantial and desperately dignified, a gentle soul who wrestled honestly but hopelessly with life's complexities without a gram of iron ever entering his soul. They lived in a world where the sun always shone, and optimism was the guiding principle. Together they walked through mayhem and catastrophe. Houses disintegrated to their component parts around them, cars fragmented and collapsed on impact after impact, trains crashed, boats sank and wives abused them, but immortals that they were, they emerged from it all physically unscathed and mentally unscarred. Suits might be tattered, eyebrows singed and the day's hopes dashed beyond redemption, but tomorrow once again they would be strolling out into the sunny, slumbering suburbs of Hollywood, where round every corner confusion, calamity or James Finlayson lay waiting to confound them.

Eventually the days arrived when John's horizons could expand beyond The Gaiety and the passing shows on the local streets. Old enough to hold his own on longer walks he moved out with his father to the more distant parts of the borough he knew so well; out to the hive of activity around and about the docks; to the swing bridges, piers and jetties of the Isle of Dogs and the press of shipping on the river; to the narrow, secret lanes leading down to ancient little-used steps onto the foreshore; to the industrial waste-lands and slums along the Limehouse Cut, and the horse-drawn narrowboats on the Regent's Canal; and everywhere the contradictory cocktail of poverty and plenty, activity and indolence of the cosmopolitan world that was the East End around the docks of London.

5

A Fishy Business

Almost opposite Stepney Junction station on the Commercial Road, just a short distance beyond the Regent's Canal, the only business enterprise owned by any member of the family was run by Lou's oldest son, Bill. A modestly successful fishmonger, he enjoyed a standard of living undoubtedly better than any one else in the family, but to a young boy it seemed that life as lived in Stepney was a whole world away from his own. Bill had once had a motorbike and now owned a car. That alone put him in a class apart, even if it was just a basic Ford utility pressed into service early each morning to carry the business stock back to the shop from Billingsgate.

Bill and his wife Em lived relatively well, but were always open-handed with the family in sharing the benefits they enjoyed. On their occasional Sunday-afternoon visits to see Louisa, they always arrived with something special for her. Of more significance to John was the knowledge that a meeting with Bill meant that he was in for a good 'drop'. He learned early on that rather than giving money, Bill always 'dropped a few bob'. To a young boy it seemed a casual way of proceeding with cash, but as long as the drop came his way he was happy – Bill was never less than generous. A drop meant at least a bob, sometimes half a dollar, and on very rare and special occasions a dollar itself. Why it was a 'dollar' was a puzzle, for Bill was as East End as they come, but in that golden age when the tourist got almost four dollars for his pound no boy was going to quibble about terms when it came to five shillings in the pocket.

If John knew they were coming he would be waiting at the end of the terrace for half an hour before their arrival. Apart from his financial expectations, he looked forward to an afternoon with his cousin Leslie, just a few months younger than himself. When the

71

car stopped and the doors opened, the scent of their own unique carte de visite billowed out and embraced him. As they walked to the house it enveloped them like an aura. When they hung their coats behind the door and settled into the warmth of Lou's room, it swelled through the passages and up the stairs, announcing their presence more effectively than any footman. Clara, whose nose was particularly finely attuned, had been known to look up from her activity in the front room on the floor above and, without being otherwise told of their arrival, sniff once or twice and announce, 'Ah! That must be Em and Bill.'

Bill certainly knew his trade exceptionally well. For his fresh fish alone he had a reputation that created a core of regular customers, but it was for his home-smoked products that he was renowned. It was the smoking operations that established and maintained his reputation, and created the distinctive aura that travelled with the family. They lived behind and over the shop and throughout the house the exhalation from Bill's smoke-hole permeated everything. The fibres of their clothing were impregnated with it. It hung in the curtains, sank into the carpets, wrapped itself around the woodwork and laid siege to the very fabric of the building. In John's innocence, with so much fish around him, he thought on his early visits that the smell was that of the sea itself.

Bill's life was demanding and active. Up early for his daily trip to the old Billingsgate fish market, he had to be back in time to have his fish prepared and on the counter when the shop opened, and before attending to his speciality, the smoking. Short and compact of stature, his fingers were callused and cracked from hard work and overexposure to cold water. His complexion was highly coloured, his cheeks flecked with broken veins and his hair thinning but not greyed. He was clean-shaven, wore horn-rimmed glasses, had knowing eyes and John could not recall meeting him when he wasn't cheerful and lively. It was mercenary, he knew, but pocket money was tight and whenever they met he waited for Bill's hand to go to his pocket.

'Here you are, Johnny-boy . . .' Always that and never John. '. . . Find something to spend that on.'

Spending never presented any problem.

Em was a more complex character and difficult to read. Dark-haired, of distinctive appearance, amply proportioned and bosomed, she was as friendly and generous as Bill, but there was an air of moodiness about her suggesting that it would be well not to cross her. She had a strong and colourful voice, could hammer out a tune on the piano 'by ear', and when in full flow and well nourished could have been taken for a performer from the halls.

If they flourished, and they did, they deserved it. They shared their success, and enjoyed it themselves in a way that was common in a community where work was hard, rewards generally few, and success all too fleeting. In White Horse Street just across the road from the shop was The Swan and there at the end of the day they were often to be found, Em at the piano with a gin and tonic, Bill at the table with his mates and a pint.

It was on visits to Stepney during the working week, sometimes with his gran sometimes with his mother, that John saw something of the mysteries of Bill's craft. The early visits were a trial for him, not only for the smell of the smokery, but also for the brooding and menacing atmosphere of the workplace. There was just one entrance alongside the shopfront which led either to the living area on the right, or straight on into the long, broad corridor that ran the length of the building. It was here that all the preparatory work on the fish was carried out. At the end a door opened into a backyard in which were smoke-hole, store sheds and lavatory.

It was the working area that played such havoc with the young boy's nerves on the early visits when he had to pass through it to the yard beyond if he wanted the lavatory. Eels writhed and twisted in vats alongside the wooden block and chopper that would give them their quietus before they went on piecemeal to the jellying process. Winkles soaking in tanks awaited their fate passively, with no visible sign of protest before they were despatched by a plunge into a vat of boiling water, an end which John thought unbearably cruel, but which they met with no more than a faint sigh of protest as the water foamed over them.

Fish prepared or awaiting preparation lay on slabs on either side of the passageway. From whole fish, large and small, moist eyes followed him reproachfully, or mouths gaped in mute protest as he passed. The neatly cleaned and trimmed fillets, divested entirely of their fishiness, would scarcely have attracted his attention had it not been for the waste bins beneath the slabs, from which disembodied heads leered at him from a sea of guts.

In normal circumstances the contents of Bill's gut bins gave rise to no concern. Regularly emptied and cleaned, as they were in peacetime, they presented no problem. The bins and their contents were placed in the backyard overnight. The yard was opened and waste collected early the following morning, and the bins emptied and cleaned before they were reused. If things went wrong, however, the contents of the gut bins had all the disruptive potential of hazardous waste, and when war came circumstances would seldom be normal and often went wrong. Despite their position at the heart of the bombers' target area in the Docklands, Bill and Em stuck it out and in the shop it was business almost as usual for much of the time. The same could not be said of a waste collection service that was understandably erratic. Bins could stand in the yard for two or even three days before they were emptied, but even that could be managed with care.

It was a simple enough combination of events that produced the crisis. There had been no collection of Wednesday's waste on the Thursday or on the Friday. The air raids had been particularly bad, so Bill and Em decided not to open on the Saturday, and on the Friday afternoon they closed the shop and left for a weekend in the relative peace of Essex. The gut bins were left in the backyard to be emptied on the Monday, but unnoticed by anyone the lid on the Wednesday bin had already been standing slightly open for two days.

It was a warm weekend. Their intended return on the Sunday night was prevented by an air raid that put the railway line out of action and it was not until the Tuesday that the line reopened. In the meantime the bins had been forgotten and Em and Bill were quite happy to have a couple of extra days away from the thick of the action. On the Tuesday after opening the shop door Em passed on through the passageway, heading for the lavatory in the yard. Her screams were followed by a call to Bill.

'Oh my God! What can we do, Bill?'

By then Bill was with her at the open door. Bluebottles had found their way under the loose lid of the gut bin, and for five days corruption had thrived and prospered without interruption. The yard was carpeted in a seething, writhing mass of maggots, and the lid on the bin stirred and shifted under the pressure of those still forcing their way into the light.

For years Bill felt queasy whenever he told the story: the sickening squelch underfoot as he crossed the yard to lift the cover from the drain; the revolting task of sweeping and washing them

74

away with buckets of water; and his tactical mistake in trying to destroy those still in the bin by pouring on a solution of bleach – they simply erupted from the bin more violently than before. It took an hour or more to clear the worst away, and for days the air in the yard was thick with bluebottles as the maggots concealed in a hundred nooks and crannies completed their life cycle.

Two large wooden doors in the backyard enclosed Bill's smoke-hole and chimney. Inside the hole every surface was layered with deposits from decades of oak smoke, and the oils slowly leached from the shoals of fish that had hung there. On walls black as the pit itself, thin, greasy, bituminous curtains sagged one over another, and from the upper reaches of the flue long treacly locks of tar hung down like pitch-dark pendants. From a bed of smoking oak chips in the bottom of the hole the choking vapours curled slowly upwards. Through rank upon rank of split and gutted fish they rose, slowly transforming the pale and pallid flesh of haddock into the soft, golden hues and delicious smoky flakes of the finnan haddie that adorned Bill's counter and made his reputation.

On the white-tiled shop counter, seductively displayed to tempt the casual shopper and reinforce the preferences of his regulars, Bill's selection may have looked like a comprehensive harvest of the seven seas, but was in fact carefully tailored to the tastes and pockets of the East End. A phalanx of oak-smoked haddocks formed the centrepiece. On either side the delicate whites, flesh-tones and pinks of filleted plaice, sole, cod steaks, whiting and skate wings blended with the rich tans and russets of smoked kippers, roes and eels, and displays of unfilleted bright-eyed herring and mackerel. At the back of the counter, and on a shelf to the side, was a selection of those much-favoured and tasty specialities that formed the basis of so many East End teas and celebrations. Jars of pickled cucumbers (wallies to the locals) and sweet-cured herrings (rollmops), tempting displays of scallops on their shells, bowls of jellied eels, boxes of sprats (smoked or fresh), and with their pint and half-pint measures at the ready, containers of prawns, shrimps, cockles, mussels, whelks and winkles.

After the calm and quiet of his home in the terrace cul-de-sac it seemed to John that the Commercial Road shop was the very hub of the East End world. Beyond the counter fronting the street a constant flow of pedestrians jostled each other on the pavement. Occasionally a face would detach itself from the passing blur to gaze over the fishy display, question a price and either purchase or move on. Trams rolled constantly down the double tracks in the centre of the road carrying passengers west towards the City, or east towards Blackwall and the docks. To the side of the tram tracks, trucks and lorries carried some small part of the relentless tide of goods that moved between London, the docks and beyond.

Opposite the shop Stepney Junction railway station, high above the pavement, marked the point where one branch of the line from the City and the west curled away over the viaduct alongside Regent's Canal Dock to divide, subdivide and finally divide again into the tangle of points, sidings, shunting yards and engine sheds that hemmed in the docks and warehouses of Poplar and the Isle of Dogs.

On the iron girders of the railway bridge over Commercial Road, just a few yards from the shop, each train on the other line drummed an announcement of its arrival or departure. At the beginning and end of the working day they passed through crowded with city workers commuting from Barking, Upminster and beyond to the dirty wastes of the terminus at Fenchurch Street station. Weekends, high days and holidays in summer saw different customers jostling in the booking hall for a day excursion to the common delights of Southend-on-Sea, the more refined air of Westcliff, or the unspoilt world of Leigh-on-Sea with its salt marshes, muddy creeks and inlets, and the tumbledown cockle sheds lining the narrow lane that ran on the seaward side of the railway line.

The need for drinking money must have separated generations of seamen from their parrots, for they could be found in all their variety in the houses around the docks. At Carters Terrace they had Mick. In Stepney they had Poll, sex undetermined, but as Poll's association was almost exclusively with Bill it was assumed that she was female. If so she was no ornament to her sex, for a fouler-tempered, more anti-social bird it would have been hard to find. She could be handled by nobody but Bill, had savaged every visitor to the house who was foolish enough to try to touch her, but had perfected a routine that ensured her survival, and should have earned Bill a fortune on the halls. Given a small cardboard box she methodically trimmed away top and bottom, thrust herself inside and, with head protruding at the top and feet at the bottom, paraded around the cage like a psittacine Ned Kelly shrieking abuse at the surrounding troopers. Pear-tree cuttings, reflectively chewed and savoured by Mick, she received with suspicion and aggression, and in the violence of her response battered and belaboured herself while screaming assault and battery at the stick.

Noisy, abusive and unfriendly as she was, her one endearing attribute was her loving bonding ritual with Bill whenever he gave her time and opportunity. Freed from the cage Poll padded across the floor, and using beak and claws climbed her way up Bill's trousers, over his waist, and up his shirt sleeve until she reached his shoulder where she perched burbling lovingly in his ear and delicately nibbling at his ear lobe with a beak that could have opened a brazil nut.

A poor speaker, she had just one phrase, delivered with an authentic cockney accent: 'Mother's gone over The Swan.' As Em favoured the nearby pub of that name this was the source of some amusement the first or second time it was heard, but rather lost its impact with repetition.

It was the nature of Bill's trade that the shop opened and closed early, and an afternoon visit meant staying for tea. For a family that lived so well in other ways their rooms, compared with those in the rambling four storeys at Carters Terrace, were confined and cramped; just two behind the shop and one upstairs. The only daylight in the living room came from the shop via a lace-curtained panel of glazing through which an eye could always be kept on the counter. During working hours the room could seem dull and dreary, but with the shutters closed on the shopfront, a fire lit, and the lights switched on it was pleasantly snug and comfortable.

In Stepney a baker or a grocer was never more than a few steps along the road, and when teatime arrived it was fresh bread and a creamy, unsalted butter that came in from the Jewish delicatessen nearby. Unsurprisingly fish was the staple ingredient of most meals and such sympathy as John had for the victims did not extend to any curb on his appetite. He found that familiarity with the spectacle soon bred indifference. His reputation as a budding trencherman went before him in the family, and Em not only took pleasure in indulging him, but knew from past experience that he would sell his soul for winkles, and if in season, winkles it would be.

Winkles, even the name can provoke a laugh, are not generally regarded as among the aristocrats of crustacean society. Unassuming, coy and tightly coiled, their shells offer but a cold, closed, virginal front to their suitors, and will not readily surrender their chaste treasure to the clumsy hands of a casual seducer. As every true aficionado will know only patience, gentleness and delicate manipulative skills will achieve the winkle's final loving surrender. Court a winkle as you would her sister, the common oyster, with brute strength and a strong knife, and it will end in tears.

Winkling is half art, half craft, and demands the right tool. A stainless-steel needle, never a pin, is essential. Not too long, about the length of the index finger is right, nor with too sharp a point, or the prize will be torn. Gently, but deftly, tease away the delicate protective shield that guards the winkle's secret, and with the needle tip catch tenderly at the flesh in the deepest recesses of the shell. At this stage most of all have care. Snatch prematurely at the prize, and the pleasure will be shallow and transitory. Have patience and the final consummation will be the sweeter. With loving, spiralling caresses draw out your prize, curled, fresh and gleaming and lay it by. Tease out another, then another, and yet another, until the last empty shell is discarded, and the final winkle tops a dark, glistening, mouth-watering pyramid of its fellows.

On a thickly buttered slice of crusty, fresh, white bread spread the winkles from edge to edge. Sprinkle with the finest available vinegar, season with freshly ground black pepper, cover with another slice of bread, halve the sandwich, and you have the food of paradise. The fragrance of the bouquet, the succulence, the melting texture and the subtle blend of flavours are a delicacy beyond description. Mocked and defamed by the uninitiated and profane as the 'humble' winkle, that diminutive crustacean is to shellfish as the truffle is to fungi – a feast for the connoisseur.

Winkling comes either naturally or not at all, and John was a natural, blessed, even as a child, with the patience and manipulative skills of the born winkler. While others were still picking their way clumsily through the shells, he was moving on to that first long, lingering bite.

On the upper deck of the tram back to Poplar, replete and satisfied with his day and fingering the shilling in his pocket, he gazed from the windows at the passing peepshow which he was still young enough, and perhaps spoilt enough, to imagine revolved by and large with him at its centre. At such times, before the passing years brought disillusionment, it did indeed seem to him that the world was his winkle.

6

Tea at Aunt Tot's

Of the three girls in her family, Louisa was the only one whose
material fortunes had not prospered following marriage. Some
might perhaps have looked back and regretted that whirlwind
romance with a revolutionary Latvian refugee, but Lou considered
herself more than compensated in other ways, nor did she envy her
sisters their material success.

Kate, the oldest of the three, married a printer in 1878, and
from a life in a Blackheath terrace was elevated to a comfortable
semi-detached in Kensington and the services of a domestic servant. By 1900 the printer had graduated to printer and publisher;
home had removed to a substantial detached establishment in the
leafy precincts of Holland Park; and the six children were attended
by a governess. After Kate died, in the early thirties, there was
little contact with the family.

Elizabeth Sarah, the second sister, was known within the family
as Aunt Tot, or by the children as aunty-granny. After a chequered
start to working life as a domestic servant in Islington she married
a mineral water manufacturer, but by the turn of the century the
husband had died leaving her with two young children, and the
business to run. This she did with considerable success until she
married again when the business was sold, and she merged her
inheritance with that of her second husband, Joe Harrod. Joe
owned land and houses in Essex, and there the city business woman
swapped the cramped manufacturing environs of West Ham for
the open, unspoilt countryside of the parish of North Benfleet,
added two more children to her family, and first introduced her
sister to the pleasures of country living. Mayfield, Tot's home, was
just a hundred yards or so along the lane from Clarence Road, and
when Mickey did his pigswill round he regularly passed the house,

but despite John's family connection was distinctly unenthusiastic when he suggested calling there.

Although a countrywoman for more than thirty years there was little about Aunt Tot that fitted the plump, apple-cheeked stereotype. In stature she and Lou were a matched pair: short, lean and wiry. Facially there was less likeness. Tot's face in repose looked more severe and forbidding, less open and generous than Lou's, but was transformed when she smiled.

She did this readily enough, but if Mickey's reluctance to call stemmed from an earlier confrontation over missing produce from Tot's vegetable plot, it was easy to see why he would not be anxious for a second encounter. Despite years surrounded by the rich, slow burr of the Essex locals her London accent was undiluted, and when she spoke it could have been her sister talking. Their appearance mirrored their characters. Lou's hair wandered in disarray and when her grandchildren hugged her, her clothes felt soft, warm and welcoming, Tot's hair was drawn back under tight control, her clothing stiff and unfriendly.

From Bayhurst the family made their occasional teatime visits to Mayfield where Tot lived in circumstances which were recognised by all the family as being very comfortable indeed by comparison with life in the terrace. Their welcome at the house was always warm and the entertainment generous, but even John realised early on that Aunt Tot was not one who was likely to be dropping him a bob or two.

The house was an impressive one for the area, with two plain sash windows up, two large bay windows down, a porch-sheltered front door and woodwork painted overall in cream and dark green. At the rear a large extension included the kitchen and pantry. It stood back from the road in a half-acre plot intensely cultivated and immaculately maintained. There were a few flower beds, some roses and sweet peas grown for cutting, but the emphasis was more on the practical than the ornamental. Joe's workshop and stable stood at the far end of the land and the rest consisted of orchard area, large vegetable plots and a soft fruit garden.

Tot didn't favour a back-door 'drop in for a chat' approach from neighbours or family, so the occasional visits were always made by prior arrangement and marked by a touch of formality. Children were well scrubbed in advance and expected to behave themselves. Louisa and her daughters always looked their best, and the men of the family generally found a good reason to be absent. The approach was always made by the porch and front door in which Louisa knew Tot took particular pride. 'That's really a lovely piece of glass, Tot,' she said as they moved into the hall. She referred to a large panel of leaded, coloured glass in the top half of the door: a stylised representation of the setting sun shedding garish geometric rays over a garden of cabbagey blooms and hovering dragonflies.

In the hall a tall grandfather clock towered above visiting children.

'Belonged to my old mum before she died, John. Would you like to have a look?'

Joe was much more approachable than Tot, and when the others moved into the front room took a simple delight in displaying the weights, pendulum, wheels, cogs, and other moving parts of his family heirloom. On the cracked enamel face an ornate multicoloured coat of arms framed the motto 'By Hand & Hand All Arts Do Stand', and below in black on the white of the dial 'J. Reed Leeds' gave its provenance. In the four corners of the face-plate the decorative work of its provincial artist still glowed with colour in naive visionary scenes of life on the four continents then known to him. In the hierarchy of long-case clocks its place would have been a lowly one, but for the young visitors it bestowed on Aunt Tot's hall the status of a palace.

The furniture, fabrics, ornaments and general display of well-heeled comfort at Mayfield seemed to John as far removed from home, as home was from the Heards' miserable establishment. He made only a few visits, and children are easily impressed so perhaps it was really not so grand, but when the Mayfield days came to an end, and he looked back to those lazy, teatime afternoons, his memories were of comfortable rooms stuffed with furniture and knick-knacks, where floorboards were polished, carpets rich and thick, and the air was filled with the scent of easy country living, of stuffed lavender bags, furniture polish, cut flowers and the sweet lingering aroma of cake and pastry baking.

When Lou and family were visiting, Tot presented afternoon tea in style in the large front room where all her best pieces were on display. Small cakes, pastries and sandwiches arrived on a two-tier stand. There was bread, butter and jam; a large fruit cake to cut at, and serviettes. Two of Tot's daughters, one married one

81

not, lived nearby, and arrived to swell the party just as tea was ready to be poured. They met together only infrequently and in the absence of anything else family affairs and gossip would keep them fully engaged for an afternoon, but were at their happiest with a little scandal to add some spice to their fruit cake.

Not that Tot shared the relaxed, free-thinking attitudes of Lou's family. Unlike them she was not amused by the reports they brought of the young king's Adriatic philandering with Mrs S which came into the docks with the American papers along with the rest of the transatlantic trade but, even while laying into 'that woman' hot and strong, was able to keep an eye on John's wanderings around her repository of treasures.

On the mantelpiece donkeys with nodding heads, tiny porcelain shoes, figurines and lustres stood between silver-framed family photographs. More photographs and handsome oil lamps in brass and crystal gleamed on lace-covered side-tables. Against the wall stood an upright piano with polished brass sconces but its lid was down and locked, and the book of hymns resting on the music stand suggested to the young boy that his aunty-granny might not perhaps be one for a good old sing-song Poplar style.

Behind the glass doors of a slender display case Tot kept her choice items: decorated plates and compotes; a collection of porcelain birds; a miniature silver-cased clock; cut-glass jugs; a pair of deep-blue vases with a banding of gilt decoration; and two pieces to which visiting youngsters invariably took an instant dislike – a pair of matched dogs each with its jaws clenched tightly on a dead rabbit. In centre place was a needle-worked cushion, an old keepsake which Joe took out to show him more clearly. Heart-sized and shaped, with fringed edges and studded with ornamental pins and decorated inserts, it showed a crest, a cannon and the sentimental verse:

> *When the golden sun is sinking,*
> *And your mind from care is free,*
> *When of others you are thinking,*
> *Will you sometimes think of me?*

A relic of Royal Artillery service in the Boer War from Joe's family, it was the one piece from Tot's many treasures that by chance, via Lou and Elsie, eventually found its way to a place in his own home.

With tea and the final cakes disposed of, and bored with the talk of the women, it was Joe as well as John who was released, and together they made their way through the garden to the house and workshops of his brother George. John met Joe only a few times before his death, but like all the children always felt quite at home with him although he was so different in speech and temperament from the pushing, articulate but edgy men of the East End. He spoke the slow, soft Essex dialect that by the end of the century would be submerged by the unrelenting tide of Estuarine. Always gentle and polite he talked to children just as he talked to adults.

He would have been in his seventies at that time, and when young had worked in partnership with his brother George who was a few years younger. But Joe had inherited what land and property had been in the family, so Joe retired while George worked on and lived nearby in accommodation owned by his brother.

Saturday was a normal working day for George, and they went first to the workshops at the far end of the garden. Electricity had been with them for a few years by then and modern tools and methods were beginning to usurp many of the old ways. Outside the workshop a new electrical circular saw stood under cover, but the old saw-pit was still there, half filled with dead leaves and garden debris, and alongside it an oven built into a domed chamber of crumbling bricks was still fired up occasionally for steaming and bending wood.

George 'hello'd' them as they entered the workshop, but then bent his head over his work and went on as before. Old habits died hard with Joe, who although retired slipped on an apron and joined him. 'Got to keep my hand in,' he said, and left John to wander round the workshop while keeping half an eye on him to see that he came to no harm. He heard them talking softly as they worked, but could not always understand what was said. 'Ellum' he came to recognise as 'elm', but 'hoppit', 'cart-rakes' and others of their old dialect words were as foreign to him as those of the sailors chatting on the steps outside the seamen's mission in Poplar.

The tools of their trade were everywhere. Rip saws, bow saws, set squares, tee squares, curves and other assorted geometric shapes hung like eccentric decorations from hooks on the walls.

Tins of waxes, oils, fillers and varnishes filled a single line of shelves. Chisels, hammers, mallets, screwdrivers, pincers and clamps stood ready to hand in brackets fixed behind the work-bench, and on a long trestle at the end of the shop clamps, drills, brace and bit lay with planes and spoke shaves of every shape and size. Left to his own devices he kicked his way through the accumulated shavings of the day's work stirring up the sweet smell of newly-worked wood, and handled the tools freely until he picked up a chisel and was sharply told to put it back.

He watched their hands as they shaved and shaped the timber, confident and unhurried in everything they did. They were thick, clumsy-looking hands, stubby fingers with lumpy knuckles and chipped nails, but they handled their tools with delicacy and sureness of touch. The dark veins on the back of their hands, hard and ridged above the flesh, he took as signs of maturity rather than mortality, and in his childish way he envied them. He wanted to be grown up like that.

At the back of the shop flat sheets of 'ellum' separated by thin strips of wood stood in stacks, slowly seasoning for future use.

'Know what they are?' George nodded towards the sheets of elm. John shook his head.

'Coffin boards! You know what coffins are for?' John nodded his head, and George smiled, turning back to his work. Coffins were their sideline: not in great demand, but a nice steady addition to their income over the years, with two or three of the finished product always stored in a side shed ready for a call from the local undertaker. Death meant nothing to John then, but later, when they were both dead, he wondered just how they had felt as they completed box after box, each time just a little bit closer to the permanent enjoyment of one of their own products.

Together they had also built much of the workaday furniture in the house, certainly everything in the kitchen, and for many other houses in the area. Stick-back chairs, tables, cupboards, shelving, doors and the fine, polished timbers on the floor of the best room had all come from the workshop many years earlier when Joe was still a young man.

Aunt Tot and both of the brothers were regular worshippers at the church of All Saints high on the ridge of the hill at North Benfleet. Sunday morning, prior to attending church, was the one occasion in the week when the brothers applied themselves to a

84

razor, and by Saturday afternoon, which was the only time John ever saw them, they were grey-faced, hairy men, even if visitors were expected.

George had remained a bachelor, living for his work and the few specimens of livestock that he kept on an acre or so of land. He had just one old cow, long since barren and dry, that he kept on out of pure love for the beast. It was the family joke that he indulged her more than he would have done any wife, and certainly in her freshly mucked and strawed barn she lived in conditions that relatively speaking were better than his own.

John went to George's house just once, when Joe walked him there on the way back from a visit to the workshop where they had left George busy completing the job in hand. The garden, mainly devoted to crops, looked tidy and carefully tended. Pens for ducks and geese and a small area for a goat were neat and well maintained, and the accommodation for the cow was immaculate.

The house windows stood half open and the door was unlocked. As they entered a cat and her kittens, disturbed at the plates on one of the tables, scattered across the floor and out of the windows. They walked through the scullery and beyond, into what passed for the sitting room. Both were piled high with the accumulated debris of unsupervised, disorganised living. Plates encrusted with old food, dirty cups, piles of newspapers, stale bread and an empty bird cage littered the two tables. Ragged items of clothing, worn-out discarded shoes, broken tools, wicker baskets, pans, assorted junk and a couple of shotguns were piled on chairs or leaning against the wall.

Just two chairs were clear of rubbish: a stick-back at the table in front of the remains of George's last meal, and an ancient easy chair by the side of the fireplace. Its sagging seat was padded out with what John took for a shaggy rug until it moved and opened two opaque and clouded eyes. 'That's Victor. He's blind and don't go out a lot.' There was a smell about the place which suggested as much.

John thought later that he must have been taken there as some sort of private joke. They stayed only a few minutes, and Joe appeared to have no reason for calling other than to watch John as he wandered around in the middle of the chaos. Nothing more was said, and if Joe was enjoying the situation he did so quietly. When they got back to Aunt Tot's, Joe grinned at the others, 'Young

John's just bin having an inspection of our George's.' They all looked at him and laughed, so at least they appreciated the joke.

In Tot's hall two framed photographs of Joe and George hung side by side. One showed young men in working clothes and a Wednesday or Thursday growth of beard, standing before a large oak tree, each with his hands resting on the long haft of a felling axe. Beneath the photo was a framed account of the volume of useful wood that had come from the tree when it had been felled and the many items including furniture, house fittings and the bell frame for one of the local churches that the brothers had made from it. The other was of the same young men together on a bowling green in front of a small, timber-built clubhouse. Clean-shaven, in white shoes and dressed overall in newly-pressed white or cream, they stood self-consciously with George holding in his great hands the tiniest of cups, their trophy from the local bowling competition. The cup still stood on the mantelpiece, but the green and clubhouse had long gone, replaced by a cycle shop and garage.

The trap that used to collect Lou from the station was still kept up, and another pony had replaced the original, but they were no longer used for arrivals and departures by train. Only once on one of their last visits did Tot decide to ask Joe to harness them up. The trap held only four, including the driver, but Moira resolved the problem by volunteering to spend the rest of her afternoon with Tot's books and magazines, and with Tot at the reins Lou, Phoebe and the boy set off on a horse-drawn tour of the lanes.

After little more than a hundred yards the last of the plot developments was behind them, and the countryside lay unchanged as it would have been for a hundred years and more. On one side the flat acres of Smiler's and Bradfield's farms stretched away towards Burnt Mills, but the buildings and large farmhouses were sadly neglected and little used. On the other the land rose up a long incline to the ridge of the hill, All Saints Church and what was left of the hamlet of North Benfleet.

It was there and then that the Essex elms had their heyday. On either side of the lane they towered above as the trap, now in deep shadow now flecked with sunlight, passed beneath them. They swept imperially up the hedgerows towards the church and along the ridge, dominating the skyline. They clustered around the churchyard where their craggy branches hung brooding over the graves where coffin timbers cut from their fellows, were decaying slowly in the greasy clays beneath. They were the physical presence of the spirit of that countryside, and when over a few years they yellowed to black, skeletal remains that spirit fled with the trees, and the land lay open for the suburbia that was to follow.

On the lane up to the church they left the trap and walked alongside while Tot drove it slowly up the hill. At the crest they turned to the infants' school once attended by her children: just one room, heated by a wood-burning stove on which the teacher baked potatoes in their jackets. A good, basic education, said Tot, and warm and cosy in winter.

Then back towards the church where the path divided around a wide pond: to the left the barns, hayricks and farm buildings that were all that was left of the fifteenth-century hall, to the right a path skirting the pond to a gate in the churchyard wall. Beside the pond, on a wider stretch of grass a rough seat had been set up, no more than two stubs of timber sunk in the ground with a plank between them, and there the four of them sat for a while. It was a retreat to which Tot went regularly, not just to church services, but for the wide, open views and the peaceful, timeless quality of the place. She used a short cut, over the stile on the main lane, along the footpath that ran up the hill under the overhang of the elms, and into the churchyard through a wicket gate at the far corner. Joe's parents, their parents, and many before them were buried there, as she and Joe would be before very long, and almost twenty years later Lou would travel up the hill to join them as one of the very last interments in that ancient burial ground.

John was too young to sense the special appeal of the place, or understand the pleasurable melancholy that time and again drew Tot to walk the hill to the church, and sit there alone immersed in her thoughts of the past. Only later did he realise that in that quiet spot, by the still waters of the pond, in the shadow of the elms, close to the church and the generations lying around it, there lingered for a while a last, shadowy image of deep, unchanging countryside and a distant, rustic life as it was in the days before the men were marched away to an earlier war. Shaded for a few years yet by its elms, it waited, remote and silent, for the changes that were to come.

Alongside the track to the farmyard the wall undulated and sagged where the fickle Essex clays had moved beneath the foundations. Rusty iron stubs in the brick pillars were the only evidence that there had once been gates, and the yard within was dusty and silent. As well as the tractor the farm horse was still in use there. Stable doors stood open, and under the roof of the barn, farm carts, drills, harrows and ploughs awaited their season. The farmhouse was large, bleak and many-windowed, reflecting the years when horse, hand and muscle were the only power sources, and the land and buildings bustled with workers.

The pond seemed never to have belonged to the farm. Its waters were unmuddied and its edges untrampled by the feet of horses or cattle. A few wild ducks moved cautiously away from them to the far side where sedges, flowering rush and yellow flag iris offered concealment. Skimming the water, damsel and dragon flies patrolled in fits and starts. Pond skaters and water boatmen danced on its surface. In the warm, shallow margins young newts and water larvae picked their way across the bottom beneath flakes of duckweed, and overall there hung the heady perfume of meadowsweet.

Above their heads, the swallows, servicing their young in the nests on the beams and ledges of the barns, swept in long arcs around the church, over the wall and skimming low and fast over the surface of the water snatched yet another mouthful for their waiting nestlings. With explanations, descriptions and encouragement from Tot, herself totally absorbed, John would have stayed and gazed the afternoon away, but the day was passing, Phoebe was finding the overpowering scent of meadowsweet offensive to her urban nose, and so they passed on into the churchyard.

By the church porch Tot paused at the grave of the local hero, dead a hundred years but still remembered: John Cole who at Waterloo rose to the call 'Up, Guards, and at them!' and carried to his grave more than twenty years later the musket ball he received during the charge. At the grave of Joe's parents she placed a small bouquet of garden flowers, pulled some ivy from the headstone, and then they wandered slowly round the church through the long grasses and meadow flowers while Tot recited a few of the rustic scandals that were buried beneath them, and pointed out the narrow plots where the protagonists lay awaiting their final reward, or not, according to Tot's judgemental histories. It was a perfect country churchyard. Nothing out of time, nothing intruding. No green chippings, no intrusive marbles, no over-zealous scouring away of ancient stones to line the walls or paths. On the older headstones and monuments the clay, as always, had worked its mysteries, nudging them this way and that, some inclining towards a neighbour as though to share some post-mortem confidence, others recoiling in distaste at the company they were forced to keep. Later monuments were still cut from the same native stone as the old. Crisp and clean at first they were readily weathered by wind, rain and frost, and their bright surface softened by a veil of algae and a slower clothing of lichen and moss. After following the cautious passage of the trap down the hill they once again climbed up to join Tot behind the pony.

From the bottom of the hill the same leafy, sleepy countryside ran on into the distance until, above the rattle of the trap wheels on the road, they heard the sound of other traffic rising swiftly, then fading soon to silence. Then lane, trees and hedgerows came to an end and Tot drew the pony to a halt at the junction with the new London to Southend road. The arterial road she called it. Little more than ten years old, with the second carriageway only just nearing completion, the long reaches of raw concrete cut like a scar across meadows and through woods. Slicing the tops off the hills and cutting deep into the gradients its two dual-lane carriage-ways and cycle tracks ran straight and true from west to east making the main road at the other end of the lane look like a country track. Wide and smooth, with clear, open vision, it had been built to speed the coaches and buses of holidaymakers: an easy, safe route from London to the fleshpots of their local watering hole.

They sat in the trap, watching the few vehicles that passed before turning back into the elm-lined lane and fields, quiet for a few years yet before their peace would be broken by the sounds of war, but before then both Joe and Tot would be gone. They lived on to see or hear some of the warning signs in their own backyard: the straws in the wind which indicated the way things were going. Along the estuary mock air attacks were being made and search-lights tested. In Southend another mock air raid and civil-defence exercise was watched by thousands and extensively reported. Tot, however, remained convinced to the last that common sense would prevail and did not live to be disillusioned. Shortly before the outbreak of war, within a few months of each other, and in coffins of George's making, they made their final journey up the hill to join the little community scattered around the All Saints' churchyard.

7

Brass Bands and Marking Ink

Pappy's atheism, although personally firm and unswerving, was not proselytising even within the family. In 1886 he and Louisa had married in church to satisfy her family, but apart from that his non-belief was absolute. He would not personally deliver his children to baptism, but viewed with amused indifference Elsie's brief flirtation with religion, and her surreptitious christening of two of the youngsters. If the occasional attendance of members of the family at religious services suggested any ambiguity in matters of belief that was misleading: it was purely love of ceremony or experimentation that motivated them. Elsie's venture was certainly as far as anyone from her generation went. Of course every wedding was a church wedding. It was the done thing, part of 'doing it in style'. His daughters also attended Christmas midnight masses, carol services, church choral concerts and the weddings of family and friends, but they went in the same spirit that they went to the People's Palace for a concert. It made a change, was a trip out, and an excuse to get dolled up in their best clothes.

At home religion had no part whatsoever to play in the life of the family, and when at the age of three nursery school began for its latest recruit his young mind was untouched by any of its concepts. God, Jesus, heaven, hell, the devil and all the angels came to John as novel, and from what little he grasped of them, exciting, colourful and interesting ideas, and at school for the first time he was introduced to prayer and children's Bible stories. Initially he accepted these as he did play and story time without giving them any more thought. Eventually however the references to Jesus, the Bible and especially Sunday school started him wondering about those things.

When, or to whom, he carried his childish speculations he could not remember. If to his mother, she would certainly have referred

90

his enquiries to his father. Religion, belief or non-belief, God or the devil were not matters to which she gave a moment's thought during her life, or if she did she never expressed them, but just got on with the day-to-day business, demanding enough for most of the time, of keeping her family well clothed, fed and watered.

If to his father, then Jack would have been as relaxed as Pappy on the matter, understanding well enough that family influences and environment would be more than enough to keep his son on the sceptic's strait and narrow way.

Jack himself had been brought up in an Irish Catholic family; devout as far as the mother was concerned, less so with the father. Mary, the mother, had died some years before John was born, and it was only by report that he came to understand her to have been hard, uncompromising, little given to showing affection, and overly fond of drink. William, the father, was a gentle, affectionate family man.

The oldest son of seven children, Jack was the least favoured by his mother who had little enough love to bestow on any within her family. When, in his mid-teens, he rejected religion in general and Catholicism in particular, dislike between them hardened into mutual antipathy and there never was any reconciliation. He was the only one in his family to make an unequivocal break with the church and an absolute rejection of religion. The rest of the family remained, or married, practising Catholics. The bond between brothers and sisters continued close throughout their lives, however, and when they met religious faith, or the absence of it, was never an issue.

When the accumulated effects of gassing, smoking and the stress of life on one lung finally caught up with Jack and he died at sixty-two, the first of his generation, he did so with his convictions unchanged, and was cremated following a secular ceremony attended by all the family. As usual on such occasions there was much reminiscing of the old days, and for the first time religion and the church was discussed, if obliquely. Only then did it become clear that the family believers were in no doubt that in some way, by some act of grace or special dispensation, Jack was going to be all right. God would understand, a corner for Jack would be found somewhere, and in due course they would all meet up again. Their generosity of spirit would have pleased him, but not the thought of life eternal in a Catholic hereafter.

Almost thirty years later, many years after his death, Jack's posthumous granddaughter married a Catholic, attended Catholic services herself, albeit with uncertain commitment, and was having her children brought up in the faith: from Rome to Rome in four generations via Marx and Engels. Jack would have appreciated the irony, but not the indoctrination of his great-grandchildren.

Despite the absence of religious belief or observance, the pace and feel of life within the house and in the neighbourhood was noticeably different on a summer Sunday morning. The distant murmur from the main road was subdued. Nothing moved on the side roads. The doors on the Board of Trade were locked, its grounds silent, and a general air of torpor embraced the terrace and its surroundings.

That was the way of things on a thirties Sunday. If you weren't heading for church, a political demonstration in Hyde Park or the entertainment to be had at Speakers' Corner there was precious little to engage the attention. At the BBC the dead hand of Sir John Reith lay like a blight on Sunday programming. Over the decade broadcasting hours improved from a 3 p.m. start to 12.30 p.m., and then to 10.30 a.m. but programmes were generally of a thoroughly improving nature in line with his doctrine that content should always be a little above what the public thought it liked: the frivolous was unthinkable, a variety show beyond the pale. In the wider world but against bitter resistance from the Lord's Day Observance Society cinemas had been allowed to open from 6 p.m., but Sunday programmes had to be approved as appropriate for the day: only films 'of a healthy and suitable nature' were allowed to be shown, and a percentage of Sunday takings had to be given to a charity. It was little wonder that many men seized the few hours of morning opening at the pub to drink themselves into afternoon oblivion until the doors opened again in the evening.

In the terrace Sunday morning saw Jack up at his usual time, and although curtains were drawn back and windows thrown open in the children's bedroom they were not rousted out as they would have been in the week, but left pretty much to their own inclinations. Unwashed and still wearing his nightclothes, John made his Sunday-morning rounds. Down one flight to the room where his gran and Clara slept. Clara carried up a tray of tea on Sunday mornings, and there would be biscuits for the asking. Next back up two flights to the very top of the house, and the rooms under the eaves, usually empty, but every four or five weeks occupied by his aunts, at home for a few days from their work. In the eastern room, empty or not, he opened the windows and hung out listening for the sounds of church bells, and peering into the distance for a glimpse of a topmast moving on the river. Eventually breakfast calls from his mother drifted up the stairs, ignored until the final summons came, 'I won't call you again.'

Once washed, dressed and out on the streets if the local youth didn't go to religion, religion in one form or another came to them. Despite the summons of the bells few, if any, of the non-Catholic families in the neighbourhood were to be seen attending church, and most boys would be out and about on the streets as usual, sometimes scrubbed and polished to be taken on a family visit, but generally just as scruffy as in the week and with one aim: to locate, follow and generally enjoy the two or three brass bands that from mid-morning onward carried the gospel around the streets of the parish. They were a regular entertainment feature of Sunday mornings, and had a number of pitches where they stopped for an extended performance followed by a few words from their speaker and a collection before they moved on. They seldom played as they moved from pitch to pitch, and it was usually the distant boom and thud of the solo bass drum beating out their marching rhythm that caught the boys' ears and sent them off at the gallop to run them down.

The Salvation Army were irregular visitors, but when they did come they provided the most impressive display. Their banner was large and colourful, their caps, hats and uniforms immaculate, their brass and silver glistened, and the sound they made was formidable. Most of all they brought what the other outfits lacked: tambourines, the young ladies who manipulated them, and a performance of virtuosity, dexterity and skill that guaranteed them a good audience wherever they stopped.

Some of the melodies, plundered from popular songs of the halls, their audience knew well, but denying the devil exclusive use of the best tunes brought its own dangers. Just across the road in Poplar High Street the Queen's Theatre was the local palace of varieties, and the songs sung there were heard repeatedly in pub and home. The boys knew the words of course, and while the

Army's tenor section was praising the Lord to the tune of 'Champagne Charlie', they and a few young men in the audience held to their own profane and racy descant.

The solo Sunday preachers who occasionally spoke in the park endured, and possibly enjoyed, the heckling that provided so much entertainment, but the Army was generally heard out in a decent silence. There wasn't much entertainment in that, and when their speaker stepped up, and the ladies moved into the crowd with copies of the *War Cry* and collecting tins the boys moved on.

The Army wasn't without competition for the ears and souls of Poplar. From the other side of the Limehouse Cut the Poplar and Bromley Baptist Tabernacle band had a regular Sunday round, but they were reckoned insipid stuff by comparison: sober-suited, a miserable self-effacing banner, dreary tunes and worst of all no tambourines and no women. The St Michael and All Angels' brass at least cut a dash in gold-braided caps, white smocks and coloured breast bands, and followed their swaggering, white-whiskered leader's command with military precision. 'Now then, lads, give it bags of swank,' and they did.

Sunny autumn mornings with all his aunts at home brought an entirely different routine to the day. With their leisurely breakfast over, and half an hour or so spent dolling themselves up, they came down ready for a morning stroll around their parish.

'I suppose we're going to be lumbered with you as usual, are we?'

Brushed and tidied by his mother, who was always happy to have him out from under her feet, John smiled his reply and was out of the door waiting for them to join him.

Poplar, in the late 1930s, was certainly no garden suburb, but an enthusiastic tree-planting campaign in the twenties meant that in the right direction, only a short distance from the house, there were well-maintained parks and churchyards where gardens, shrubs and trees flourished, and many of the streets on their walk were leafy and shaded. Plane trees, the London tree of choice, predominated and prospered, shrugging off the winter fogs and daily pollution. In the gardens of the Board of Trade, in the churchyards and in the parks, tall, broad domes of twisted, thickly-leafed branches threw a welcome summer shade. In autumn their leaves lay thick on the pavements and carpeted the walks through the park. Large yellow-brown leaves, crisp as parchment huddled together in deep drifts, or crackled under foot, throwing a fine dust and the faint, mysterious odour of decay into the air as John stamped his way through them. From the terrace it was just a couple of hundred yards to the swings and roundabouts of Poplar recreation ground where the aunts performed the pushing and shoving required to the best of their matronly ability, and Clara, always the flighty one, joined him on the roundabout.

'In memory of 18 children who were killed by a bomb dropped from a German Aeroplane upon the L.C.C. School, Upper North Street, on 13th June 1917.' Elsie stopped before the memorial erected in the park to the memory of the Poplar Outrage and read out the words. After twenty years the incident was still fresh in her mind, and once again she told him the story. He had listened to it so many times he could have corrected her on detail, but he sat on the bench alongside her and heard it out to the end.

Kath, apart from her suicidal urge to read the newspaper aloud at breakfast, was the quietest one of the three and said little. While Elsie talked she sat gazing into the trees entirely immersed in her own private world, as she so often was. Clara, never one for sitting long or listening patiently to Elsie's repetitions, wandered off to inspect the flower beds.

They stopped at the drinking fountain before they moved on. Long banished for reasons of public hygiene, the fountains, with their dented metal cups hanging from long links of chain, were in common use in all the public places of the city. The one in the park, in solid marble with incised, gold-lettered inscription, was particularly impressive. At its base inset basins provided easy access to the water for dogs, but small children had to be helped up to the edge of the great bowl into which water flowed continuously from ornamental mouths. John took up a cup, and Elsie helped him reach to fill it. Those cups must have been carried to tens of thousands of lips over the years. Moira wouldn't drink from them, but he wasn't so squeamish, and with a quick rinse around the rim put it to his lips and drank his fill, but kept his tongue from the metal which had an unpleasant taste, acrid and sharp.

After a circuit of the bandstand in the centre of the grounds they passed through to St Matthias' Church. The morning service was still in progress, and the sound of voices raised in praise drifted out across the graveyard. Not the mournful dirge of the 'perishers', but some lively marching song of the church militant that had

95

Clara singing along in her bright soprano as they moved out into Poplar High Street. Tram free, and always something of a backwater compared with the main road, it was quieter still without the weekday traffic to and from the docks.

There were few houses in the shabby buildings on either side of the long narrow street, where the mix of businesses was much the same as on the main road: council offices, pub, newsagent, Home & Colonial, pub, chandler's, printer's, pub, baker's, greengrocer's, corn chandler's, pub. So it went on, and as all were closed there seemed to John little to detain them as they moved towards Blackwall, but the three sisters dawdled along, happily reminiscing on the high times they had in the area when they were young, and the lively turns they saw at the Queen's Theatre: Chaplin, Little Titch, Ella Shields, or Gertie Gitana knocking out her 'Nellie Dean' which the audience carried in their hearts to echo in the bars of The Ship, The White Hart, The Resolute Tavern or any one of a half-dozen pubs within strolling distance of the theatre.

Occasionally a chandler's window or the view into a workyard would catch his eye and detain him. Forgetful for the moment of their charge his aunts wandered on ahead absorbed in their talk. He looked after them and wondered, not for the first time, why his Three Graces had no uncles or cousins for him, but it was only a passing thought, he had uncles and cousins enough.

There was little more than six years between the three of them: Elsie the first born of the family, Kath following on four years later and then Clara, two years after Kath. By the time he was walking out with them Elsie was into her fifties, and the other two well into their forties. He was himself nearly sixty when Clara, the last of them, died but not once over the many years that followed those early walks did he hear them, or anyone within the family, make any comment on the fact that they had never married.

When old enough to have an informed opinion on the matter he could see clearly enough that there had been nothing about their appearance that might have deterred suitors. Early photographs showed them to be good-looking and attractive enough to have received a few offers, and perhaps they had, but he had always assumed that they were simply three of the many of that sad generation whose lovers and husbands were the cannon fodder of the Great War. The boys who dreamed of home, but were never to see it again.

96

There was, it was true, a certain imperial severity about Elsie's features, but Kath had an open attractive face, and Clara was really rather pretty, and she knew it. Even in old age she was fastidious in her attention to appearance and dress, and for almost fifty years, continuing until she was into her seventies, she received a card on St Valentine's Day from an anonymous admirer. Always written in the same hand and posted in central London, it was a continuing source of pride to Clara while intriguing and frustrating her sisters, but they were all a little sad when a Valentine's Day arrived and it became clear that a card had come for the last time. If Clara herself knew the identity of her Valentine she kept her secret to the end.

A few years after Clara, the last of the sisters, had died, a tape was transcribed of an interview that Elsie had given in the closing months of her life to a researcher from Oxford. It contained the one comment that seemed to cast some light on their attitude. Talking of her suffragette activities, the reason for the interview, and referring to the freedom that they were allowed as young women she said:

My parents never interfered, we girls came in at night and went out at night and we didn't tell them where we were going, but we were always in at a respectable time. They knew that and didn't trouble. We didn't trouble much about men – you know. I could have gone to Canada when I was about nineteen and married but I didn't want to.

Perhaps that was also how her sisters felt, and they had evidence enough in the streets around them that early marriage and children was the near-certain route to lifelong poverty and deprivation.

It may have had little part to play in any decisions they made about marriage, but from the time that Pappy ceased to work, and even more so after his death, the contributions that the three of them made were an important part of the economy of the house. None of them had at any time been out of work for any extended period. Certainly working women earned little enough then, but at least what they earned was regular, reasonably secure and it was theirs, no husbands looking to have a hand in its spending.

A couple of years before the outbreak of war a bout of rheumatic fever left Phoebe so seriously weakened that she was packed off to a convalescent home to recover, and John had to be minded during the school holidays as and where it was convenient. As Lou herself was under the weather the lot fell to Clara who at that time was managing the receiving office of the Stepney Laundry in East India Dock Road. Clara ran her laundry operation with little interference from above, and so there were many days when John spent his time with her at the laundry. With her nephew clasped by one hand, and their sandwiches and refreshments for the day in the other, Clara set off for her walk to the laundry receiving office. By eight-thirty they had picked up the bottle of milk from the shop steps, and were behind the counter waiting for the early customers.

The overwhelming and abiding impression of the office was the smell: not of laundry, but of the black marking ink used by the gallon. Beneath one end of the broad counter vast sheets of brown paper, impress stamps and pads, piles of tags, great balls of string, marking pencils and counterfoil books were kept in orderly fashion. At the other end used books of counterfoils and other rubbish was piled high. Tall, deep racks of slatted timber filled the back half of the shop, some crammed with string-tied brown-paper parcels of newly-laundered items, others empty. Wheeled steps were used to reach the upper sections of the racks.

John started the day on a stool behind the counter with a marking pencil and some old counterfoil books to scribble and draw in.

'Hello then, young man. You're in charge today are you?'

Most customers were struck with the originality and humour of their greeting. He responded with a winning smile and endured their chat with patience, but always had half an eye on the main chance. Some of the callers were regulars bringing laundry in daily from lodging houses and missions, and by the end of his days with Clara he was doing a good trade in sweets and pieces of chocolate.

In the furthest corner of the shop was the 'dead laundry' rack: bundles of laundry long past their due date, and eventually to be disposed of, but kept long enough to ensure that they were never going to be collected. From these Clara found a parcel of thick, laundered curtains and laid them out high in the racking to form a snug couch. When the counter palled he climbed the steps to his retreat and there, secret and unobserved as he thought looked out on to the passing scene or spied on the customers as they came and went. It was not unusual for Clara to find him asleep there at the end of the day.

With the experience of many years Clara had an easy line of small talk with her callers, some of whom came as much for the pleasure of chewing the cud as to bring or collect the laundry. He was astonished how much they seemed to know about his family.

'How's Ma and your sister then, Clara?'

Ma was his gran, and it was soon clear from Clara's reply that the sister was his mother, still in the convalescent home. Having satisfied the caller on her initial enquiry, advising her that Elsie was much happier back with the LCC, Charlie settled in his new job and Rene engaged, Clara's liberal disclosure of family news might have continued longer had another customer not arrived. It was John's first introduction to the art of gossip, and he realised in due course that he had been listening to an expert at work. Clara was exceedingly fond of a chat.

Diversions of a quite different kind came in from the docks. The ships running into the Port of London in the 1930s were not turned round as container ships are in a matter of a day or so. Discharging cargo was a time-consuming process which gave sea-men the opportunity to have their gear properly laundered while the ship was in port. From around the globe they arrived at the counter, many of them either with no English, or so thick an accent that what they had to say was incomprehensible.

Years of experience had made Clara a match for most of them. It was when words failed that the entertainment began, and Clara entered into a silent routine that had been developed and carefully refined over the years. With props consisting of a few items of clothing and an old iron from under the counter she mimed her way through the basic laundering processes, and with encouraging or questioning looks, nods of the head and waving of the arms tried to establish just what was wanted. John was most impressed. This was his aunt as he had never seen her before and apparently enjoying having an audience for her performance. Initially the mime seemed meaningless to her customers, but gradually the confusion or astonishment on their faces was replaced with a smile of understanding and a gesture of thanks.

Only once did he see a complete breakdown in communication. After an initial exchange of words Clara was heard repeatedly saying 'No' as she pushed a pile of laundry back across the counter.

99

There was apparently something about its nature or condition that was unacceptable. Without comment the clothing was pushed back towards her. Clara repeated her action two or three times with the same response, and the two stood looking at each other in silence. By this time other customers had come in and were watching with evident interest. Clara looked her opponent in the eye, gathered up the clothing in her arms, leaned over the counter and distributed it on to the floor before pointing magisterially to the door. The contest was over. The clothing was collected in silence and carried from the shop. Clara triumphant.

At one o'clock the main door was locked. Clara made tea in a scullery at the rear of the shop, and if the weather was fine they had their break outside. A couple of old chairs were taken out, and in a narrow disused space between the receiving office and the laundry they opened their packs of sandwiches and took their lunch in a flourishing oasis set in a desert of bricks and mortar.

Midsummer and the prolific, wandering weeds of the city had softened and transformed the mean, neglected yard. Toadflax, mosses and ferns invaded the soft mortar and prospered high in the brickwork. Green curtains of white-spangled bindweed rambled across its decaying walls, and in between the crumbling stones that paved the yard tufts of rank grass, dandelions, groundsel, chickweed and poppies flourished, and set their seeds for the year to follow.

While they had their break the operations of the laundry thundered on behind them. Clara had no authority to take him inside, but he learned early on that the unceasing rumble was the sound of drums tumbling the laundry. The gushing hisses were the steam presses at work, and high on the walls a constant mist drifted from the ventilators, moistening the mosses and ferns before dissipating in the dry summer air. Pressing his face close to the grimy windows he was able to look in at the bustle and movement within, and was rewarded with a wave and smile from the workers. There was plenty to keep him occupied while Clara buried her head in a newspaper or magazine. When their break was over he collected the best of the chickweed to take back as a treat for the parrot. Those laundry days spent together, and the fact that Clara always lived at home, meant that in his early years he got to know her much better than he did her sisters.

From school Elsie and Kath had gone into domestic service and that was their work for a number of years, always living away from home and moving into and out of jobs when young, without any serious unemployment. By the mid-1930s they were engaged on a permanent basis as cooks at council establishments where they also had to live in. Kath was in Hertfordshire working in a home for maladjusted children, Elsie in a nursery home. They each earned the same 1s an hour for a 48-hour week out of which they paid 12s 6d for their board and lodging. Somehow from the residue they made regular contributions to Louisa for the upkeep of the Poplar house, kept themselves clothed, had an occasional trip out and managed a holiday.

From the early years of the century until just before the Second World War the same old box Brownie chronicled their trips away. John had looked through the fading, curling snaps many times: formal groupings during suffragette conferences and meetings at Yarmouth and the Isle of Wight; summer holidays at Eastbourne, Southsea and Weymouth, on the promenade casually dressed in their flowing summer dresses or self-consciously posed by the beach hut in their one-piece costumes; crowded into a horse-drawn cart for an excursion, 'Upwey Wishing Well. 1s Return Fare'; or Elsie, always the pioneering spirit, climbing down a rickety step-ladder, wind-blasted and dishevelled from her flight in an early open-cockpit biplane with the Surrey Air Service at Croydon.

'Come on, John. We haven't got all day.'

At last they had noticed that he was no longer with them and turned to give him a call. From the High Street they passed through Robin Hood Lane and into the gardens running beside the approach road to the tunnel where it dropped down from East India Dock Road to burrow under the Thames.

Tunnel Gardens – the changes and redevelopment that successive years have brought to the area have been so far-reaching and absolute, the destruction of every aspect that he remembered so complete, that it seemed that it was not just in another time, but in another world that he had followed the three of them into the tree-lined terrace that ran through to the main road and the tunnel entrance. There, while they rested for a moment from their walk he joined them on one of the long park benches overlooking the gardens.

Behind them ivy and climbing plants screened the brickwork of the high walls guarding the warehouses of the East India Import

101

Dock, and at their feet shrubs and young trees grew in a narrow strip of soil fronted by low iron fencing. Between the terrace and the walls guarding the drop into the tunnel approach road, children played on the swings and roundabout of a narrow playground, supervised closely by mothers or aunts, or more casually attended by fathers reading their Sunday papers. Beyond the walls a few lorries or buses passed by, either climbing slowly into view up the long incline from the tunnel, or disappearing as they dropped down on their way to the south bank.

After a drinking stop at another garden fountain they walked out into the light bustle of Sunday lunchtime traffic on East India Dock Road. A few vehicles filtered through the tunnel gateway all turning in from east or west. From the Brunswick Road, now almost totally overlaid by the new northern approach road, nothing came and nothing went.

After the rest in the gardens there was not much lingering by his aunts on the way home. A loop around the churchyard of All Saints' where his parents were married, a resentful and uneasy glance by John towards Poplar police station where his father had spent a night in the cells following arrest at a political demonstration, and then quickly home for Sunday lunch, always a substantial meal and taken together in Louisa's room when the aunts were at home.

By the time they returned a cut of beef and the potatoes were already roasting in the oven. Other vegetable were prepared and ready for the pot, but the Yorkshire pudding was left for Elsie. Nobody dared or wanted to dispute her title as batter-maker extraordinary. Without fail her puddings came from the oven crisp, golden brown, delicately crusted on the outside, soft, crumbling and mouth-watering on the inside.

Friendships have foundered and families fragmented on the rock of Yorkshire pudding protocol: by itself, or with the meat and veg, with gravy or without. Elsie's law was absolute. Her pudding came to the table hot from the oven with the meat and veg, and no one was expected to reduce its crumbly, crisp texture to a soggy mess with gravy. Nobody did.

For the meat and veg, gravy was certainly available, but genuine, succulent gravy conjured up from the juices of the meat. For Elsie, Bisto and its like were an abomination.

Sunday afternoon post-lunch each played out in her own way.

There was a gap of almost nine years between Phoebe and the youngest of her three older sisters, and they had few interests or friends in common. She had been born a little too late to join in suffragette activities and, despite her background, showed about as much interest and involvement in political and social issues as she did in religious ones, in short very little. Sunday afternoons were a time for meeting old friends from her schooldays or the working years before the children came along. Jack would either have his head in a book, be out meeting political friends or visiting his brothers.

Left to their own devices John and his sister went their separate ways. She had her school friends or tucked herself away with her school books. At the age of eleven she had won a scholarship to Coburn High School, and that brought homework at weekends as well as in the week.

For Louisa and the older sisters Sunday afternoons were somnolent, heavy-eyed affairs when they retreated to the front room upstairs. In winter a fire would have been lit in the morning, and winter or summer, if the skies were cloudless, it was flooded with sunshine from early afternoon until evening.

John was past the age when an afternoon rest was thought appropriate, but after the long morning walk the streets and his mates had little appeal, so he joined the gathering in the front room. The perishers from the Seaman's Rest still threw out the lifeline, but they no longer had the power to move him. Books had little appeal, and so he took a few old comics and settled down out of the way to see how the afternoon developed.

His gran was of an age when she was resigned to the fact that within ten minutes of settling in her easy chair after a good lunch she would be snoozing. She prepared for her nap by removing her false teeth. As her sleep deepened, her face relaxed. The jaw dropped open, the mouth gaped, thin lips sank over toothless gums, and her gentle breathing became a windy gasp. Familiar as he was with this unnerving display, John found the performance unsettling and was unable to join in the whispered laughter of his aunts.

Sunday-afternoon entertainment varied. If there were visitors, as there frequently were, he was content to sit and listen, or drift off into his comics. If not then the front room became the music room.

'Give us a tune then, Else.'

The request was made a little after his gran woke up, and Clara arrived with a tray of tea. The piano was an upright of unknown provenance and uncertain temperament. Keys that played one week failed the next, introducing an interesting element of chance into each performance. Elsie was the only one in the family who had learned to read music. This gave her a certain amount of status among family and friends until it was realised that of itself it did not make for proficiency. The final combination was not an unhappy one, however. If Elsie's performance was only more or less reliable, it was much the same with the piano and they got along pretty well together.

The sheet music was kept in a compartment under the lid of the ornamental piano stool. When it was next lifted after Clara died, the last of the three sisters, more than forty years had elapsed since the end of the war but the sheets were still there: torn, well worn and a little dust-covered, but otherwise much as John remembered them from those early days in London. The collection had been added to only a little since the thirties, and not at all since the war. How familiar they seemed!

Clara had the best of the voices, closely followed by Phoebe, and it was the sound of their singing drifting out into the garden where he played as a child or through the house on a Sunday afternoon that formed his musical memories of those early years. He thumbed through the sheets:

'When I Grow Too Old to Dream,' 'One Day When We Were Young' – romantic old favourites from Hollywood musicals.

'Red Sails in the Sunset' – very popular, the theme song of Suzette Tarry on the halls and radio, and a great favourite at parties as the chorus made demands neither on vocal range nor sobriety. The inner page was marked mysteriously 'C Bra'. Some obscure musical notation he wondered, or some more intimate reference for one of his aunts?

'Ah Sweet Mystery of Life at Last I've Found Thee' from *Naughty Marietta* – he wondered what Marie Lloyd would have done with the ambiguity of that line.

'Dinner for One Please, James' – guaranteed to have strong men weeping in their beer.

It was strange considering their political and social allegiances that they were also happy to sing those ghastly, chirpy ditties that promised the underpaid, underprivileged and undervalued a silver lining to their clouds. *Sing as you go and let the world go by, It's a lovely day tomorrow . . . so forget your troubles* etc.

Charlie, like so many, had a tough time in the hard years of the Depression and, if present, gave that sort of thing short shrift.

'Promises, promises. Nothing but bloody promises,' he would call and drown them out.

> *You will eat, bye and bye, in that glorious land in the sky;*
> *Work and Pray, live on hay, you'll get pie in the sky when*
>   *you die.*

Charlie, the only other member of the family with any sort of musical talent, had a self-taught proficiency on flute and squeeze box, both a little too melancholy in character to lend themselves to large party sing-songs when Elsie was always the musician of choice, but there were occasions when the mood was reflective and Charlie came into his own. 'Play us that one that Dad used to like, Charlie,' Kath would say. Then with Charlie on the squeeze box they hummed or sang their way through a few of the old sentimental melodies. But melancholy and nostalgia were not strong features in the Lagsding character, and they soon turned to their old favourites, the songs from the halls or popular operettas.

If Elsie wasn't available for the piano the alternative was a handsome His Master's Voice gramophone, a wedding present to Phoebe and Jack but kept for general use in the front room. The cabinet, in dark polished wood, stood at table height on elegant legs and was considered by all to be a fine piece of furniture in its own right. It contained a mixed but not very extensive collection, as the old 78rpm shellac records took up a lot of space. Vintage Caruso performances on heavy, one-sided discs rubbed shoulders with the Glasgow Orpheus and Don Cossack choirs, 'Silver Threads Among the Gold' with 'Voices of Spring', and McCormack's 'Lark in the Clear Air' with Nellie Melba's 'Home Sweet Home'.

As a youngster he had listened to them with less than enthusiasm, but in later years came to see the error of his ways, and it needed only the nostalgic hiss of steel on shellac to carry him back to those drowsy Poplar afternoons; to Louisa snoozing in her corner, the aunts sipping their second cup of tea, and Musetta's song soaring out into the summer air.

Fortunately for him there was also a popular side to the collection, and when the light or heavy classics had run their course he was allowed a little Harry Lauder, a brass band or an assignation with Wilhelmina, the buxom blonde from Holland and the saloon-bar tenor who sang her praises. Like much in Holland itself the record did not survive the rigours of war, but the memory was fresh: the pinched nasal tones of the singer, the oompa-band accompaniment, and the final rousing chorus:

> *Wilhelmina is plump and round, plump and round, plump*
>   *and round.*
> *Jacob and Peter and Fritz and Hans*
> *Ask her permission to put up the bans.*
> *All she says is 'Nein, nein, nein', no wedding bells for me.*
> *Each day they get keener on plump little Wilhelmina*
> *The pride of the Zuider Zee.*

But soon the music making was over, the afternoon was gone and Elsie and Kath were thinking of catching the tram on the first leg of the journey back to their workplace. They wouldn't be seen again for five or six weeks and for that time weekends would be much, much less interesting.

8

Elsie: An Accidental Suffragette

8th September 1887: Victoria Empress of India for more than ten years; Britain at the height of its Imperial power; the country basking in the afterglow of the Queen's Golden Jubilee celebrations in June; and Louisa Henrietta Lagsding brought to bed of Elsie, her firstborn.

If any faint remnant of that Jubilee glow penetrated into the alleys and courts of Canning Town, it could do nothing to relieve the gloom of the cramped and miserable tenement in which Elsie was born, to be followed in quick succession by William and Kathleen. By 1893 with the family bursting out of their two rooms, and Louisa swelling with Clara-to-be, a move was made across Bow Creek to a larger house in Chilcot Street where Elsie was to spend most of her school years.

Operated at that time by the School Board of London, and a little later by the LCC the schools provided a thorough, if basic, education that was reflected in one of Elsie's final letters written a few months before she died, aged eighty-nine:

> *Dear John,*
> *I now take up my pen to write these few lines to you hoping to find you quite well as it leaves me at present. This is how I was taught to begin a letter eighty years ago.*

At fourteen education ended, work began and Elsie entered service. Of this and later periods she left her own partial record and can speak for herself:

> *After I left school I went away into domestic service. I was always on the shy side and didn't want to go mixing with a lot of people. I went local first of all, but I soon cleared off there*

107

because the couple I worked for used to go on the booze. Very nice people they were but they did like a drop. He was a superintendent for the Prudential Company but used to go on the tiddly and she would get me to go out with the jug. I used to wear a cape and with the jug tucked under my arm beneath the cape nobody saw it. It was a big house and they were very decent to me. I've got no complaints about them.

From there I went to the West End, to Curzon Street Mayfair – Major Arthur Griffiths and his wife. I was upstairs downstairs there: upstairs in the morning and downstairs in the evening to help the cook. I remember once the cook was ill and they asked me to do the dinner. I was scared stiff, I had to fry whitebait. They just looked like tiddlers to me, like the kids bring home on a Sunday afternoon when they have been fishing in the canal. I got these whitebait and put them in and anyhow the message came down from the dining room congratulating me on the dinner and I was only fifteen. I was there about a year but then they packed up and went abroad.

Before they left she said her niece wanted a maid and would I think about it. Of course I was only too glad. I didn't like to go past a job and so I went there and was there for about two years. Mrs Marshall she was. She wrote to me afterwards that her husband had been killed in the First World War and he was such a nice man. He was the oldest son of Marshal Snelgrove. Of course his father had money and he used to go up to London every day for the firm. They were quite comfortable and she was a marvellous pianist – she used to play beautifully. They lived in a small flat, only about four rooms, and there was only me.

Then they moved to Watford and that was just an ordinary working man's house, six rooms and I did it all. I even took the cooking on. Of course I never had any washing anywhere wherever I went, nor any flights of stone steps like there were to do. I was pretty lucky really. I liked it there and Mr Marshall too. He was really a nice chap – it seemed such a shame. They had a baby there and that died at birth. Shortly after that I left them.

Her time with the Marshalls brought Elsie's period in service to an end. The cookery experience she had acquired enabled her to obtain work in a school kitchen in Poplar and so she returned to live with the family.

Despite her father's radical and revolutionary thinking, it was not any ideological commitment to the suffragette cause that drew Elsie to them. The initial contact was accidental and casual:

It must have been at the end of 1911 or the beginning of 1912 when I first met Sylvia Pankhurst. She had rented a couple of rooms in a large house in East India Dock Road near Poplar hospital facing the dock wall. I was passing with a friend and she was speaking to quite a large crowd from one of the windows. She was a really passionate speaker and we stood outside listening for a while until she invited people to go in and join her. 'Come on,' I said 'Let's go in and hear what she has got to say.' So in we went and after a bit of a talk we both joined because we found it interesting. From then on we would meet every week somewhere and go to a meeting with her. There was a lot of talk about the name but eventually they settled on the East London Federation of Suffragettes.

Elsie understood that she herself had neither the education nor ability to further the cause on the platform or in print, but she was throughout a hard-working, enthusiastic and at times frightened worker, not only in the cause of votes for women, but later in Sylvia's fight for pacifism, and an end to the slaughter of the First World War:

I never spoke at any of the Federation meetings. I was always too scared and don't think I could have done it anyway. That was all left to Sylvia and those who had it at their fingertips, but I was there for all the protests and activities.

The first turnout after I met her was at a meeting in Bow Baths. Sylvia was there with Daisy Lansbury and the meeting was going on with Sylvia on the platform speaking when all of a sudden the police rushed in. They were after Sylvia to arrest her and in no time chairs were being flung all over the place. I was really terrified because I had never imagined anything like it. I rushed and stood back against the wall under the balcony because chairs were being thrown off the balcony at the police. While they fought back the police Sylvia

*disappeared and they got her safely away out of it. Of course
she was all right as she wasn't ill then. In the end Daisy
Lansbury was arrested in her place. The police took her for
Sylvia as she was about the same size, so she ended up at the
police station and Sylvia got away that night.*

It is possible that Elsie's memory failed her here. There were two
incidents at Bow Baths on 12th October and 5th November 1913.
The confrontation with the police was at the first and the mistaken
arrest of Daisy Lansbury at the second when a similar confrontation took place but outside the hall after the meeting.

*Most of our demonstrations started from the dock gates and
members from other branches like the Canning Town people
would come over to Poplar and join us. We would line up
there, get organised and then march off wherever Sylvia
wanted us to go. We had quite a lot of marching about to do
and I remember one day we had just lined up and were ready
to go when this woman came up spat at me, called me some
very choice names and pulled my hat off just as we were ready
to start off in the procession.*

*Of course we always dressed nicely and properly for those
affairs. If it was summertime we'd be in summer dresses, white
shoes, white stockings like we wore then and all made up. It
was summertime when I got arrested in Hyde Park where we
went for lots of our demonstrations and meetings. I was there
as usual with my bundle of* Dreadnoughts. *I knew it wasn't
allowed to sell them in the park so I just had them hanging
over my arm, casual like. Of course if anyone came up and
asked for one I didn't refuse them. I just took the tuppence
and anything more they liked to give and I sold quite a few
before I got caught.*

*Well I was standing there and this man came up to me. He
was a smart chap, well dressed with a straw hat and buttonhole. He asked me for a paper so I sold him one and got a
shilling for it. A shilling – I thought I was well away. Shortly
afterwards a policeman came up and took hold of my arm.*
'Will you come down to the station with me?' he said.
'What for?' I asked and he said, 'You're breaking the law.'

110

So I called out to Sylvia, 'I'm pinched,' and off we all went for they all followed me to the station.

I must say everyone was very nice and the police too. There was a sergeant there and when we had been sat waiting for a very long time he said to me,

'I'm sorry I can't offer you a cup of tea.'

So I sat there for a couple of hours until one of my friends, Miss Smythe, came along and bailed me out.

A little later I had to appear at one of the West End police courts and who turned up but the well-dressed chap I'd seen with the straw hat and buttonhole. He turned out to be a detective and gave evidence that I was selling the Dreadnoughts. *Then I was sworn in and told the magistrate that I hadn't been selling papers.*

'You sold him one,' he said, meaning the detective.

'Yes, but I didn't offer it to him. He came up and asked me for it and gave me a shilling for it.' Well, that didn't wash. If I wasn't offering them for sale I suppose in a way I was selling them.

'If we gave you permission to sell your Dreadnought *in Hyde Park they'd be selling peanuts and winkles before it was finished and we can't have that. You'll be fined five shillings.'*

So I stood down and Miss Smythe paid the fine for me.

The affair which really put the wind up me was at the Albert Hall. I knew roughly what the idea was but didn't fancy it and hadn't volunteered until I heard my friend Daisy calling out,

'We'll go, me and Elsie,' and so of course I was stuck with it.

We were given a banner which we were told to hold up at a certain time. So we got the bus up to the hall and got ourselves in and sat down with the rest of the girls who were there as well. We found out then that it was a patriotic meeting that was taking place, not an anti-war meeting, and the hall was packed. Well, I don't mind admitting I'm a bit of a coward and I was frightened. I sat there shivering and feeling sick, whispering to Daisy every few minutes, 'Are we going to hold it up now?'

It was a good-sized banner with a couple of short poles to hold it up. The girls had prepared its message a couple of days earlier painted in red and black on white calico, 'British War Ships Are Firing on the Soviet Republic.' Well I didn't know whether they were or not but I suppose they must have been.

Anyway the time comes round and up we stand with our banner shouting out our message. That causes a right rumpus and the first thing is that the woman in front of me turns round and gives me a right mouthful. Then the attendants arrive and take us to the back of the hall. They were very kind, they didn't push us about at all but just kept us there until a policeman came up.

'Had you got permission to hold that banner up, madam?' he asks.

'Now ask yourself,' I said, feeling a bit cheeky by now.

Well, they took the banner, led us downstairs and saw us safely out but they didn't touch us or harm us in any way. So we went across the road and sat by the Albert Memorial chatting until the others came out and we all went home. I didn't realise that we had been photographed but the next day there we were in the papers with our great big banner.

When it came to the big processions the police were always looking for the excuse to break them up and it could turn very nasty, although most of the time I must say that I enjoyed it. I was a bit of a coward and always cleared off if there was any fighting so I didn't get hurt at any time, although there were a few near misses like the time I got my hat bashed in.

That was during the war and it was one of the worst ones for me. It was a good, big procession because all the men were joining in as well. The plan was to march down one of the roads off Bow Road and hold a meeting outside a councillor's house. There was the railway on one side of the road and rather nice houses with steps and basements on the other. It all started out nice and orderly with a band in the front to keep us swinging along.

Well, the police were there in full force and a bloke on a white horse nearly always met the procession. When he did you knew you weren't going to get very far. We got nearly to the bottom of the road before it turned really nasty. Then the police in the front turned round their horses and charged the crowd and the police behind charged from the back.

Everybody ran and scattered all over the place and we lost one another. It was a pretty mad scramble and I was shouting out, 'Where's my sister? I want my sister.'

I was holding a red flag when we started and that was yanked out of my hand right away. Then a man pulled me inside the gate to one of the houses and shut the gate. Lots of the others were doing the same, rushing into the front areas of the houses and shutting the gates because there was nowhere else to get away from the police who were lashing out left and right. One of them on a horse came up on the pavement and tried to open the gate to pull us out but this man called out, 'Leave them alone,' and kept the gate shut. So there I was with the old horse leaning its head over the gate and spitting in my face. I started out the day with a lovely black, velvet hat nicely wired all round with two beautiful bows. Well, by the time I got clear that was in a right mess.

Finally it quietened down and we all picked up with one another in Bow Road and ended up having a good laugh while we tried to straighten out the wire and tidy up the bows in my poor old hat. Nobody was really hurt at the end of the day but all the band's gear went for a burton. They smashed the drum and the flags, the instruments, the lot. They were all thrown down the embankment onto the railway line.

They were all a great crowd and there were good times of course as well as bad. We got together from time to time for the evening and at one of the concerts Sylvia organised, Elsa Lanchester, the wife of Charles Laughton, came along and danced for us. In 1915 a few of us met up in Railway Street for a party on my birthday when we heard the sound of an air-raid warning. No sirens then of course, just someone going round the streets blowing a whistle or calling out. I saw Arthur Dinham standing in the doorway gazing up and asked him what he was looking at. He told me to get inside but of course they all went tumbling out to have an eyeful and there was this great elegant thing sailing calmly through the air like a huge silver cigar. It looked such a beautiful, peaceful sight but as we learned later it killed quite a few people and did a lot of damage in the city.

When the war started in 1914 Sylvia started a restaurant. The Cost Price Restaurant it was called in Railway Street,

Poplar, and she asked me if I would go and work there. Well, I didn't want to go really because I was quite settled in my cookery job with the council.

It was just before Christmas and my father said, 'Why don't you go? You keep messing about with the woman. Why don't you tell her what you are going to do one way or the other?' So eventually I said that I would leave. I was getting about fourteen or fifteen shillings a week then working for the council – well, that was a good wage really at that time. They offered me £1 at the canteen and that was a bit of an attraction, four or five shillings a week extra, so I went.

But it wasn't much of a job, you could get vegetables and things like that but you couldn't get meat. The girls working there wouldn't give up their food coupons naturally and so it was mainly offal that we had. We used to mince it up and make pies and puddings and stews. It was all right at that time I suppose and they liked it. We also used to get pots of jam from time to time that one or the other of the girls would bring in. There were a few other workers but not many working there and I had a young girl of about fifteen working with me in the kitchen. They were all a jolly good crowd together and it could be hectic really.

The dinners were not free. They paid about threepence or fourpence for a dinner and that was a two-course affair. Then they had a cup of tea afterwards – that was about a ha'penny, but of course a ha'penny was a ha'penny in those days, it wasn't like we've got now. I suppose about thirty or forty people came in at any one time. We didn't have waitresses. They came up and were served from the bar. All we did were the midday dinners from twelve to two and then they had a cup of tea if they wanted it. We cleared up, which took us all the afternoon till finishing-up time.

That went on all through the war in Railway Street in Poplar in an old-fashioned little pub that had been empty for years. It had one big room that had been two bars and there was another big long room with an old-fashioned stove in it that was used as an office. Upstairs there were three small rooms where Sylvia opened up a clinic, which was another of her operations. There was a doctor's room and a nurse's room. The nurse used to come every day and the doctor twice

114

a week and they looked after the children and examined them there. The mothers would come and sit out in the big room where they could have drinks while they waited.

I was working there all through the war and right through to 1919 but then I went on holiday to Yarmouth and had a bad accident. When I came back I couldn't get back to work again so Sylvia closed it up just like that. It wasn't making any profit or anything – if it paid its way and the wages they were lucky. Of course the wages were very small. I never got more than the £1 I started with all through the war but I wouldn't have gone on munitions so I suppose I wouldn't have earned much more anyhow. Although they did get more money on the council, they paid out extra increases and that, but they knocked them off after the war when the food began to get a bit more normal.

We had a few strange turnouts while I was there. A woman came in one day and asked for a dinner which we served up for her. She had a baby in her arms, looked around her and suddenly said, 'Oh will you hold my baby – I've left my bag up at Bromley station'. Well, I was a right mug. I took the baby as she bunged it in my arms and stood there waiting. Of course she never came back. We phoned Sylvia and asked her what to do and she said to go to the police station. So down we trotted to the police station with the baby and they sent us on to the workhouse in Poplar High Street. That's where we left the baby but I never knew what happened to the poor little thing after that. The police came and questioned me but we never heard any more or saw the woman again.

We left the canteen about four o'clock and went home for a meal and of course at weekends the canteen was closed but there was always plenty to do when we weren't there, collections, meetings, demonstrations or selling the Dreadnought. We used to go down to the docks at Millwall and stand outside shaking our boxes. One was for Babies' Milk the other for the Dreadnought. There was one man who gave me five shillings every week when he bought the Dreadnought. We got quite a bit that way, collecting for milk. Of course we weren't the only ones doing that sort of thing.

We walked from Poplar right up to Trafalgar Square no end of times and from there on to other places with the *processions. I'd been up for Sylvia's trial when she got the six months and remember her saying, 'Why should I be arrested for saying what my father said years ago that if all men held the view that war was wrong there would be no more war.' But I think she had said a bit more than that.*

One of the processions went up to Holloway where she was in prison. It was winter and a shocking, mucky night as we walked up in mud and slosh with all the snow melting. When we were there we all assembled outside calling out for the release of Sylvia Pankhurst. Much good that did us. It was so bad we all ended up coming back on the train.

Of course if they went on hunger strike they had a terrible time in and out of prison on cat-and-mouse licence. Out when they started to get too ill and then snatched back in as soon as they were a little better. We all went to a big demonstration in Victoria Park when Sylvia was just out on licence and wanted to speak. Well, that was a proper do then and it got very rough. One of my friends ended up with a terrific black eye. Sylvia was so bad she had been brought to the park on a stretcher but the police took her again in the park, stretcher and all. That was what it was like for them, in then out and in again.

All the girls liked Sylvia and thought a lot of her. To her face or if she was about they spoke of her as Miss Pankhurst but behind her back amongst ourselves it was always 'Old Pank'. She was a good, kind person and if anyone was in trouble she would help them out as she did me.

When I had the accident that stopped me working in the canteen I had been in Yarmouth with suffragette friends who lived there. We were walking back home when I got caught and dragged against a wall by a wagon and horses carrying a load of copper ore and ended up with both shoulders and my collar bone fractured. A borough councillor told us to write to the firm and what to do, and I got a reply but it didn't get me very far. When Sylvia heard what was going on she came along to see me and said that she would put it in the hands of her solicitor. She also sent me to her doctor and he gave a report. I went to the solicitor to talk to him two or three times. The firm had offered me £15 but Sylvia's solicitor took it further and they offered £73 which he advised me to take but

I had been out of work for eight months so that didn't go very far. That was the sort of thing Sylvia did.

But she liked her own way too. Always wanted to be the one and get what she wanted and if people didn't agree with her she didn't like it. She could be difficult to work with in that way.

By about the time of the General Strike I wasn't seeing so much of Sylvia and we only met a few times. I went over to see her in Woodford once where she had a house in Charteris Road. I went over because she had borrowed a book from me. It was The French Revolution *by Kropotkin. My father said it gave a very different view from the other ones. But I didn't get it back from her and she still had it when she went out to Abyssinia. We never had it back.*

How that Kropotkin book, her father's treasure, rankled with Elsie. There she was more than fifty years later, putting her own thoughts on that time together, and still she hadn't forgotten it.

The events and people she referred to were discussed time and time again when John was young. Friends called, and the old photographs were passed around to much laughter and chatter, but he struggled in vain to make any connection between the grainy black-and-white images of a slim young lady self-consciously displaying her poster in Hyde Park in 1913 and the substantial, comfortable old aunty sipping her afternoon tea.

9

Dockland Diversions

At the beginning of the twentieth century educational prospects for the working-class children of Limehouse were grim, but a few flourished despite the system and Jack was one of the lucky ones. He fell into a good senior school with an exceptional teacher who recognised his abilities, and encouraged by father and teacher he took advantage of every opportunity that came his way. Following school, both before and after the war, he continued his education through the Workers Educational Association and it wasn't long before the offer came of a scholarship to Ruskin College, founded a decade or so earlier to promote higher education among working men and women. The offer may at some other time have seemed tempting, but by then any pipe dreams of a post-war land fit for heroes had evaporated. Poplar was one of the areas hit hardest by the deepening Depression and growing unemployment, and Jack saw the only way forward as a radical reform of society through active involvement in politics. Politics brought him to a meeting with Pappy at a local political rally. An invitation to the Lagsding home in Carters Terrace followed. There he found a warm welcome in the lively, radical background and a wife in Pappy's young daughter Phoebe.

Like many thousands of others Jack brought a legacy of the war back with him from France. Caught on the fringes of a gas attack, one of his lungs had been substantially and permanently damaged. It left him incapable of the hard physical labour that was the lot of most men in the East End, but even during the periods of depression he was fortunate and seldom unable to find clerical employment in the offices of one of the many businesses and factories that clustered around the docks and wharves of Poplar or Millwall.

For a few years up to the outbreak of the Second World War

118

that work was with Russian Oil Products at their storage depot alongside the Thames on the Isle of Dogs. It would be one of many prime targets along the river when the bombers came and didn't last long after the initial raid. For the time and place it was a good job, with wages that were considered a little better than average. A five-day working week meant that the weekends were free for his other interests and activities, and from the time that his son was old enough and willing to walk a mile or more without complaining Jack set about introducing him to the world and its ways.

Sometimes with one or two of Jack's friends, but more often just by themselves, they went out and about for a morning or afternoon in the streets, along the canals, or on to the piers and foreshore of the river. It made little difference which direction they took from home; it was a complex, multifaceted world of its own, full of activity, fascination and novelty and there would be little enough opportunity for the young boy to get to know it. In Guernica the Luftwaffe had already been honing its terror-bombing techniques, Austria had been absorbed into the Third Reich, and in Czechoslovakia the familiar orchestrated reign of disorder, assassination or fabricated 'border incidents' formed a prelude to the Nazi occupation of the Sudetenland. However, despite the many warning voices raised, the continuing policy of appeasement – the supine surrender to increasingly outrageous demands from Hitler – would give them a couple of years of seeming normality for their walks.

To the north of the terrace three or four quiet streets of mean, depressing, back-to-back terraced houses took them to the road to Bow Common, and a noisy, smelly conglomeration of residential, retail, commercial and industrial activities that was typical of a score of working-class districts in the East End. At the end of the road a gentle incline led up to the bridge over the Limehouse Cut, and from its parapet a view for the young boy of life on and around its waters.

On the Bow side, rising from the greasy surface of the cut, the crumbling brick walls of an old warehouse gave way from the third floor upwards to grey, weather-worn timber boarding. From the topmost floor a wooden balcony sagged over the water and the derrick of a simple crane was swung out to haul to the upper storeys the cargoes of the barges tied up below: heavy, bulging bales, sack-wrapped and closely stitched at the seams. In the

119

shadow of the bridge sweating stevedores manoeuvred their loads with deceptive ease, striking hooks deep into the sacking and dragging the bales to the chains of the crane to be hauled high up the walls to the doors and hatches standing open to receive them. And from the open hatchways a heavy, sweet-smelling aroma spilled out across the bridge to mingle uneasily with the other less wholesome emanations that drifted over the surface of the cut.

The decay and dissolution of trade on the narrow canals further inland was already well under way by then, but the broad waters of the Limehouse Cut were still full of life and movement with traffic passing through from the Lea to the Thames and back, or stopping to unload at the factories and businesses that lined the banks. It was mostly routine river traffic: flat-bottomed barges, battered and rusting from their jostling on the Thames, piled high with bulk goods, coal, gravel or timber, or sheeted over with tarry black tarpaulins and towed along by dirty, noisy motor boats.

The men of the cut were a stolid, phlegmatic band. Flat cap on head, pipe clamped firmly in the mouth, each gazed impassively ahead as he passed under the bridge and along the cut towards the distant clock tower of St Anne's and on to Limehouse basin. If there was any response to a shout and a wave it was at best an upward glance and a wobble of the pipe. From Stinkhouse Bridge (the local name was well chosen) steps led down to the towpath walk towards the River Lea. Shrouded in the mists that hissed and steamed from the tanks, pipes and vats of the Phoenix Chemical Works, it marked the start of a stretch of canal-side Poplar that embodied all that was worst of the East End. Areas where industrial works and factories were crammed cheek by jowl with residential slums, and men returning home from a day's work in the stinking, noxious atmosphere of one unregulated, polluting enterprise lay down to sleep inhaling the fumes of another.

The banks of the Limehouse Cut were thick with such industries, and if the walk was a fascinating experience, it was also a gut-churning and testing one for a sensitive nose. Fumes and stinks from bone boiling, glue making, and fish or guano processing embraced those from charcoal manufacturing, tar distilling and chemical works to form their own heady mix before making common cause with exhalations from a disinfectant factory, lead works or any one of a dozen malodorous processes. Day in, day

120

out the final complex, breath-catching cocktail of vapours, drifting on the soft summer air or wreathed in the winter fogs, was the industrial legacy of the cut to the homes in the streets around it.

Beyond open gates or through the fencing, something of the canal-side activity could be seen from the towpath as they passed along. Behind one malodorous factory mounds of animal bones, clouded by swarms of flies, fouled the air of the men who casually barrowed them inside for processing. In the corner of another yard stacks of damaged and rusting drums oozed their dregs on to the greasy black sludge that surrounded them, and from a pipe beneath the towpath an oily slick spread out across the water. From the open-sided sheds of the sawmills a haze of dust and drifting chips carried the refreshing scent of newly sawn timber for a few yards before they were overwhelmed by the reeking odours from the rag-and-bone sorting yard or the acrid vapours from the varnish works. And from factory to barge and back there was a constant movement of the commodities of their trade: barrels, sacks, timber, boxes, chains, bags of cement, bricks, pig iron, sheet iron, waste paper and a hundred other items.

At Prospect Place (where the residents enjoyed a panorama that ranged from varnish works through engine sheds to the match factory) they left the cut and before they turned for home Jack called in to see Jimmy Bellamy an old friend from the war years. They had their politics and social attitudes in common and a ten-minute stop easily spun itself out into half an hour or longer. Jim, who worked for the LCC, was a rolling, round barrel of a man – round face, round glasses and round eyes over a little clipped moustache – but if Jim was a barrel Kate his wife was a hogshead, and if things got physical at political demonstrations they carried all before them. After work their involvement in politics and social reform occupied all their waking hours. They had no family of their own and took little interest in the niceties of domestic life, but as a matter of policy kept a few toys to occupy visiting children while the parents talked politics, always politics.

After politics, and presumably his wife, the love of Jim's life was a tandem bicycle kept in, and half occupying, the scullery. It was their one escape from work and their sordid surroundings, and when time and weather permitted they left the slums behind them and travelled far out to the east and the countryside of Essex. On

121

a good flat road with their combined tonnage thrusting at the pedals they went like a steam train; on a downhill run with the wind behind them they made an awesome sight.

Beyond East India Dock Road the great bursiform mass of the Isle of Dogs fell away into the sweeping meander of the Thames that runs from Blackwall Point to the Lower Pool. The island stood divorced and isolated from the rest of the borough, and did not invite or welcome casual strollers into its heartland. Little more than four hundred yards to the south of Carters Terrace, just beyond the tangle of railway lines, sidings, junctions and shunting yards that were the arteries of the port, the bonded warehouses of the Import Dock rose like a curtain wall against all intruders. Five storeys high, well guarded, and unbroken for almost three-quarters of a mile they barred any access to the island except by the perimeter road that enclosed it.

Beyond the wall lay the vast expanse of the docks themselves – West India Import, Export and South Docks, Millwall Inner and Outer – over one hundred and thirty five acres of secure deep water moorings for just some of the 60,000 ships a year that moved to and from London. Around and between the docks, strung along the road, or occupying the Thames foreshore from Limehouse pier to Blackwall, were all the ancillary activities and facilities that served or thrived on the docks and the tens of thousands who worked in them: swing bridges, dry docks, customs houses, iron-works, graving docks, grain silos, locks, cranes, engineering works, oil works, landing stages: in short all the commercial and industrial activities that, with the docks themselves and the ships in them, would be the prime targets of the German bombers in 1940.

Behind the walls of the grain silos, alongside the factories, in between the railway sidings, next to the oil depots, and in a great horseshoe sweep that hugged the docks, were the cramped streets of terraced houses, and the shops, churches, pubs and halls of the Dockland workers. Jerry-built from the cheapest of materials, they would offer no resistance to the high explosives and incendiaries when they came, and their destruction would be over, and by and large forgotten, long before the euphemism 'collateral damage' was coined.

Avoiding the barriers and intricacies of the island, it was to the byways of Poplar and the waterside haunts of Limehouse that Jack turned on their walks. That was his home ground: he had been born there, spent his childhood there, and as a young boy explored its streets and alleys with his father on the horse-van. He knew its secret places and loved the history to be found at every one of their stopping points.

In the recreation ground the man-sized model of the West Indiaman *Hibbert*, taken from the central arch of the demolished old Clock Gate, was the only visible reminder of the opening of the docks more than a century earlier. Beyond the *Hibbert*, in the corner of the graveyard, St Matthias' Church had been founded by the East India Company. The oldest church in the borough it embodied in its fabric Poplar's ancient links with the sea and trade: columns, it was said, from the wrecks of the Spanish Armada, and a ceiling decorated with the arms of the founding company. It survived the Blitz and the twentieth century unscathed but deconsecrated, and at the beginning of the new millennium was one of the few remaining links with the glory days of Poplar's maritime past; days when tea clippers built by Richard Green in his Poplar yards beat off the American challenge for the China trade in a last hurrah for sail as steam began to rule the seas.

On past the bowling green. No white flannels in Poplar, just the local men tidily dressed either playing or lounging on the benches around the green. There was a call from under the trees.

'Morning, Jack. Introducing the boy to his great inheritance?'

'Just letting him see the idle rich taking their ease. Nothing doing in the docks today, Arthur?'

'Well, you know the score, Jack. One day on and three days off. The old story.'

As the pleasantries turned to more serious matters John wandered off to watch the bowlers at play while Jack and Arthur sat in conversation. They smoked as they talked, and when John returned he caught the homely whiff of tobacco and beer on Arthur's breath: the Queen's Head pub, conveniently placed for the bowlers, was just a few steps along the High Street.

The local library, just across the road from the green, was Jack's second home, and he called in to return a recent loan before they went any further. When he could afford to, he bought his books second-hand, but he read much more than he could buy. The Poplar libraries were well provided, open to their readers from nine in the morning till nine at night, and if Jack couldn't borrow a book the family lost him to the reference room for as long as it took him to read it. When he died more than twenty years after the Blitz, the books on his shelves included two that bore witness to the event: date-stamped for return to the library on 17th September 1940.

By way of Pennyfields and Limehouse Causeway their route took them through the heart of the East End's Chinatown where the names on shopfronts and businesses were rich in entertainment value for any young child versed in the stereotypes of comics and Saturday-morning cinema: Poy Fong, Wong Tam, Sing San Sam and Sing Ching Foo How, who owned the refreshment rooms. But there was nothing sinister or mysterious about the Orientals they passed: the Chinese were no novelty to a boy who saw them moving to and from the Seamen's Rest every day.

A shorter route through Garford Street brought them soonest to the river and the first of the steps down on to the foreshore. In the 1850s Mayhew wrote of fourteen stairways to the river between Execution Dock and Limehouse Hole. Eighty years later most of them remained, together with lingering traces of the dark Victorian world that he and Dickens would have known. Soon, with the sights, sounds and smells of the river close to hand, they were in streets and alleys redolent of the murky undercurrents of that cheerless Thames-side underworld, where the scum of humanity had exercised their doubtful trades and Gaffer Hexam slipped his boat from the mud of Limey Hole in a grim search for the human flotsam thrown up by the river. The sailing ships and most of the villains had gone, but on both sides of the street beyond the Hole there were industries and occupations that Dickens would have recognised: ships' chandlers, barge builders, wharfingers, sail and mast makers, tug and barge owners, riverside warehouses, and the pubs and cheap refreshment rooms that kept the workers fuelled and oiled.

At Limekiln Dock the sweet, rich aroma from the caramel manufactory, the beery waftings from the Barley Mow brewery and the frowsy, rafty smells of the foreshore and its decaying timbers mingled to welcome them. Beyond the dock and the Dunbar warehouses they passed into Narrow Street that would take them through to another passageway and the Thames foreshore at Kidney Stairs: a cramped set of stone steps squeezed between the riverside buildings close to the entrance to the Regent's Canal Dock and Limehouse Cut.

Throughout the length of Narrow Street from the Causeway to Ratcliffe Cross Stairs the world was one of hectic maritime, industrial and marketing activity, with ships and lighters moving into and out of the river locks on the tide; horses and carts, lorries and hand-barrows jostling for a way through on the roads; and pavements a constant press of workers, seamen and casual passers-by.

At the broad ship-lock on the full tide, colliers, lighters and freighters passed up from the river into Regent's Canal Dock with their cargoes of coal from the north of England, timber from the Baltic and German ports, and fruit from Spain. With timing critical, the river traffic was given priority and along with everyone else on the street Jack stopped and waited as ahead of them, through the open swing bridge, a freighter moving up from the river drifted leisurely across the road and into the lock. Incongruous in size and appearance, it towered above the customs' office and dwarfed the carts and lorries brought to a standstill by its passage. Pedestrians on the pavement looked up at it curiously, and two sailors, idle for a few moments, smoked their cigarettes as they hung over the deck rails and gazed as curiously back until the ship passed through and swung away to its quay and out of sight.

Opposite Shoulder of Mutton Lane, they turned away from the crush and passed down the narrow entry to Kidney Stairs where a century or so earlier a fare of sixpence to one of the many watermen operating there would have bought them a river trip back to the steps at Limey Hole. The watermen were long gone but on either side of the steps wherries, cutters and dinghies bounced and tugged at lines tied to posts and rings on the lower levels of the riverside buildings, and the incoming tide swirled the river eddies at their feet.

Ahead of them the Thames opened up, full to the brim from shore to shore at high tide, and immediately across the river lay the broad expanse of the Surrey Commercial Docks named for their maritime and trading connections: Norway, Canada, Greenland, Quebec and Russia. Around the docks spread acre upon acre of yards and sheds crammed with the imported timbers that would burn so well and for so long in the firestorms of the Blitz. To their left the long, straight stretch of Limehouse Reach ran down towards the Greenwich bend. To their right the waters of the Lower Pool swung away towards the London and St Katherine Docks, the Upper Pool and Tower Bridge.

Out of the main stream broad rafts of lighters and barges strained against their moorings, and beyond, on the deep-water channel, well separated and moving in orderly procession, that tide's burden of the sixty-two million tons of shipping that passed through the Port of London each year steamed to its dockside moorings. Great seagoing freighters, scruffy coasters, colliers and elegant passenger ships moved onwards to the Upper Pool, or blasted out a warning as they slowed and swung in towards the locks or a mooring. Slipping alongside them river tugs churned the water to foam as they towed their lines of laden barges upstream to wharves and warehouses, or downriver, full to the gunnels with London's waste, and heading for the marshland dumps of Kent and Essex. Between and around the heavy river traffic, pilot boats, police launches, motor boats and wherries wove their way, and occasionally the sails of a Thames spritsail barge drifted sedately by with its burden of timber, grain, coal or cement.

That was the way of the Dockland world during those pre-war walks: the river thronged with shipping great and small, the streets vibrant with life and activity, and the lighters in Limekiln dock bustling with stevedores discharging the cargoes to the upper storeys of the warehouses at Dunbar Wharf. The Blitz brought the first of the changes and from then on things never really recovered. Slowly at first, and then in one great sweep it all went. The river is deserted, the docks and dockers gone, and in his luxury bijou apartment high in the Dunbar warehouse, a snip at £350,000, the weary executive sips his malt and gazes out at the promised 'distant river views' of a dead and featureless waterway utterly devoid of romance, life and interest.

At low water the stones of the bottom steps at Kidney Stairs, still wet from the outgoing tide, were green, slippery and treacherous, and the breeze carried the distinctive smell of exposed Thames foreshore. Traffic on the river had virtually ceased: nothing of any size moved, and the river ran sluggishly in the narrowing channel. Away from the steps the surface was surprisingly firm beneath their feet; a natural mix of shingle, stone and mud.

The picture was one in which Mayhew or his mudlarks would have recognised much of the Thames they knew: long, gently shelving stretches of dark foreshore; dinghies, skiffs and other small boats lying on the mud at the limit of their lines; dolphins, mooring posts and embankment stanchions stained and greasy with the deposits of a dirty river; and the planks and rotten cross-timbers on the shadowy undersides of jetties and piers dripping steadily through thin curtains of green slime.

Only the rubbish might have surprised them. Without the scavengers that picked the bones of Victorian London clean of waste the foreshore was littered with the detritus of industry and daily living: fragmentary lengths of rope and chain; broken packing cases and clean, freshly sawn timber lost from one of the many woodyards; bottles and broken glass; old sacks and pieces of clothing caught and held by the nails on waterlogged woodwork. Anything in short that might have been thrown or lost from ship or shore. There were still some pickings for latter-day mudlarks, and as they made their way across the gravel and mud towards Duke Shore Steps they passed one heading for home with his morning's haul: several lengths of useful-looking timber on one shoulder, and a coir fender draped across the other.

It was never difficult in the East End to find a pub at the halfway point of their walks. On the foreshore it was The Grapes Inn where Jack climbed the wooden steps to a sagging balcony and passed out of sight in search of their refreshments before they set off for home.

Inland and a little further west was the Regent's Canal where the locks from the river led north to the waterways of the Midlands. It was the longest of their walks, and they could have taken a tram, but trams cost money, and legs were made for using then even if they were young ones. So walk they did, along roads thick with the traffic that flowed east and west from the docks.

On either side of the road were the many smaller commercial and manufacturing businesses that serviced the docks and the industries and factories grouped around them. It was an eclectic mix: ironmongers, coppersmiths, garages, boot and shoemakers, clothing manufacturers, watchmakers, printers, flag makers, under-takers, boiler cleaners, stewed eel shops, and open doors and gateways were a constant invitation to linger, watch and wonder.

Food and drink was there to suit all tastes, save the discriminat-ing and delicate. Outside coffee houses, eating rooms and pie shops, boards propped against the walls commended menus that the odours drifting from open doors and windows did little to endorse. About pub after pub the reeking, sour smell of stale beer hung in the air whatever the time of day, and from each adjacent urinal drifted the same sharp breath-catching stench.

Tobacconists, grocers, doctors, dentists, letter writers; all were there advertising their goods and services, and in the heart of an area satisfying the demands of the seamen of the world, there were other more intimate ministrations available that John was too young to recognise.

Competing to satisfy the spiritual needs of the Docklands' fixed and floating population were the assorted churches, chapels, mission houses and Salvation Army halls scattered along their route, but on a Saturday they showed few signs of activity. Pressed between his sandwich boards one of life's losers shuffled the old message along the pavement, 'Repent Ye and believe the Gospel' and 'The Wages of Sin is Death', and at one of the busier corners a solitary eccentric preached his own idiosyncratic gospel from a box. He was a regular at the spot and had a good audience, there for the laughs most of them, and changing all the time.

Short rows of houses broke up the pattern of business occupation. Many offered cheap apartments or lodgings, and together with the seamen's rests or missions they provided a bed for the night for the constantly changing population that came from the docks. Anywhere else at that time the colourfully varied and cosmopolitan mix of people that filled the streets would have been the focus of intense interest, and probably of suspicion, but in Commercial Road they passed without notice. African, Asiatic, Oriental and Indian faces under turbans, skullcaps, puggarees and fezes mingled with the grey, pinched features of the East End locals, and not a cloth-capped head was turned.

Pawnbrokers thrived on the needs of the shifting population of seamen and a local community that with few exceptions lived on a hand-to-mouth, day-to-day basis. In windows stuffed to overflowing, a sad display of intimate and personal belongings, popped 'just 'til next pay-day', but never redeemed, rubbed shoulders with the exotic and practical possessions of the tide of seamen that flooded into and out of the docks. Household utensils, sandalwood chests, cigarette cases, lacquered tea caddies, ornamental daggers, second-hand shoes and suits, compasses, patent logs and sounding gear, musical instruments, books on stowage, navigation, knots and splices, stuffed monkeys, birds, and animal horns of all shapes and sizes, plain and decorated: a young boy's eyes could be dazzled and his mind baffled by the variety of the display and by speculation on procurement if pocket money were saved for a week or two.

In Limehouse, where the West and East India Dock Roads, joined with Burdett and Commercial Roads, the tramlines met in a complex intersection to create a large, triangular traffic island, where two sets of steps, framed by ornamental wrought-iron railings, descended to subterranean lavatories that raised sanitary engineering to the realms of fine art. A far cry from the mean, black-iron, purely functional urinals that serviced the pubs and docks, they were public utility showpieces created by their Victorian builders with the same confidence, pride and attention to detail and design that the architects gave to their grander institutions above ground, and no Moor in the fastness of the Alhambra was ever as enchanted by his water gardens and fountain courts as was John by his occasional visits to the Limehouse public lavatories.

Above the entrance an arch of curiously interwoven ironwork supported an illuminated globe that both advertised the services and threw a welcoming light on steps descending between tiled walls always newly washed and gleaming. At the foot of the steps a uniformed factotum presided over the mysteries of the place from a cubbyhole of varnished wood and glass. On duty throughout opening hours, he cleaned, scrubbed and polished every inch as though it was his personal domain.

It was cool and fresh underground, with a faint earthy smell, but free of any taint from its basic operations. High on the walls, on decorated iron brackets, gleaming white vitreous-enamel cisterns hung beneath a richly coloured, decorated cornice. Below the cisterns copper pipes, burnished and glowing from years of devoted attention, dropped and extended along the walls through bulbous brass junctions, smoothed and rounded by their daily polishing.

When John stood in one of the massive, deeply curving bays of urinals, his head barely reached to the manufacturer's name and device fused into the vitreous china. Through bullseyes of glass in the roof above him the rays of the high sun, refracted and scattered, glinted and danced on the copper and brass before him, and he listened in satisfaction to the music of the water coursing through the pipes as he added his own miniscule dribble to the flood. He had the gratifying feeling of growing up, of being one of the men. It was perhaps his father's amused understanding of this that allowed him the indulgence of a visit whenever they passed.

Opposite the urinals, behind varnished doors guarded by gleaming brass locks, the water closets were closed off inside a long line of cubicles. He had seen the penny payments being made, heard the click of the locks, and those secret cabinets filled him with curiosity.

Just once, having convinced his father of a genuine need, he slipped in his penny, drew back the lock, and passed at last into the inner sanctum. The door closed with a heavy, satisfying clunk. Perched on the glossy, varnished seat he gazed around him at the glazed tiles, the glossy timber and the bright brass fittings. He pulled some paper from the roll; proper toilet paper, not torn-up sheets from the *Herald*. He had no use for it, but he'd paid his money and intended to have his pennyworth. He could hear his father talking to the custodian – there was no need to hurry.

Above him he watched the shadowy shapes of pedestrians hurrying across the bullseyes. He heard the occasional thunder of the trams rumbling over the junction tracks, the regular flushing of water over the urinals, and then the sound of his father's voice telling him he'd been in there long enough.

From that day the lavatory at home, with its scrubbed wooden seat of common deal, its whitewashed brick walls, its lead piping and black iron cistern, and the torn sheets of yesterday's daily, tied by string to a nail in the wall, seemed a very undistinguished affair. For just a penny, he decided, the Limehouse public conveniences were very good value. Their splendours faded and decayed during and after the war, and today only a solitary, rusting ventilation shaft rises up to mark the site and their passing.

On a bench beneath the trees in the churchyard of St Anne's they sat together before they moved on. Ships and the sea entered into the very fabric of Limehouse and Poplar, and no more so than at St Anne's. For a century and more its tower had been a landmark for every ship working its way up Limehouse Reach into the lower pool, and babies born on British vessels at sea were registered and baptised at its font when the ship returned to its home port.

From St Anne's it was only a short walk to the canal at Salmon Lane lock. There a broader stretch of water ran south to Regent's

130

Canal Dock and the river locks that opened into the Thames. Barges piled high with timber moved up from the dock to the canal to discharge at the many timberyards that lined its banks. Motor narrowboats manoeuvred to warehouses or moorings on gently idling engines, and with studied negligence the boatmen poled their butty boats into position, leaning casually against their long shafts as if it was all just too easy and relaxing.

To the north the canal curved away beyond Johnson's lock to the waters of the Grand Union. In both directions, tied up to long lines of mooring posts, were the narrowboats that carried some small part of the imports of the docks to the Midlands and beyond, and returned from the Black Country or the Potteries laden with the goods that were outward bound. Many, loading or unloading, clustered around the wharves across the canal from the towing path, while others moved on to drop down into Regent's Canal Dock, or start the long climb that would take them through the heart of London Zoo, and then into the suburbs on their way to the north.

From Salmon Lane lock to Victory Bridge the towpath passed little blocks of stables attached to a couple of pubs used mainly by passing canal traffic. Horse-drawn boats were disappearing fast from the canals, but there were generally six or seven horses in the stables, shuffling their feet as they pulled twists of hay from the racks on the walls, or standing shaking their heads over the stable doors as they waited to be led out and harnessed up. In the hands of the experienced boatmen it seldom took long: the collar to be slipped on, the harness strapped tight, the tow rope attached to horse and mast, a final check of the brasses if the boatman took a pride in his work and they were ready. Then with his master at his head the horse took the first few steps in the long haul ahead. The tow rope rose dripping from the water, snapped tight, spangling the surface of the cut with a shower of droplets, and slowly the boat moved forward. From then on until journey's end the only accompaniment to their passage would be the steady plod of the horse, the jangle of brasses and harness, and the splash and rush of water at locks or weirs.

Others boats were less reticent in announcing their presence and were heard before they were seen: a distinctive, arresting voice. First the regular beat of an engine deep under the railway bridge, hammering out a rhythm caught and echoed by the build-

131

ings that lined the cut. Then, from the gloom beneath the bridge a pair of narrowboats, firmly breasted-up, swung into view. Many were unexceptional in any way – just workhorses for the job in hand, plain and unadorned. But there were others that reflected all the pride of possession, devotion and decorative skills that their owners could bring to them.

Bold lettering on painted side panels proclaimed name of boat, owner and base. Brightly coloured hatch covers were patterned in hearts, spades, diamonds or clubs. Above the engine hole the decorated pigeon box was capped with polished brass work, and alternating narrow bands of brass and colour topped two gleaming black chimneys. On the cabin roof water cans and dippers embellished with roses and imaginary vistas stood ready for use, and flowers blooming in brightly painted troughs brought a touch of cottage garden into the industrial heart of London. Visitors from the north, they seemed to come from another world of limpid waters, wooded cuttings and open fields.

From the crossing planks on the top gates they could look down on to the boat and through open double doors, decorated with visionary castles and swags of cabbagey English roses, into the back cabin. A compact iron stove, newly black-leaded, glowed under a couple of steaming pans. On a narrow bench a cat was stretched out asleep on a pile of patchwork cushions. Add the whiff of stew drifting up from the pots and it had the welcoming, comforting look and feel of home.

Further on in the dimly lit interior glimpses of family treasures and possessions could just be seen. Narrow shelves fringed with lace hangings held the cups, saucers and jugs in daily use and a few choice china ornaments like those that Lou treasured. Fancy furnishings varied from boat to boat: ornamental horse brasses, copper display pieces, intricate sconces holding brass oil lamps, lace plates threaded and hung with red ribbon, and family photographs in ornate frames – all had a place on the walls. Almost anything that glistened, gleamed or carried a splash of bright colour into the little cabin was grist to the decorative mill.

The boats passed on their way through the lock to an audience of young boys green with envy at the sight of a canal boy, not much older than themselves, at the tiller of a breasted-up pair as it sank into the depths of the lock. In the empty butty boat alongside, younger children could be seen scrambling around in the hold, with

132

a dog or two – there were always dogs – scampering excitedly at their feet. With the bottom gates open, the young lad put his hand to the engine control and, contemptuously casual in front of his audience, took the boats out of the lock and to within an inch or two of the towing path for his father to step aboard after closing the lock gates.

There was one other visitor from the north seen only rarely, but she sang a siren song that turned every head and drew the boys running from their games in the street. She sounded at first like a score of others, but then her engine coughed coyly and dropped into a syncopated rhythm and string of variations that set the feet tapping and intoxicated the soul. Her appearance did little to commend her for she was rather flash in her decorations, but the fascinating, perverse rhythm of the engine hypnotised her audience as she eased her way into the lock. Then through the open hatchway they could look down on an engine beyond their wildest imaginings. Shining and bright under a sheen of engine oil, every working part seemed to be visible, and all that was visible was in perpetual, intriguing motion.

At the front the dark steel of a massive flywheel shimmered and gleamed as it rotated to the pulse of the idling engine. From the bowels of the boat a thick, round engine trunk rose to a tangle of polished copper pipes wound round a silvery dome. To one side of the engine a moving metal striker hammered out a strange eccentric beat to which the deep exhaust kept time: tunc, tunc, tunc, pause, tunc-tunc, tunc, tunc, pause, tunc-tunc. From the base of the engine, long levers rising to the cabin roof were extended by rods to the boatman at the stern. As he put his hand to them they rotated or moved to and fro, and the note and rhythm of the engine changed, as the boat edged slowly forwards or back. From steel boxes at the foot of the engine, slender copper piping extended to the moving parts, and low down just above the keelson a greasy, rotating shaft disappeared beneath the metal plates of the floor towards the stern. All was movement, vibration and excitement. Screwed to the head of the cylinder a polished brass plate carried the legend 'Bolinder: Sweden'.

Slowly the boat dropped away into the depths of the lock and the engine was lost to view. With the bottom gates open the boatman reached in to his controls. The speed of the engine increased, its note hardened, and now to a steady unvarying beat

133

the boat slipped out of the lock, and passed away down the cut and into the distance.

Following those canal visits with his father, narrowboats were to John as railway engines were to boys who wanted to be engine drivers – they engendered a passion of longing. Their walks to the canal were all made in the fine weather of summer of course, and life on the cut was seen only in the sunshine hours. There was no thought then of long, dark November evenings with the family cramped together in a stuffy, rain-swept cabin, or February mornings with the snow and ice just a few inches from their heads and a long day's run in sleet and snow ahead of them.

When the war came narrowboats were conscripted along with the rest, and roses, castles and traditional eye-catching decorations gave way to an austere wartime livery. Munitions, copper, aluminium and other materials essential to the war effort were added to the coal, metals and pottery moving regularly between London and the Midlands, and water girls as well as land girls joined the national effort. Operating in teams of three they moved a pair of boats, motor boat and butty, across the waterways in work that was dirty, hard and unremitting. The German bombers too found occasional use for the waterways, the clear, sharp lines across the countryside as good a guide to their Midland targets as the Thames had been from the coast to London.

10

The Cockle Sheds

The fine weekends and long school holiday of 1939 saw Bayhurst filled to overflowing with aunts, uncles, cousins and friends. The thought that it might be the last summer of peace when they could be together was never openly expressed, but that was certainly the conviction growing in most minds. Two years earlier the atrocities of the Luftwaffe's Condor Legion over Guernica had defined the nature of Hitler's regime. His subsequent words and actions in Europe left little scope for doubt that events were moving towards a climax that could only be violent. There was certainly no one left in the family who shared the optimism that Aunt Tot had carried with her to the grave

Nor was it necessary to look to the news from Europe. Already at home there were more than enough indications of the way the government thought things were going. As early as 1938 blackout trials were being selectively conducted across the country. Leicester, Paddington, Hampshire and the Midlands all had their turn, and to general amusement Hertfordshire's trial was appointed for Guy Fawkes Night. In the same year articles on Air Raid Protection began to appear in the daily newspapers, and their readers learned that twenty-six million gas masks and fifty million ration cards were already on hand. Planning began for the evacuation of children, and the start of the Bayhurst 'season' in May of 1939 brought matters much closer to home when Phoebe and Jack were called to the children's schools to register them for evacuation.

All in all there was precious little reason to view the future with anything but a jaundiced eye, and for that very reason all those who crammed themselves into their plotland retreat were more than ever determined to make the most of their time there. Where numbers exceeded capacity, as they sometimes did, there was Aunt Tot's family to soak up the excess with a bed for the night.

For most of the thousands of pleasure seekers from the East End the fleshpots of Southend-on-Sea were the main attraction. Crammed into the excursion trains that ran from Fenchurch Street and stations east, a few of them dropped off at the two more restrained resorts just short of the town, but most pressed on into Southend where they spilled out and flooded down the High Street towards the sea. There the beaches offered a little sand but much mud, and the pier, the Kursaal amusement park, the arcades, the shops, pubs and refreshment rooms that lined the front all competed hotly to relieve the punters of their cash. Noisy, brash and crowded, its gimcracks, slot machines and candyfloss were a dreamland for the children of the family when they could get there, but the overriding adult preference was for something quieter with a little more character. They found this closer to hand at Leigh-on-Sea.

On most family excursions, with economy always an overriding consideration, they would have taken their own refreshments: sandwiches, cakes and Thermos flasks of tea, but Leigh had its own gourmet delights to tempt them, and they carried nothing with them but towels and costumes. Progress up the lane was leisurely; the adults strolling and chatting, the children tumbling along backwards and forwards over the deep drainage ditches lining the lane, or racing ahead to choose something for their journey at the sweet shop.

If the Essex bus service lacked the frequency and reliability of Poplar public transport, the country bus stop was a pleasant place to wait. There was little passing traffic and when harvesting was in progress the fields were full of life and activity. If the harvesters had already passed that way then the children played their games around the standing shocks of corn, or wandered the stubble seeking and chewing the grain from the few ears of corn missed by the gleaners.

The road to Leigh had nothing of interest to offer. Half a mile beyond Bowers Gifford the countryside ended in the cluster of shops and houses at Tarpots, and from there to Southend, apart from the woodlands of Bread and Cheese Hill and a few acres of farmed land on a Salvation Army colony, patchy ribbon development stretched in a broad no-man's-land between the unspoilt country inland and the coastline of the estuary.

Close to Leigh, penny-watching as always, they cut away from

136

the bus a fare stage early and walked the longer but scenic route to the sea. It took them down a rough unsurfaced track with distant views of the ragged stumps of Hadleigh Castle, and the estuary gradually opening out before them. Then along the ridge of the hill above the estuary, past houses beside which Aunt Tot's shrunk to a very modest establishment in the eyes of her grand-nephew. Garages, leaded glazing, conservatories, wrought ironwork, decorative garden ornaments and sun-drenched balconies marked them out as homes to those enjoying a life of comfortable retirement or still 'something in the City'; all conveniently placed for a brisk but short walk to the station and the fast train up to town at a civilised hour in the morning.

Their windows looked out across lawns, ornamental gardens and neatly trimmed grassland to the mudflats and sands of the estuary shallows, and beyond through the haze, over the deeper waters of the channel, to the Kent shore and the Isle of Grain. It was a prospect that attracted the watercolourists, where the nuances of light and shade varied with every hour of the day and every shift of water and wind. At low tide the foreshore was a tangle of creeks and inlets cutting through black islands that slowly disappeared as the waters rose. On the deeply cut, curving banks of the channels, boats sagged on the mud, waiting for the returning waters to lift them to life once again. Here and there a hull more deeply buried, or the entombed remains of ribs and planking, marked those that had failed to rise to a new tide's challenge. Beyond the flats and marshes the sea receded to a distant glimmer fringing the Chapman Sands where, high tide or low, the imports and exports of the London docks passed slowly along the deep-water channel.

When the tide turned from ebb to flood, the waters seeped back into the winding channels stealthily and imperceptibly. To the watchers on the hill they gave no sign of their return until the slight, tentative movement of a mast on one of the grounded boats marked the start of its journey back to the vertical, and one by one the others followed. All would be afloat and swinging into line with tide or wind before the blank expanses of the flats started to be broken with runnels of water, and the waders probing the mud retreated little by little on the shrinking islands that were left to them. The changes were swift then as the tide outflanked, surrounded and finally overwhelmed them, and for the few hours of high tide the sea rolled unbroken from Leigh to the coast of Kent, while above the Chapman Sands the dredgers renewed their work recovering sand for the brickfields.

As they strolled the ridge of the hill in the summer of 1939 their talk reflected the mood of the times, now light holiday chatter, now more thoughtful and subdued. It stopped entirely as they paused and listened when the easterly wind carried to them the distant thunder of test firings by the big guns on the artillery ranges at Shoeburyness. At the bottom of the hill their route took them over the railway at the new station, along a gravel track by the side of the creek, and then into the old town. It was the furthest point from the beaches but it was Old Leigh itself that was the prime attraction, not its few patches of sand.

When the railway arrived at Leigh in the mid-nineteenth century, the high ground inland forced it to slice its way through the edges of the hill just thirty yards or so from the creek, leaving a sliver of the town, just one road and its buildings, isolated below the line.

On the heights above, late-Victorian and Edwardian villas sprang up, hotels were built and businesses flourished. Down below, Old Leigh was in every sense on the wrong side of the track. Changing little with the years, it turned its back on high town and railway and, as it had done for centuries, looked to, and worked on, the sea. It was a down-at-heel, ramshackle sort of place. Here and there on a few old, weatherboarded houses, roofs sagged over timbers that had twisted and warped as foundations slipped and settled. Chandlers' shops, pubs, sail lofts, marine engineers, workshops and a smithy were scattered in between retail shops, refreshment rooms, cockle merchants, pubs and narrow terraces of two-up, two-down brick-built houses: mean little dwellings like those they had left behind in Poplar. Everywhere passages, slipways or steps gave access across the foreshore to the creek and the boats of the fishermen.

If time and tide were right as they approached, steam would be rising from the roofs of their objective, a huddle of sheds at the edge of the main channel. On an easterly wind the scent of the creek and the sheds would be heavy in the air at half a mile. It spoke of the sea, the sands, the salt marshes and the flats, but above all it spoke of lunch. It was a breeze that teased the nose and moistened the mouth with anticipation of the pleasures to

138

come. It carried the scent, the rich aroma, the irresistible fragrance of the cockle sheds, and it promised fresh, sweet-tasting, succulent sea flesh, newly harvested and landed from the fleet of boats that came up the creek on the morning tide.

Apart from a few old boathouses and workshops beside the path, the cockle sheds were the first buildings they came to as they entered the old town. They were a rambling, irregular hotchpotch that had grown by process of accretion to suit the increasing and changing demands of the years. From an old wharf by the creek a ramp and hardstanding ran to a shed where the haze of rising steam marked the passing of that morning's catch. Beyond, a long, low extension led to the shop and counters on which the seductive selection of shellfish was displayed.

It was past noon when the Pound Lane visitors arrived, and after the long walk in the sea air they were set on self-indulgence. In the low, central section of the building tables, cloths and chairs were set out under cover, but except in the worst of weather they were ignored and unoccupied. On the open ground beside the shed, wooden benches and well-scrubbed tables provided an open-air dining room where the bite of sea air sharpened the appetite and the eye could run on into the hazy distance, where just a few hours earlier their lunch had been busying itself in the sands.

Places were staked at the table nearest to the creek. From the Cooked Billet behind them beer arrived for the men and lemonade for the children; the ladies sipped tea with their seafood but would be enjoying a little drop of something short after the meal. At Osborne's counter, desire was both inflamed and frustrated by the display: large, white-enamel bowls heaped with cockles, mussels, shrimps, prawns, whelks and winkles; whole crabs or their shells filled with fresh white and brown crabmeat; bowls of jellied eels, and for those with slightly deeper pockets, piles of gleaming pearly-grey oysters.

At the front of the counter, choice selections were set out in shallow dishes, large or small and priced accordingly, to tempt the casual passers-by. They stopped for a few moments, splashed on the pepper and vinegar, downed their cockles or whelks with a fragment of bread and were off, but the family were there on more serious business.

For the children the dilemma of choice was just part of the pleasure. John as an aficionado knew that winkles, although the

139

pick of the crop, demanded serious application and were far too time-consuming for the occasion. Whelks though tasty were gristly, but whatever the personal choice, by the time they all sat down the table held a broad selection of most that was on offer, plus dressed crab for general use, and plates of bread and butter or crusty white rolls. A light sprinkling of vinegar and a dusting of pepper completed the preliminaries.

Informal and alfresco the setting may have been, but a code of etiquette was imposed as rigid as that on the highest of hall tables. Knives and forks were out, fingers de rigeur. To take cockles on the cold, metallic prongs of a fork was the creek-side equivalent of eating peas on a knife at the Savoy. Before and after the meal hands were washed under a tap on the side of the shed and dried in the sun and wind.

As they ate, gulls swept in circles overhead or clustered on the eaves of the surrounding buildings. Raucous and aggressive, they burst into frantic, squabbling warfare when fragments of food were thrown their way, as they frequently were just for the pleasure of the entertainment provided. Behind the pub an occasional train coughed and puffed its way into or out of the nearby station, and a haze of sooty smoke drifted over their tables and out to sea. At low tide, as the sea streamed out through the creeks, the mud of the flats and banks that edged the channels shimmered in the sun, and on a clear day, far in the distance, the cockle boats might just be seen, high and dry on the sands, as the cocklers raked up the next harvest. When the tide was on the flood the boats returned again from the distant cockle beds. Line astern they skirted the muddy shallows, following with easy familiarity the twists and turns of a creek now invisible under the risen waters, until they moored just a few yards from their sheds. Then, basket by basket, their harvest came ashore to the sheds and once again the steam began to rise.

Until they next moved out to the cockle grounds the boats lay moored up, or at anchor swinging this way and that as breeze or current took them. It looked a peaceful unchanging scene with no conceivable threat beyond that of wind and weather, but within less than a year, a small fleet of cockle boats and many like them, together with their crews, would be lying under shellfire and air attack off the beaches of Dunkirk, some not to return. The family would have seen them all as they sat at lunch in that last summer before war erupted – *Endeavour, Reliance, Resolute* and *Renown* – pretentious names perhaps on the creeks and fleets of the estuary, but the boats and their crews earned the right to them in May 1940.

'What are you going to have then, Ma?'

'Oh, thanks, Jack, a port and lemon I think.'

While the ladies enjoyed their tipple, and the men lingered over their cigarettes, the children were released upon the town. Its diversions were limited, but the railway was a good start. The station wasn't far away, and the trains travelled slowly on a stretch where only a fence and a few yards separated the line from the footpath. There they assembled and waited for the carriages to pass. From open carriage windows young faces gazed out towards the estuary, those on their way home wistful and dejected, those outward bound looking eagerly towards the sea, the pier and their holiday,

They sent them on their way with a shouted exchange of pleasantries and physical expressions of derision that might have surprised their parents, and then over rough paths and access ramps between decaying wharves and storehouses they passed through to the foreshore, a waste of shale and mud except behind the cockle sheds where hills of golden sand beckoned only to resolve themselves on close inspection into mounds of empty cockle shells. They spilled out like dunes along the edges of the creek – countless generations piled upon generations slowly drifting back under their own weight towards the creek and the mud from which they had been dredged.

The old town did not extend very far; there was no traffic, and children could roam safely along the one lane shoving their noses into boatyards until they were hounded away, or scouring the slipways and ramps leading through to the foreshore. There were idle winches to wind, shell mounds to climb and defend, and dead crabs to gawp at. They searched for the secret passages into the caverns beneath the old Peter Boat Inn, clambered over and into any boats that were on the shore, and hauled at every rope they could get their hands on. When the adults finally emerged from their extended lunch break they moved off down the narrow street, stopping only at the last group of buildings where ice cream, nut rings or coconut ice from Mrs Trot's strategically placed sweet shop provided the children with sustenance for the next hour or so.

141

From the eastern end of town, squeezed in between the railway and the sea, a narrow footpath led to the promenade that stretched from Westcliff to Southend and beyond. At the start of the path, for a couple of hundred yards, were the few beaches that Leigh had to offer. A line of timber groins running down towards the creek anchored narrow stretches of sand against the effects of waves and wind, but they were narrow and soon petered out into shingle, shingle and mud, and finally mud. The restrained old-fashioned character of Leigh never drew the crowds, however, and there was always plenty of space in which to spread out.

Deckchairs were hired, the children were costumed, and for the rest of the afternoon the members of the party went their separate ways. The men set off on the path to Westcliff, smoking and talking as they went, and Lou settled in her chair to doze the afternoon away. Even the hottest weather could no longer tempt Phoebe and her sisters into costumes, but if the sea was up to the sand and well clear of mud and shingle then off came their shoes and stockings, and they paddled around with their dresses held discreetly just above knee level. Sedate and modest to start with, they were too far advanced in years it seemed to show their enjoyment, but it wasn't long before one or the other reverted to type. A splash here would be followed by a shout and a splash there, and before long they were going at one another like children, until like children one was over-enthusiastic with the water. Then after an exchange of words there would be a sulky withdrawal to deckchairs, and from being entertained observers the children proper passed on to their own occupations.

If it was high tide, they had to be content with sand. That was fine in its own way, but sand was to be had at most beaches. The Leigh ooze on the other hand, had its own special attractions, and if the waters were far enough out it was a muddy wallow that made the day. At the fringes of the beach, where the sand and gravel petered out, the mud was firm and supportive, but as it shelved towards the creek it softened and oozed away beneath their feet. Alongside the water of the creek they were more than ankle-deep in the stuff – clinging, viscous, possessive mud from which their feet were dragged laboriously.

Like the sand, the mud warmed quickly in the sun, and at the edges of the creek they stretched out like basking seals. With legs and feet cool in the water, and thighs and body warm in the sun, they rolled, twisted and slithered, luxuriating in the silky-soft embrace, until from neck to toe they were gleaming black and fragrant with the distinctive and powerful odour of the creeks. Phoebe watched the performance with equanimity. She had seen it all before and knew that the remedy was readily to hand. When they had finally exhausted themselves she ushered them along the fringes of the beach to a concrete slipway, where after soaking for a while to soften up the encrusted deposits, they washed themselves clean in the waters of the creek.

The journey home began with a short, sharp climb to the top of Church Hill. A mix of cobbles and shallow steps, it was a steeper route back to the main road but was chosen by the ladies for the pleasure of walking a little down the terraces along the side of the hill where they could admire the gardens and frontages of the attractive, old weatherboarded houses that had occupied the slopes long before the Victorian and Edwardian villas arrived with the railway. At the top of the climb the church of St Clement's stood high on the ridge above the old town. While the ladies caught their breath and took in the view, the children goggled at the Cutlass Stone scored, Jack assured them, by the blades of press-gang cutlasses as they sharpened them before raiding the inns of the old town.

The youngsters were not denied an occasional taste of the vulgar delights of Southend, however, but if John was taken at all it was usually by his aunts, generous as ever, on one of their longer summer visits to the country. Even with them his excesses were limited to the ghost train, bumper cars and a penny or two wasted on the slot machines. Their indulgence did not extend to the scenic railway, giant swings or the wall of death. For those none of his powers of persuasion or wheedling worked. They would not let him ride alone, were not prepared to ride with him, nor were they, as he proposed, prepared to entrust him to any other adult waiting to ride. Compensation came in the form of creamy Rossi's ice cream and candyfloss.

On the pier they walked out and took the train back. It was a long walk, but not without its diversions if the tide was out. From time to time a train rumbled past them, and far below mud artists with pegs, scrapers and smoothing boards followed the waters as they flowed out over the level flats, and for the hours available between the tides covered the surface of the mud with their transient art. Sailing ships, pictures of the steamers calling at the pier head, images of the pier itself, or of the scenic railway were all favourite themes. A couple of buckets placed for walkers to show their appreciation proved difficult targets, but the artists were more than adept at retrieving misdirected coins from the mud. On a fine day there were plenty of walkers, and donations must have been good for the artists kept coming.

When the tide turned the first shallow surge of the returning water moved smoothly at walking speed over the surface, scarcely disturbing the picture as it passed. The second ripple softened the outlines, the next swilled up a haze of mud, and then it took very few minutes for the artist's work to fade back into the ooze.

At the end of the pier they called in for refreshments: tea and cake for the aunts, lemonade and a sticky bun for John. They had been late on to the pier, and the refreshment room was closing as they left. After ten minutes or so on the sun deck, with the aunts sprawled in deckchairs before the return home, he missed the model car they had bought him. A few questions convinced Elsie that he had left it in the refreshment room, and nephew in hand she set off on a recovery mission.

The room was closed, and the glass-topped doors locked, but there was a bell. Elsie pressed it briefly without response. When a second and then a third longer ring were also ignored, she lent on the bell until eventually a figure emerged inside, and a man looked hard towards the door. Elsie kept her finger on the bell. He crossed the room, glared at them, and then called through the glass,

'You can ring the bell till your teeth drop out. We're closed.'

The old suffragette warhorse stiffened as she snapped out her reply. 'I'll ring your nose till your eyes pop out. Don't be so bloody cheeky. The boy's left his toy in there and he wants it back.'

He looked her in the face for a second or two, slid back the latch, and Elsie was inside and back out again with the car in no time. John had a lot of admiration for his Aunt Elsie.

Throughout the holiday season a small fleet of coastal steamers from the Upper Pool of London ran day trips to the coastal resorts of Margate, Ramsgate and Clacton, or on to the nearer Continental ports calling in at the pier on their way. They, too, would play their part with the cockle boats at Dunkirk, but before the war they provided a summer treat that was very popular – for those who could afford it.

With Elsie's hand clamped to his coat collar he watched at the railings of the upper deck as the *Royal Eagle* came sweeping in from the outer reaches of the estuary to the landing stage below, slowing and manoeuvring against the ebbing tide. Whistles and the bridge telegraph bell sounded out across the water, and hidden in their casings the paddle wheels responded to hard astern, flushing up a surge of mud and sediment from the bottom. With a confidence born of practice she was nudged into the landing stage, mooring lines made fast, and gangways were rolled out.

If anything could have displaced the working narrowboat from a boy's heart it would have been that elegant and fascinating vision: the slim black hull trimmed with a band of white; her name gleaming in gold; the long line of portholes hinting at the mysteries of the engines throbbing deep within her; the bridge, deck cabins and superstructure glistening with paint; the rich mahogany glow of her freshly varnished timber, and everywhere the glint of polished brass.

Beyond the wide windows of the dining saloon flower-decorated tables were laid with crystal glassware, napkins and sparkling cutlery. White-jacketed waiters moved discreetly with trays and bottles serving those who were travelling on upriver to London. A vision from another world, it all looked very opulent and expensive, but there were few children to be seen. Stylish ladies in long coats and fancy hats promenaded their handbags up and down the open sun deck. Old men lounged, nodded off to sleep in comfortable wicker chairs, or hung nonchalantly over the rails watching proceedings. Casual informality was decades away. Suits, waistcoats, shirts, ties and hats were worn as standard; there were even a few topcoats.

Royal Eagle was at the luxury end of the river cruising market: 11s for a Ramsgate return from Tower Pier plus 2s for use of the upper sun deck. Add the cost of a meal and that would be almost half of a weekly pay packet for Elsie, and John did not even begin to dream that one day he might himself be a passenger. He had seen the prices displayed on the lower pier deck, looked into the world of her dining saloon and smoking rooms, and knew well enough that it was all beyond his best powers of pleading or persuasion and the depth of the family pocket.

The disembarkation was soon done. The forward rope was cleared, the bow swung from the pier into the ebbing tide, and the telegraph rang for slow ahead. With a surge of mud from her paddles the *Royal Eagle* moved out into the haze of the river on her way back to London.

By mid-August what would prove to be the final pre-war visit to Bayhurst was coming to its end. London had a barrage balloon exercise and blackout trial, but it ran only from midnight to 4 a.m. As far as the general population was concerned it had little impact, provided nothing by way of practical experience, and left the effectiveness of domestic blackout completely untested. The last of a string of information leaflets had been received: 'If War Should Come', 'Your Food in Wartime', 'Your Gas Mask – How to Keep and Use It'. They didn't need to open them to judge how quickly time was running out.

In those days Bayhurst had no wireless but early each morning the daily paper was collected from the post office. Its news formed the only topic of discussion at breakfast, but if the younger children were aware of any unusual earnestness and concern in the voices around them none of the anxiety that must have haunted the family as they considered their return to London and life just a stone's throw from the docks was communicated to them. They played out their daily rounds as usual, returning from the thickets at the end of the garden or clambering down from the boughs of their one great tree to present themselves to each of the many visitors who came down from London for a day in the country. Their expectation, seldom unfulfilled, was of chocolate or sweets from the visitors, and perhaps sixpence when they left. They were generally old friends of the aunts' generation from school, work or suffragette days. They were female, unmarried and loving, seeing themselves as, and behaving like, surrogate aunts to the many children in the family.

The work put into the garden was now showing results, and it flourished with a last abundance of summer flowers. Verbena, astilbe, rudbeckia, aster and others, but above all long spikes of gladioli, Jack's special plantings for cutting, were assembled into parting bouquets, and visitors' departures were a sequence of hugs, kisses and the overwhelming scent of cut stalks, blossoms and shop perfume. That year there were sometimes tears which John found puzzling.

Farewell calls were made to the neighbours, and John had his last morning with the Heard boys. By early afternoon the key had been turned in the lock, and Bayhurst was left to slumber in silence in the heat of the day. They set off up the lane laden with cases and as many bunches of flowers as could be carried.

It was a late-summer afternoon at their remote country station. All was silence and drowsy warmth. Beyond the platform cattle grazed in the narrow strip of fields that skirted the railway line, and over the marshes and creeks they had their last sightings for that year of the seabirds and a few wild fowl. In the far distance, glinting in the sun, the towers and tanks of the oil refineries and storage depots at Coryton, Thames Haven and Shell Haven marked the point where the estuary narrowed and the Thames, like a finger, pointed the way to the industries and docks of London.

Across the fields, beyond the spire of the church at Bowers Gifford, a few puffs of smoke marked the approach of the train on the long curve of track skirting the marshes. John was called from his wandering and together they bundled into the compartment for the journey. Within moments the marshes, the estuary and the distant river were gone, and he was on his way home. With his family around him he was looking forward to the remainder of his holiday, to canal-side and dockland walks with his father, and then to school once again, and kicking his feet through the autumn leaves in the parks: August 1939.

PART TWO

11

Evacuation

A few days before the outbreak of war Poplar Council posted notices giving details of the shelters that would be available to the general public in the event of air raids. For the tens of thousands in the Borough with no room in their cramped backyards for their own Anderson shelter it made less than reassuring reading: the location of a dozen or so slit trenches, a few large basements in commercial premises and some church crypts. More than two years had passed since civilians had died in their hundreds in just one raid on Guernica, and an example had followed more recently in the bombing of Barcelona, yet not one custom-built shelter had been built to provide protection against the onslaught that experience should have led the authorities to expect.

More strategic foresight and no little business acumen had been shown in other quarters. From as early as 1937, high-class flats with specially constructed blast-proof and gas-proof shelters were being offered adjacent to Regent's Park at £350 to £650 pa, but with privates still on a shilling a day and skilled engineers earning less than £200 a year the people of Poplar weren't going to be queuing at the agent's door. By the summer of 1938 well-heeled and discerning buyers had the choice of luxury apartments with the royal parks adjacent providing all the amenities and pleasures of country life and a gas- and bomb-proof shelter conveniently to hand in the basement for themselves and their staff. Display advertisements appeared offering the installation of shelters – 'in these days as obviously desirable as lifeboats on a ship.' And in Essex ARP (air-raid precautions) bungalows were on offer in sleepy Hornchurch 'each with its own precast concrete bomb-proof and gas-proof dugout – can also be used as wine cellar.' At £850 freehold (reduced from £1250) they may not have seemed such a bargain less than a year later when the Luftwaffe turned

151

its attention to the Hornchurch Fighter Station in the Battle of Britain.

A latter-day version of an age-old theme, one war for the rich, one for the poor, it went hand in hand with that first casualty of war, truth. For somehow, somewhere in the last two or three days of peace, a major newspaper had found quite a different world: the East End its old irrepressible, cheerful self; evacuation a great adventure and welcomed by many mothers as a reduction in their housekeeping costs; adequate air-raid protection of a high standard including deep gas-proof and fireproof shelters beneath the children's playgrounds; even a Poplar wag or halfwit who proudly proclaimed that protection in his borough was better than in any other part of London.

The inadequacy of the preparations had not escaped the notice of most of Dockland's residents, and had John been old enough to grasp the significance of the news and events that he heard the family discussing, or to interpret correctly the slow transformation of the streets and parks of Poplar, he would have been less sanguine in his hopes for the autumn. He was still young enough, however, for his expectations for the future to be founded on his own wishes and limited experience of the past. The rest of the family were not so naive and had seen what was coming for more than a year.

In the late summer of 1938 gas masks had been issued. He didn't particularly enjoy their heavy, nauseating odour of rubber and chemicals, but otherwise was quite unconcerned by the strange and novel experience of trying them on. Indeed they soon acquired considerable nuisance and entertainment value when the street grapevine passed on a technique of rapid exhalation which vibrated the rubber around the mask to the sound of a ripe and fruity fart. A performance that failed to amuse at home where his experiments were short-lived.

For many months changes had been taking place around him that marked the passage towards war. The entrances to the Board of Trade, the Seamen's Rest, the Town Hall and many other buildings were gradually screened off with walls of sandbags. Deep trenches appeared in the lawns of the recreation ground, and on the streets around the docks army and Royal Navy uniforms were increasingly to be seen. At home Louisa had been busy for weeks

152

at her sewing machine preparing blackout curtains for the many rooms of the house, and one by one the view from each of the windows was obscured by triangular patterns of anti-blast tape. All of that he saw. None of it figured in his plans and expectations for the immediate future.

Soon after the return from Essex, however, he began to understand that things were not going to be as he expected that autumn. Jack spent a long time explaining to him the plans for evacuation, what they would mean, and what the family might have to do. He was old enough to understand in his own childish way what it was that was likely to happen. War, air raids, shelters and terror-bombing were terms that were not new to him. He had heard them talked about when the Spanish Civil War was discussed within the family who had watched the newsreel pictures of the city bombings at the cinemas and heard the stark conclusion to the commentary: 'This was a war, and these were homes – like yours.' The reality of it all and the significance of his own personal involvement was quite beyond him.

The thought that he might be sent away to the country while the rest of the family stayed behind did not greatly concern him. It was part of his character to mix in well wherever he was, if only he was given half a chance, and he viewed the prospect of evacuation as akin to an extended visit to Aunt Tot's. Moira, however, had a realistic idea of what was coming, and although much older than her brother found the prospect altogether more daunting. She was shy and fastidious, a very private person whose life was focused on her school activities, on home, family and, in particular, her father. Breaking new ground and making new friends would not come easily to her.

He had not been to the park since early summer, and when he next went with Elsie and Clara it was as much for them to look over the changes that had been made, as for him to have a last chance to enjoy the swings. The gardens and lawn that Clara so much admired had been sacrificed to a long, open, air-raid trench. The bandstand was piled high with sandbags, and the park buildings had been occupied by the offices of the local ARP. They didn't stay long and there were no more walks. Events moved much too quickly.

Jack's brother Dan called unexpectedly. A merchant seaman,

he was leaving for Liverpool the following day to join a ship on the North Atlantic run. The youngest of the four brothers, his bond with Jack was particularly close, and he wanted to see him again before he left. Still in his late twenties, Dan was normally good for a laugh and some games with the children, but on this occasion all that was forgotten. After talking together for an hour or so he was ready to leave. John followed them through the passage to the door where his mother and gran were waiting. A few whispered words that John didn't catch, a handshake and a kiss, and then finally: 'All the best, Dan. We'll be thinking of you. Look after yourself.' It was a kindly thought, but it would soon be clear that on the North Atlantic run survival was a matter of luck in a lottery against the odds.

Elsie and Kath made brief, unexpected visits home. His pocket money received a substantial and unanticipated boost, but they were so unlike their usual selves when they left him that the surprise lost some of its gloss. The few remaining days in his old world were busy and dreamlike. On the Monday after what would prove to be his last weekend at home he was taken by Phoebe for a full-dress rehearsal of the evacuation arrangements. With his luggage, clothes and ration of food they assembled with the other mothers and children first in the playground and then in the hall. All the teachers were there, but at the end when all the business had been done it was a stranger who spoke just to the children. Nothing that he heard did anything to shake John's original impression of an extended country holiday. Shortly after they returned home Moira and his father came back from a similar meeting at her school.

Following the meeting a few items of clothing for the children were renewed in Chrisp Street, and time and time again they heard the lecture: 'Keep your gas masks safely with you. Watch your suitcases while travelling. Keep yourselves clean and tidy while you are away. Write home and say where you are as soon as you can, and above all behave yourselves wherever you are.' He suspected that most of those directives were aimed specifically at him. Moira could be relied on in all such matters.

Although leaving on the same day they were not to be travelling together, but in company with the rest of their schools, and by the end of the following day they would be far apart. For one last night they shared a bedroom and their thoughts, chatting and rambling on with no thought of sleep, and then he felt his father shaking his shoulder, and telling him it was time to get up. Despite all the excitement and tensions of the preparation for departure they had slept well enough, but it was early and barely light when they woke on the morning of 1st September. They both had to be at their schools by seven, but Moira's was further away in Bow Road, and their father would be taking her there half an hour or so before John had to leave for North Street.

He pulled back a curtain and for one last time opened the window and looked out. In the yard below Terry heard the noise, looked up and greeted him with a bark. Dimly, in the distance, he could just make out the old, familiar landmarks. Over the warehouses, factories, wharves and berths of the Docklands the haze of night lights still glowed, but was fading with the dawn. At the end of the following day those lights would go out and the blackouts would go up. More than five years would pass before they were seen again, and by then much that he looked out on would lie in rubble and the world would have been transformed.

Louisa looked after their breakfast on that special morning and prepared something cooked and tasty; 'to keep them going for a few hours,' as she said. Then it was time for Moira and his father to go. It was a quiet goodbye: hugs, kisses, a few hasty last words, but no tears. They left in the early light of dawn, turned into the terrace, paused briefly at the top to wave, and were gone. By now Lou's friend Carrie Enwright from next door had joined them, so the kettle went on once again, and he was encouraged to eat some more if he could. They seemed to have a fair idea of what might be coming.

All too soon he was being buttoned and strapped into his raincoat despite the fact that the morning was warm and dry. Then came the pre-departure check: identity tags with name, home address and school (three of them just to be safe) pinned in strategic places on his coat; gas mask, with the same information printed inside the box; a case similarly marked containing his clothing; two comics stuffed into his coat pocket; food for the day in a carrier bag that he could sling over his shoulder; sandwiches, biscuits, raisins, an apple, an orange and some boiled sweets to suck.

Finally, more important than anything else, his gollywog. Goll had been the last thing packed inside his case, a guarantee that whatever else he lost he would look after that. He said his goodbyes to Terry, gave Mick a final tickle, looked for the cat, but couldn't find it, received a hug and a shilling from Clara who was getting ready for work, and then with his mother and gran, walked up the terrace to join the disconsolate stream of mums, dads and children making their way to North Street School. In the schoolyard crowds clustered around the main entrance where goodbyes were being said and last-minute advice whispered. 'Remember now, behave yourself, and don't forget to let us know where you are as soon as you can.'

After more cuddles and kisses (there were a lot about that morning) they passed him into the keeping of the mistress on the door, gave him a final wave and turned for home. They were a close family, but displays of emotion were private not public affairs, and there were no tears. All the children went first to their classes, but were soon called together in the hall for final instructions before filing out into the playground to board the buses waiting to take them to the station. Many mothers still stood in groups outside the playground looking on at the preparation for departure, calling out to their children, and prompting yet more tears from those who were already distressed. His mother and gran were not among them.

For the first time he began to feel the sense of loss and uncertainty that must have been general that morning, but they were left with little time to indulge their feelings before Miss Roberts, their usual teacher, was ushering them forward through the gate. Once on the bus the struggle for the best seat on top, and the babble of chatter as they waited for the start kept them occupied with other thoughts, and soon they were moving at the start of what was to be a long, long journey into the west.

The roads from the East End into the city were a strange sight that morning. Buses and trams were running as on any other day, but instead of the usual bevies of workers and shoppers on their way to city offices or West End shops they were mainly occupied by evacuees: schoolchildren with their teachers or mothers with babies, toddlers and accompanying helpers, all of them heading towards the central bus, coach or train stations. And from the centre of town, for that one day, many roads to the north, south and west would be one-way only carrying the exodus that was fleeing the city.

He arrived at the station expecting something the size of Barking, and the unhurried, easy familiarity that marked their departures for Essex. The reality of that morning was something altogether different. The noise of engines echoing round roofs and walls, of booming, unintelligible public-address announcements, of officials calling, children crying and shouting, and adults consoling and remonstrating, combined into one overwhelming, intimidating roar. With his raincoat belted tight around his waist, and three identity labels prominently attached, he looked more like a special-delivery parcel for the guard's van than a passenger.

The delays were longer than expected, and soon there were urgent demands for the lavatory. The risk that children would get confused and lost if they went by themselves meant that little groups had to be taken across under escort. That took time to organise, and while they waited there was at least one accident where the culprit had to be marched off to be cleaned up in private. One by one, as fatigue set in, their cases and neatly wrapped bundles were put to use as seats, and gradually they made a start on their refreshments. Eventually Miss Roberts was called, and staying closely behind her they shuffled forward alongside other creeping crocodiles of children, through the barrier, and on to their train.

Either providence, or the wisdom of some distant administrator familiar with the urinary requirements of young and excited children, had assigned them a corridor carriage with lavatories. In view of the journey they were to embark on that was just as well. Even the delay before their departure created urgent demands. The proscription on use while standing at the platform was soon declared a dead letter, possibly for the duration, and they were able to wait for the start of their journey in comfort. It was almost ten o'clock before they left.

His experience of one-hour journeys to Essex had ill prepared him for the tedium of the long haul that was to come. Once the comforting and homely backstreets, factories and houses of the London suburbs had been left behind, the countryside seemed alien and unfamiliar, and the sense of loneliness and separation

157

increased. The excitement at the start of the journey and the pleasure of a corridor to explore soon faded. Even the novelty of using the lavatory while on the move, and gazing down the pan at the passing blur of railway sleepers soon lost its fascination. Comics had been exhausted, many children were sleeping after their early-morning starts, and here and there some were quietly crying.

As well as the teachers who travelled with them, there were also nurses who passed through the train every couple of hours checking how they were and carrying water for those who wanted a drink. But until they arrived at their destination, whenever that might be, there would be nothing to eat except the food they had set out with at the start of their journey, much of it already seriously depleted.

The morning dragged on interminably, and their passage was frequently interrupted as the train slowed, came to a halt and stood puffing idly. For a while they took that as a sign that their journey might be coming to an end, and rushed to the windows in the hope that something encouraging might be seen. Then the carriages lurched forwards and once again they moved on through the same tedious sequence of bridge, cutting, river, village, bridge. Only the tunnels that swallowed the train without warning woke them from their stupor to an excited chatter or screams of panic as they were plunged briefly into utter darkness before the lights came on. Even those seasoned travellers with experience of the Underground were taken by surprise at the rush and roar as a tunnel engulfed them, and the stink of engine smoke flooded into the carriages.

Morning turned to afternoon, and their progress into the west continued. By then they had passed through several towns and many stations, but the names that they saw meant nothing to them. Eventually, well into the afternoon, they slowed and stopped at a station in one of the larger towns, but their carriages stood isolated on the middle track of three. It was clearly not their final destination and once again the train was only waiting to move on. Children flooded into the corridor, and faces were pressed to every window.

It was a strange sight they presented to those waiting on the platforms on either side: hundreds of young faces gazing out at them, some glum, some optimistic, some sad, some smiling. For a few moments train and platform watched each other silently. Then there was just one wave from the platform, and the floodgates opened. Windows dropped, heads were thrust out, and a dialogue opened from engine to guard's van.

'Where are you all off to then?'

'We don't know. Where are we?'

'Exeter.'

'Where's that?'

'Devon.'

'How far is that from London?'

'About two hundred miles.'

The conversations continued, but that was the one message that passed down the train: two hundred miles from London. John knew how far it was from his home to Pitsea. Exeter seemed a desperate extension of those twenty miles. How much further were they being taken? Would anyone from home ever get to visit them? How long were they going to be so far away? Those were the thoughts and questions that troubled them all. Gradually the teachers went the length of the train. Heads were drawn in, windows were closed, and eventually, to many waves and shouts wishing them luck, they moved on once again.

It was after seven by the station clock when they arrived at their final destination. They were at St Austell in Cornwall, more than two hundred and fifty miles from home. On the platform they were once again marshalled into the separate groups that had started out on the journey, and then marched off to a large hall nearby where tables of sandwiches, plain cake and milk were waiting. The last fragments of their home rations had been consumed hours before, and for a while eating and chattering sustained their spirits.

Then began the final parting of the ways between friends and schoolfellows that was so hard to bear. For some, things would work out well. For others, the desolation and loneliness would remain, and the process by which they were dispersed into the community would have seemed a complete mystery to all of them. A few wives arrived at the hall with their husbands, but it was mostly women by themselves who called. They talked with Miss Roberts and the local organisers, looked over the assorted lots of children as though they were in a jumble sale, and then, on what seemed to be a completely random basis, left with one or more of them. John saw two of his friends disappearing without a chance to learn where they might be going or whom they were with.

There were still many children in the hall when Miss Roberts called the remainder of her flock together and told them that they would be staying in St Austell for only a few days and then moving on. When, eventually, John left the hall it was with three others and not by himself. They were shepherded to a large house nearby where they slept together on truckle beds in one large room – that was comforting and eased their first night of separation from home.

The days immediately following the evacuation saw London a city transformed and the papers full of reports describing the scene for those who were not reminded of it all too often by the vacant beds, silent rooms and gaps at the table around them. To be in London, said the reports, was to know what Hamelin must have been like after the Pied Piper had passed that way. In childless, desolate parks and playgrounds swings hung idle, slides and round-abouts deserted, and park keepers looked in vain for the usual suspects trespassing on the grass. At forsaken schools only the solitary tread of the caretaker echoing through the corridors broke a hushed, unnatural silence. And at The Gaiety and a score of fleapits like her Saturday morning saw the entrance grills firmly closed and padlocked and the streets around empty of the usual eager crowds pushing towards their next appointment with the Lone Ranger or Old Mother Riley.

Two hundred and fifty miles away in St Austell John was to land on his feet – a destiny to which he was born according to his mother – but his evacuation luck was not to be shared by his sister. Moira's journey had been shorter, but at its end she found a billet where she was desperately unhappy, and treated shamefully by the couple to whom she was entrusted. Thanks to Elsie a few of the family wartime letters survived, including one from Moira written some six weeks or so after she arrived:

Dear Aunty Clara and Clara Dent,
I am pracktically certain now that I am not going to be moved, the girl Peggy Hayden who I was going to be moved with has been moved and I did not go with her.
*   Last night I went for a walk and met Miss Philpot, she just*

160

said in a vague way 'It might become possible for you to be moved.'

Before, they said I would be moved definitly, the people have gone out for the day and I have got to get my own dinner and tea, last night I was alone from six till half past ten. Tell Daddy I will not stay in this house much longer.

The pictures are open but I have no one to go with and I get tired of looking around shops.

I have lots of dirty socks, undercloths and towels, in fact I am ashamed to use my towel it makes me dirtier than ever.

I don't know how to wash and dry dresses and under clothes, and they have to be ironed with an electric iron which I wouldn't touch.

I am now going to spend a delightful morning writing out and learning 20 French sentences. I will then get my dinner and wash up and go to school, come home have tea and wash up, and sit alone for a few hours, go to bed.

This is typical of every day except that I don't usually get my own dinner.

This house is freezing, my hands are so cold I can hardly write, no hot water except twice a week,

Love from your miserable neice Moira.

P.S. I have got an awful cold

P.P.S. I sometimes get only a slice of toast for breakfast with marmalade, when I get porridge and bread and butter I don't even see the jam or marmalade, and get three slices of stale bread and butter for tea. Did I say butter I haven't seen any for about a week, she gets margarine now, I don't suppose she eats it herself because she has breakfast before I come down and tea before I come home from school. She had egg and bacon for breakfast, what does bacon taste like I've forgotten, we have eggs for dinner with chips once a week.

She buys big blocks of nut and fruit chocolate and always eats it in her bedroom, I offered her some chocolate once but not now. I am wiser now.

Love from your starving neice Moira.

P.P.P.S. Now laugh, I don't think it funny.

P.S. I'd like a rose tree planted on my grave, please let me have this sort of tombstone.

161

There followed a drawing of a grave with a tombstone inscribed:

Sacred to the memory of Moira O'Sullivan.
Passed away from this life October 1939.
Died of starvation and misery,
Peace at last.

In October 1939, when the letter was written, all foods were still unrationed. There was no especial shortage of bacon, eggs, butter or sweets, and Moira was unfortunate, but would not have been alone, in falling into the care of a couple so selfish, mean-minded and penny-pinching. More than fifty years rolled by before Moira passed on a copy of the letter on which she noted: 'Enclosed just for a laugh – but it was all true. The woman was a bitch – a Woolworth's shop girl who had landed the son of a local shoe manufacturer. The letter reduced poor auntie Clara to tears but it got me moved.'

After the four days in St Austell John's time in Cornwall was spent in Lostwithiel, but it was not to last for more than a few months and would leave little permanent impression on him. He was comfortably placed with a kind and caring couple who told him they were to be Aunt Enid and Uncle Dick, and with his home background of aunts and uncles by the score that suited him fine. Schooling should have started when he arrived, but under the pressures created by the flood of evacuees was non-existent, irregular or much dislocated for the time he was there. He posted his pre-addressed stamped card to say where he was, but the distance from home was such that he had no realistic expectation of any visits, and he settled into a life which proved to be much as he had expected: an extended holiday with Aunt Tot.

Within a year or so of his return home the details had faded and blurred into a vague dream of streams where the water ran like liquid chalk, of a town quiet and safe to play in, of ancient echoing arches under the bridge by the river, and games beneath the massive barbican of Restormel Castle.

When he heard at the beginning of December that his short Cornish venture would soon be at an end his feelings were not unmixed. He had grown fond of his foster aunt and uncle, and enjoyed the town, the castle and his new friends, but the thought of Christmas anywhere other than home with his family, pets and belongings around him once again was more than enough to override those minor regrets.

12

The Last Christmas

In October 1939 a few Luftwaffe intrusions into Scottish airspace
saw the first bombs fall on British soil and the first raider downed,
but in London all had been quiet. The terror raids that everyone
had expected and dreaded had not materialised. No bombs had
fallen and no one had died. In many ways life went on much as it
always had, and as Christmas approached more and more parents
began to bring their evacuated children home despite official
opposition. Government notices in the papers and cinema newsreels all carried the same message, 'Leave Them in the Country,'
but to little purpose.

The situation was not new. Almost from the outset there were
signs of the very problems that had always been anticipated but
could not be avoided. The town mice and the country mice were
not finding it easy to live together, and within a week of the exodus
there were the first signs of a drift back to home. Initially the
return was of mothers with babies and toddlers, but soon schoolchildren too were being brought back. Official warnings that
schools in evacuated areas would remain closed and that there
would be no provision for education had little effect, and matters
were not helped by some of the intemperate language used in
letters of complaint about the East End evacuees – 'half savage,
verminous, wholly illiterate, untrained animals,' as one writer
described them.

As soon as rumours began to circulate that the LCC would be
reopening schools after Christmas Phoebe, like so many parents,
was determined to have her family back with her before the end of
the year. She wrote to say that arrangements were already made
for Moira to return to London, and to tell Enid that she would be
travelling down by coach to take John home.

She arrived in Lostwithiel in mid-December. Enid had offered

164

her a bed for the night, and for the few hours they were together they settled down like old friends. They were both keen knitters and family-centred, so the evening passed away comfortably with Enid knitting, and the two of them chatting away to the background drone of the wireless. John's endless prattle about home during the twelve weeks or so he was with her must have given Enid quite an insight into his background, but if Phoebe was surprised at her knowledge of home life and family, she saw quickly enough how things were, and ended up talking about Lou, the aunts and others as if they were all well known to Enid, as indeed they were, through John.

They started early the following morning. He was happy to be travelling homeward, unlabelled this time and with his mother to carry the case, but it was a miserably tedious and tiring journey. The weather continued foul, with rain and high winds. The coach was crowded, stuffy and smoky. Apart from occasional brief stops for the lavatory, or to pick up or put down passengers, there was no opportunity for any exercise, and Phoebe was tired and irritable from her long journey down the previous day. Altogether it was an experience he was more than happy to forget, apart from the crossing of Salisbury Plain.

The rain had stopped, but the clouds were still sullen and threatening, and a turbulent wind buffeted the coach as it moved out on to the open stretches of the downs. Then on the horizon, for the first time that day, the solid, black mass of cloud fractured and opened to the cold, dark blue of a late December sky. Silhouetted against that dramatic backdrop Stonehenge appeared to him, lonely, stark and elemental. It was a fleeting, haunting vision but it stayed with him long after they passed on into the approaching night.

They returned to a London in profound darkness. On the day he left for Cornwall the blackout had been fully implemented and was now all-embracing. Within days of its introduction the first obituary notices were appearing of deaths 'owing to the blackout', and from then on the numbers soared. In December, when not one civilian life had been lost as a result of enemy action, almost 1,200 were to die on the roads, most as a result of the blackout.

As they drew into the station the hazy illumination threw only a dim half-light over the crowds swirling around the coaches. Beyond the exit doors they stepped into a black void, and hand clasping hand shuffled forward hesitantly to find the tram for the final stages of their return home. They climbed aboard and sat in the gloom, cramped and crushed by the crowd of passengers who either travelled in silence, or spoke in hushed and hesitant whispers that the near-darkness seemed to impose. On the last leg of the journey along Commercial and East India Dock roads he looked in vain for the lights that would normally have marked their passage at the Hippodrome and Gaiety, but unlit and shrouded by the night they were both passed unnoticed, and Phoebe would have missed her own stop without the conductor's call based on the sixth sense for location that he had already developed.

They stepped from the tram and paused. The clouds had cleared and there was no moon. In normal times any faint illumination from the night sky would have been lost in the general haze of light from un-curtained windows, street lamps and the headlights of passing traffic. Now from the darkened street they looked up to a sky stuffed full of stars and in their faint glow could just make out the bulk of the Board of Trade. They followed the line of its walls along the main road, felt their way carefully along its railings into Rigden Street, inched themselves to the bottom of a pitch-dark terrace, through the gate, down the steps and into the shadowy passage. As they closed the door the lights came on, and the sights and smells of the old house wrapped themselves around him, a reminder of all he had been missing. Through the open door the warmth from the stove in his gran's room and the chattering of the parrot spilled out into the passage where the faces and voices of home surrounded him. So to kisses from his gran and Clara, and a welcoming hug from his father, he settled back into the old routine. 'Oh God, they haven't brought you back again, have they?' Moira had survived her evacuation experience without any damage to her customary form then. He was pleased to hear that.

They installed him at the head of the table with the fire burning in the black-leaded range at his back, and the family gathered around him. Lou had been on a special shopping expedition to Bill's during the afternoon and his contentment was absolute as he turned his attention to winkles, jellied eels, buttered bread fresh from Chrisp Street just a couple of hours earlier, hot tea and a Dundee cake made by his mother to celebrate his return. It already

166

seemed a bit like Christmas, which was still more than a week away.

Excused the usual early-morning call from his father he was left to sleep on, and Moira was already washed, dressed and downstairs when he woke. It was not yet fully light, and the blackout curtains in the bedroom were still closed, but after breakfast, as the daylight increased, he climbed the stairs to his customary lookout at the window of the top-floor back. The aunts were not at home, and the rooms were empty. He threw open the casement and gazed out. In the yard below Terry bounced and barked at the end of his chain in response to a call.

The friendly rumble of dock-bound traffic that he had missed so much in the silent streets of Lostwithiel rose up to greet him, and to the east the sun was rising over the old, familiar scene: long lines of roofs, slates, gutters and chimney pots; the weathervane topping the spire of All Saints' glinting in the sun; distant cranes dipping and turning about their business in the docks; but looming over all, lazily twisting and swinging in the wind, the gross, silver barrage balloons straining at their tethers were another reminder of the way the world had changed since his departure in the last days of peace. From the front of the house more balloons could be seen dotting the sky towards Stepney and beyond. The windows of the Board of Trade, the Seamen's Rest and every house within view were latticed with strips of blast-protection tape, and in the gardens beyond the terrace wall a line of earth-covered shelters stood like latter-day tumuli.

Christmas shopping was still in hand, and in mid-afternoon shortly after his return home he joined his mother and gran on a shopping trip to Chrisp Street. A year earlier it would have been bustling with barrows and carts as the stallholders began to set up their lights to work on through the darkening December afternoon and into the early evening. There had been a special Christmas concession allowing some lighting on street stalls during the black-out hours, but despite the traders' best efforts Chrisp Street was a muted, shadowy image of its former self. Many shopfronts were boarded up with timber panels, or screened with mounds of sandbags. Most had abandoned any attempt to celebrate the season with decorations. Just a few had simple Christmas scenes in their windows, but even those were half obscured by the web of anti-

167

blast tapes across the glass. There were no lights winking on Christmas trees and little in the way of overt displays of Christmas spirit: all unwelcome auguries of the increasing austerity that each succeeding Christmas would bring.

Just one year earlier it had been so different: a rare and extended white Christmas that eclipsed even the extravagant, Dickensian scenes on the cards that fell through the letter box. Snow had fallen daily for more than a week, with the heaviest fall just a couple of days before Christmas. It clung to the trunk and branches of the solitary pear tree, capped the walls, and blanketed the roofs. On the stones of the terrace, the gardens beyond and the streets around it lay deep and crisp and even, muting the sound of every wheel and footfall. There were snowmen in the park, giant snowballs in the streets and every morning's paper brought fresh pictures of the city's winter sports: skiing on Hampstead Heath, skating on Kingsmere, and toboggans on the roads of Perivale.

Elsie and Kath had been home for a whole week and dispensing their Christmas treats to the children. Moira was indulged in a matinee visit to the theatre, and then they set off for a trip 'up West' with their nephew. Snow was still falling as the tram made its way through an East End where for a few winter days all that was filthy, shabby and workaday wore a fleeting beauty. At Aldgate they switched to the bus for the second leg of their journey: past the display windows of the cruise-line offices, brilliantly decorated, blazing with lights, and full of enticing offers (for the leisured and well-breeched) of New Year voyages to the warmth and romance of the southern seas; past Mansion House, St Paul's and the Old Bailey all shrouded in white; and finally to Holborn Circus, the icy pavements and Gamages. Not really West End, but who cared when window after window, each framed with flickering, sparkling lights, was stuffed with such collections of delights: rocking horses, bicycles, dolls, toy soldiers, train sets, books, model yachts, teddy bears, forts and more, more, yet more.

Inside it was rambling, sprawling muddle of a building: a three-dimensional maze where steps, ramps and confined, narrow passages opened into vast display rooms, no two of which seemed to be at the same level, each stuffed with a confusion of the largesse of Christmas under the glitter of tinsel, artificial snow and shimmering decorations. There was a visit to a model railway display, many young boys and not a few fathers all sick with desire; a train

168

ride (faked as even the youngest could see) to visit Father Christmas; and a blowout of his own choosing in the restaurant. But it hadn't all been indulgence. After he had been given his head he was led to other departments of his aunts' choosing, where the overwhelming scent of perfumes, leather and fabrics sickened him, and soon had him ready for the cold, fresh air and the journey home. He had taken little away with him, but knew that come Christmas morning some of the things he wanted would be waiting for him.

The year 1939 brought no snow but happily there was as yet no noticeable shortage in the shops of food, drink and the other assorted trimmings that a good old-fashioned Christmas demanded. Phoebe collected a choice cut of beef and the saltpetre, sugar and allspice in which it would be turned daily before being cooked to serve cold-cut on Christmas night. Icing sugar, marzipan, mixed dried fruit and peel, nuts, cake decorations, butter, eggs, chocolate and sweets, including Elvas sugar plums, Lou's favourite, all of them and more were on the shopping list and still available.

Nobody had any doubt what was coming, certainly not Lou or anyone who had lived through the rationing of 1914–18. Even before the declaration of war it had been made an offence to buy or store more than a week's supply of any kind of food, and as it was to do increasingly in all aspects of life the government took draconian new powers under the Emergency Regulations for its officers to enter and inspect any premises where it was thought the regulation may have been breeched. By mid-November they were all leafing glumly through the recently issued ration books. Early December brought ministerial appeals to the nation's housewives to play fair when they were shopping. Rationing was not to be imposed until the New Year, but until then the patriotic thing to do was to ration yourself – there should be no Christmas feasting. The result was predictable and inevitable – almost everyone was determined to spend as much as could be afforded on one last glorious blowout. The Lagsdings were to be no exception.

In a normal year pudding-mixing day with their mother was the children's big pre-Christmas event. Stealing the fruit and nuts, stirring the mix and making a wish, dropping in the sixpenny pieces, the final scouring of the bowl with their fingers, and the rich, raw flavours of the mix as they sucked them clean: it was better even than Christmas Day when they came to the pudding already sated. In 1939, far away in Oxfordshire and Cornwall, they had missed the event.

It was Phoebe's custom to make several puddings six or seven weeks before Christmas using a mix laced liberally with rum or brandy which was then basined up, covered with a double layer of linen, cooked and left to mature until Christmas. As a cook she favoured the intuitive method: 'Just judging it,' as she said. Most of the time it seemed to work well, and her family survived and flourished. One of her intuitions was that the puddings, if really well braced with spirit, would keep for a year, and like fine wine, be the better for it. For several years she had been fully vindicated in the results. The pre-cooked puddings were boiled once again on the day they were to be eaten, and the vintage pudding from the previous year, if not noticeably better, had never been noticeably worse.

At their last pre-war Christmas the fresh 1938 pudding was consumed to everyone's satisfaction on Christmas Day. On the morning of Boxing Day Phoebe was unusually silent as she brought in the basin containing the 1937 pudding prior to putting it on to boil. 'Feel that, Jack,' she said. The children sensed something unusual and gathered round with interest. He weighed the basin in the palm of his hand, placed it on the table, and cutting the string whipped away the linen shroud. Instead of a dark, substantial pudding, a pale, translucent dome of crust gleamed at them for a few moments before crumbling into dust at the bottom of a basin that, except for a few other crumbs, was singularly empty. They stood in decent, silent tribute to the spectacular failure of the intuitive method, until Moira laughed. All the 1938 puddings were eaten within a month of Christmas, and no one could offer any explanation for the mysterious chemistry, a sort of cold spontaneous combustion, that had consumed the substance of the '37 vintage.

Preparations for Christmas Day 1939 went ahead much as they always had. From corner cupboards tucked away in recesses of the top floor, boxes with the accumulated decorations of previous years were brought down to the large front room that would be the centre of family jollifications, and together they dressed it overall. They were cheap and cheerful things most of them: multi-cut, many-coloured hangings, brash, gaudy, and bright. After years of use they may have been a little torn and faded, but in uncertain

170

times their very familiarity was reassuring. Things were to be as they had been – no one wanted any change. From corner to corner and along the picture rails the swags festooned the rooms, and from every available projection stars, diamonds and spirals hung twisting and turning as the moving currents of air caught them. The lights were screened with Chinese lanterns and hung with sprigs of mistletoe, balloons were inflated, and everywhere there was the glint of silver tinsel. Elsewhere there were no decorations except in the children's bedroom where they hung their own handmade paper chains and a few balloons to mark the season.

Early on the afternoon of Christmas Eve Jack lit the fire in the front room. The first bottles were opened. Lou brought out the mince pies and together they settled down to the wireless. Forty-five minutes of *Christmas at Dingley Dell* followed by a selection of the *Nine Lessons and Carols from King's* had them nicely in festive mood by the time the curtains and blackout were drawn against the night. The Santa Claus myth might long have been exploded, but the children liked to keep up the old traditions, and when they went to sleep that night it was with a stocking and pillowcase tied to the foot of their beds as they had always done.

Christmas morning saw them awake and exploring the contents long before the rest of the house was moving, and despite the war, they found things much as usual. The extended family they lived with, their gran, the three maiden aunts and their large circle of friends, many unmarried, meant that on birthdays and at Christmas they were seldom disappointed. In relative terms, by the day-to-day comparisons they made with their friends, they realised that they did pretty well. Beyond such comparisons there was nothing to stuff their heads with unreasonable hopes and expectations. The relentless, never-ending exploitation and moulding of young minds by business and the advertising industry was decades away, and a pre-Christmas trip to the West End to see the street and shop decorations, and the toy treasure-caverns of Selfridges, Gamages and Hamleys was a fleeting whirl through a kaleidoscope of wonders that dazzled the eye, but confused and baffled desire.

Presents unwrapped, they turned to the rest of the house with a round of thanks which although unreasonably early was well received. After that came breakfast, and then their Christmas Day slipped into its customary pattern for the last time. When the aunts at last made a belated appearance John joined them for a second breakfast and to give Mick a tickle and his Christmas Day fix of tea-soaked and sugared bread crust. Breakfast over, Clara and Elsie, who were expecting friends, moved to the upstairs room where the fire had been burning since early morning.

In the scullery Phoebe and Lou had started early preparation of vegetables for the Christmas dinner, while Jack slipped an extension leaf into the dining table and brought in extra chairs in preparation for the numbers expected. From the floor above the sounds of two carols drifted down from the gramophone before Elsie turned to the piano, and as John and his father were putting on their coats for a morning walk they could hear Clara's soprano tremulously enquiring, 'Sweetheart, sweetheart, sweetheart – will you love me ever?' They left her waiting for a reply, and set off up the terrace.

The usual sounds of a Poplar working day were hushed. Little traffic moved on the main road, and the engines of industry crammed into the streets and riverside of the Isle of Dogs were still. Only a tumbling peal from the bells of All Saints' broke the silence of the morning. Soon, throughout the country, all the bells would be falling silent. If they were heard again it would be as the signal of invasion, or briefly for a few hours on Christmas mornings. Far, far away in the uncertain future they would also be heard in celebration of victories as yet beyond imagining.

They ignored the canal-side path, taking instead the short route to Jimmy's, and on their way saw more of the wartime changes that had taken place since last they walked that way together: entrances, kerbstones, lamp posts and trees splashed with white paint to pick them out in the blackout; newly built surface shelters that closed the streets to traffic and directions to other refuges, scarcely shelters, in the cellars and basements beneath larger buildings.

Jim and his wife didn't bother with decorations; with no children in the house there was little point. Their fire had only just been lit, and the room was cold. After the warmth, colour and glitter of home it was a dark and depressing spot to be on Christmas morning, but Jack had some papers that he wanted Jimmy to see, and as they looked through them and talked, whiskies were poured and cigarettes rolled. Drink and tobacco: John sat and watched, fascinated by those twin evils of flesh and the devil. To sit with a

172

glass, and quietly roll a smoke while chatting away with a mate seemed the most companionable and friendly of activities, and he couldn't wait to qualify.

Jimmy was the local air-raid warden and a member of the ARP. When the talking was done and the drink finished, he took them with him to his local ARP centre, and up to the fire-watching post, high on the roof of the tallest building. It looked out across the factories lining the Limehouse Cut, the power station and distant gasworks, the engine sheds and sidings of the railway, and row upon row of densely packed, back-to-back jerry-built houses. Jimmy's task would be to spot and report the fall of incendiary bombs. Beyond the canal, an unfortunate group of squaddies were busy, even on Christmas morning, around a couple of anti-aircraft guns that had been sited on derelict land well away from houses. Apart from the sound of distant bells all was silent in Dockland. Christmas 1939 – waiting.

They were back home with time to spare before Christmas dinner. They made a later start than usual so that Lou and the aunts could hear the King's address to the nation. In normal circumstances a royal broadcast would have passed them by without anyone thinking of listening, but circumstances were far from normal. The wireless was in the room where they would be eating, and as they waited round the table drinks were poured: whisky or beer for the men, sherry or a liqueur for the ladies. Jack switched on the wireless, and as they sipped their drinks the valves slowly warmed, and the set gathered its resources.

The broadcast was heard out in silence. The King said nothing unexpected, but unsurprisingly, considering the circumstances and the general tenor of the speech, it managed to cast a shadow over what until then had been lively and convivial proceedings. Things improved again with the arrival of the bird and vegetables from the kitchen. When they finally sat down to eat the late-afternoon sun was still strong enough for them to make a start without any other light, but as it was impossible to have even a candle lit with the curtains open they soon had to draw them, put up the blackout, and settle down to the rest of the day quite closed off from the outside world.

There were nine of them at table. Lou's youngest daughter, Irene, and her husband Dick had joined the household and were

173

living in the little room above the scullery. Their numbers were also swelled, but scarcely noticeably, by the diminutive figure of Carrie Enwright.

There might have been a standard mould for East End matriarchs in which Lou and Carrie were cast. They looked like sisters and after a friendship of more than thirty years were as close as sisters. Carrie was living at number three with her husband and children when Lou first moved into the terrace with her own young family. Then an accident in the docks left the husband disabled and unable to work. This began a descent into poverty, accelerated by his death a few years later, from which Carrie never escaped. Of her children only two boys survived childhood. One was killed in the First World War. The other, after serving in the navy, settled in Canada and within a few years faded into the wastes of that country, and was heard of no more. From occupying the whole house, Carrie retreated gradually to just two ground-floor rooms where she somehow survived on an old-age pension stuck at ten shillings a week since 1919, plus whatever niggardly public assistance she received. Occasional petitions for an increase in the pension had consistently been denied. According to the prime minister a gradual fall in the cost of living meant that pensioners in 1939 were in fact better off than they had been in 1919. What a difference it would have made for Carrie if only she had known that.

She was as meticulous as Lou with her housework, but whenever John visited Carrie with his gran he was conscious of a home that looked even more depressing than the Heards'. The same bare floorboards with only a couple of rag rugs, the same bald walls, precious little comfort, and the minimum of plain, rough furniture. It may not have been pervaded with the odour of pigswill, but it lacked the spirit and vitality that two young boys brought into the Essex home.

All Lou's children had grown up with Carrie, regarded her as one of the family, and tried without patronising to ease things for her as and when they could. The daily paper and women's magazines found their way to her as a matter of course, as did any surpluses of flowers or fruit from the Essex trips, and a device adopted by Lou many years earlier on a casual, irregular basis had long since settled into a regular routine. Twice a week she popped next door with a serving from the family dinner, and twice a week

Carrie could be seen slipping through the passages of the house like a wraith to return the washed plates to the rack in the scullery. But it was Charlie who transformed her days and restored a little of the daily companionship she had been missing. A man of many parts, with a keen eye for a bargain, he picked up a simple but defunct wireless set for next to nothing, restored it to working order, and presented it to Carrie. It opened a window on to a new world, and from then on the BBC was Carrie's life.

On Christmas afternoon, as was customary, she joined the family for dinner and the rest of the evening. Throughout the year she was in no position to return anything but thanks for Lou's kindness, but at Christmas she arrived with a bottle of port. It was a good port that would have cost her months of scrimping and saving, and the bottle was set close to hand as they sat down to eat.

The Lagsding women were great talkers, and a dinner with everyone present was a noisy affair, but one in which Carrie played little part. Accustomed only to her own company and the sound of the wireless for most of the year she looked, listened and nibbled her way in silence through the minute portions she selected. When a decent interval had elapsed after the pudding they turned to Carrie's gift.

'Right, Carrie, let's try some of that port shall we?'

'That'll be very nice, Jack.'

She sipped her way quietly through the contents of a generously sized glass. Except for a large sherry before the meal it was her first drop of tipple since the previous Christmas. Her cheeks were flushed and her eyes brighter, when she started the second, and all reticence faded as the glass was emptied. Replete, relaxed and well lubricated, Carrie was at last in full spate. The early years when Lou and her family arrived at the terrace, the parties they had when Pappy was alive, and speculation on where it was all going to end now they were at war: she had her say on all of them, but on the subject of Charlie's wireless she waxed lyrical.

Radio was universally popular with those who had it, but Carrie brought to her listening the devotion and commitment of the newly converted. The announcers were her friends, Gert and Daisy her neighbours. She talked of Uncle Mac with the same delight and enthusiasm as the children, and a more than passable imitation of Suzette Tarry earned her a round of applause. For an hour or so on Christmas afternoon Carrie held court, and the rest of the family were in attendance.

Two glasses each for the ladies had almost emptied the bottle, and Carrie was sitting with her third, and what would be her final glass in hand, when the move was made to the front room above. It was early evening when they filed out into the passage leaving two volunteers to clear the table, wash up and set things ready for the late supper.

For Carrie the unaccustomed combination of excitement, drink and stairs proved too much, and while Clara took her glass, Jack and Dick ushered her up to a comfortable chair by the fire where she finished her port and fell asleep. In the back room the bed was still in place, but the dividing doors were opened for extra space, and chairs brought up from around the house for visitors expected and unexpected. Charlie and Doll arrived with their young daughter Valerie, followed by the first of the friends and neighbours, some to stay for an hour or so, others just passing through on a general round of Christmas calls. The fire was made up, drinks poured, and Clara celebrated the occasion by passing round a pack of Balkan Sobranie Black Russian, an annual extravagance at 3s 8d a packet. She then enjoyed with the men one of the five or six cigarettes that she smoked each year, and they settled down for the evening.

Elsie was having a preliminary canter at the piano when Carrie woke, looked confusedly at the crowd around her, and decided that she would now be better off at home. Charlie went ahead to draw the curtains and check her fire, and then Carrie was half escorted, half carried, through the front door, down the steps and into her own front room where she settled down to slumber her way through the rest of her Christmas beside the wireless.

With Carrie safely tucked away the evening resumed a pattern that was superficially familiar: a generous selection of the aunts' favourites from Frumkins stood on the sideboard; the aroma of cheap cigars filled the air; neighbours called in, chatted and moved on; and Elsie coaxed a medley of popular songs from the piano. But beneath the surface of normality, celebration and conviviality, they could not forget that their world was changing, and probably for good. There were absences from the family ranks. Dan was at sea; cousins serving in the army and RAF were away from home; and Kath was absent on duty rota over Christmas.

In the past their family celebrations had embraced the neighbourhood. Doors stood open, curtains were drawn back, and light streamed out over the garden and balcony. Flushed and noisy conga dancers sang and snaked their way through the house, along the passages, up the stairs, out of one door and in at the other, and finally up and down the terrace to drag in any neighbour who showed his face. Now garden, balcony and terrace stood dark and silent, and if Pappy's spirit had returned to the lower room for the evening it could have rested in his old corner undisturbed by the creak of the joists in the ceiling, and the tramp of dancing feet on the floor above. Such thoughts set the pattern for an evening that all too easily slipped into nostalgia and sentimental reminiscing, reflecting the thought at the back of their minds that it might be the last time they would meet there together.

It was to the old ballads, the songs of the halls, and of the earlier war that Elsie turned on the piano. Everyone knew them; they made for easy harmonising, and were homely and comforting in a changing world where nothing could be seen but uncertainty. 'Call Round Any Old Time', 'If You Were the Only Girl in the World', 'Just Like the Ivy': they wrapped themselves in the old, familiar tunes and words with a loving, sentimental excess. As each song ended, one or the other opened with the verse of another. Elsie picked up the tune on the piano, and they all came in on the choruses. If invention flagged they had the *News Chronicle Song Book*. It came complete with tonic sol-fa and sixty old-time songs by the stars of the halls.

Solo performances were always welcome, with Clara top of the bill, but when Lou put down her port and lemon, stepped forward and assumed the familiar declamatory pose her audience sighed. They really hadn't much enthusiasm for yet one more repeat of Lou's old schoolroom texts, but it was Christmas and a time to be charitable so they sat back, took a stiff swig of something comforting and resigned themselves to four or five minutes of improving verse. Standing tall, hands behind her back, feet together and head up, she paused, wiggled, and with Elsie in collusion on the piano twisted and insinuated herself through all three verses of 'Every Little Movement Has a Meaning of Its Own'.

'You should be thoroughly ashamed of yourself, Ma.'

She took Charlie's comment as the compliment intended and received her applause graciously, and the company's thoughts turned again to the bar and then to the refreshments set out downstairs.

Christmas supper was traditional in nature and mostly home produced. Phoebe's dry-salted beef kept company with a bought-in ham. Bill provided jellied eels, sweet-cured herring and succulent wallies. Kath had made the cake, and Elsie iced it. The mince pies, tarts and home-made pickles were all Lou's. Cheese, brought in from a speciality shop in Stepney included, if only for Jack and Charlie, a large, hostile and overripe wedge of stinking Gorgonzola. They bore the abuse this generated with a grin and equanimity. Fresh bread, butter, salad, watercress, tea for those who wanted it, nuts and miscellaneous titbits from the Jewish delicatessen filled any vacant spaces on the table. Plates were loaded and everyone settled down to eat wherever a convenient place could be found. A few with an eye to the main chance squeezed into a space at the table with the refreshments, the rest did the best they could on their laps in the front room.

John's attack on refreshments so late at night was closely supervised and regulated by his mother, who favoured him for the umpteenth time with her opinion that his eyes were bigger than his belly. The physiological falsity of this was patently obvious, and as his capacity as a consumer had never been tested to destruction, so to speak, he harboured deep resentment at his premature separation from the loaded table.

By supper time his cousin, after an early start and a long day, had given up the struggle and been tucked into the bed in the back room where, despite the noise, she was already sleeping soundly. Moira was too old not to be allowed a really late night on such occasions, but for John and his mother it was time to play out the ritual departure, and so she ushered him away to be tucked up alone in his bedroom one floor above the party. His door was open, the landing light was on, and all the sounds of the evening floated up to him. It was a game that followed well-established rules, and he knew it would be folly to return too early. Only after a decent interval did he slip into his dressing gown, creep down the stairs, and sneak again into the back room. Clara was sitting by the door with a glass of advocaat. She gave him a wink, settled him down between her chair and the bed, and held the glass towards him. He dipped in a finger, sucked it dry, and made himself as inconspicuous as possible.

No further visitors were expected, but the front door had been left unlocked for any late arrivals, and no one heard it open and close before Em and Bill walked in with Leslie. They had not been expected, but their two older children had left home during the year, one on marriage and the other into the RAF, and the quiet Christmas Day eventually proved too much for them. When the evening came, the longing for some family company finally overwhelmed them, and with a little of their precious petrol ration in the car they made their way to Poplar with all the caution that the blackout restrictions and Bill's excess of Johnny Walker imposed.

Their arrival was well timed. Jack had drifted into his Celtic humour as the evening and whisky consumption progressed, and his melancholy offering of 'The Parting Glass' had left the party in a subdued, reflective mood from which it might not have recovered without the gale of enthusiasm that now blew in. When Em was in the party vein with a few gins behind her she was the irresistible force that swept all before it. Elsie surrendered her seat at the piano, a large gin and Italian was poured and placed conveniently to hand, and Em assumed control of the proceedings. She played by ear, with a thumping, rhythmic bass, and an uncompromising assault on the keyboard. Under the remorseless weight of a left hand that gave no quarter the piano shuddered; keys that had long lain silent leapt into life; and glasses standing on the top began a trembling dance towards the edge.

With her right hand, in a judicious compromise between dexterity, speed and accuracy, she called up all the old, favourite tunes that the house had heard so many times before. 'My Old Man', 'A Little of what You Fancy', 'Are we to Part Like This Bill', and her own solo piece, 'Abe, Abe, Abe My Boy What Are You Waiting for Now?' Her resources were inexhaustible, and a pause only came when a second adjournment was made for refreshments. John had been spotted by his mother long before then, but ignored apart from a meaningful glare. He realised that a second run at the food was out of the question, and when he was dropped into his gran's bed to join his two cousins it was the best he could have hoped for. For the rest of the evening and into the night his dozing and dreaming merged with snatches of song, piano, laughter and talk, until finally a deep sleep divorced him from it all.

'Come on, you, time to make a move; Gran wants to get to bed.'

His mother's call awakened him to a room that was silent, cold and almost deserted. The dividing doors were half closed, just one low light burned, and behind the blackout curtains the sash windows had been raised to allow a flow of night air to clear some of the tobacco fumes. Clara passed to and fro moving glasses, ashtrays and party debris from the bedroom into the front room, where they would be left until morning. She sang softly as she moved around,

> After the ball was over,
> After the break of morn,
> After the dancers' leaving,
> After the stars are gone,
> Many a heart is aching
> If you could read them all,
> Many the hopes that have vanished
> After the ball.

Since the early years of the century, in those familiar surroundings, the family had drawn together countless times in celebration, and just once in mourning. Clara's song marked the end of all that. After more than thirty years they had scattered from the house for the last time.

13

Hitler Has Missed the Bus

The celebrations of Christmas night had exhausted the party spirit, and New Year's Eve passed quietly. In earlier years it had often been the occasion for family reunions and parties that eclipsed those of Christmas, but with Elsie back at work the days after Christmas were flat and the mood increasingly sober. It seemed like one long morning after the night before with everyone pre-occupied with the uncertainty of the year to come.

The months to the end of 1939 and into the early summer of the following year were often called the Phoney War. On the western front just across the Channel the British Expeditionary Force was still building its strength, action was desultory, and the French waited with a false sense of security behind the Maginot Line. Only at sea, for Dan and thousands of other merchant seamen on the Atlantic, was there nothing phoney about it. There, as everyone around the docks well knew, the war was being played out in deadly earnest, and by the end of the year German surface raiders and U-boats would have claimed more than a hundred ships and their crews. The scuttling of the *Graf Spee* following the battle of the River Plate was one of a few British successes, but the price paid was a heavy one.

At home just one week into the New Year saw food rationing up and running and gave a whole new meaning to bringing home the bacon when Phoebe returned with the family allocation for the week and dropped it on the table with the accompanying sugar and butter and a meaningful glance at her son.

'Well, that's going to slow you down a bit. No more larding on the butter or chasing the aunts for their bacon off-cuts. It's belt tightening time for all of us.'

The threat would mean little to him until the screw began to tighten, which it would soon enough. As far as he was concerned

181

things could not have been much better. Not only was he back at home, but it looked as though he was on extended holiday from school. When Phoebe made enquiries a few days into the New Year it was clear that rumour, unsurprisingly, had got it wrong. At North Street she found a situation of utter confusion with no provision for schooling to be resumed. It had never been anticipated that children would return to the city as they had, and in their absence parts of the school had been assigned to the ARP and other wartime organisations. Nor had all children returned. Most stayed where they were, and with them stayed the teachers who had accompanied them.

Not until the middle of January was the matter finally resolved by the LCC with a decision that selected schools would be reopened, but only children over eleven years of age would be allowed to attend, and only for a few hours a day: morning or afternoon but not both. For the under-elevens it would be impossible to provide any form of education before Easter and even that would have to be on a part-time basis. So for Moira there was some sort of return to normality, but for John and his like the schools remained firmly closed.

For those children on unexpected and extended holiday, however, January was to bring little pleasure either at home or on the streets. The fires that had been blazing when Phoebe and John returned from Lostwithiel and during Christmas had been a rash indulgence that cut deeply into a restricted allowance of coal, and left them to skimp and scrape their way through a January that was to be altogether unforgiving and test them miserably. Before they had reached the middle of the month, a frost that was unrelenting and deep gripped the house and the world about them. Water had to be drained from the boiler and pipes in the bathhouse. Oil lamps were left burning night and day under the cistern in the lavatory and the water pipes in the scullery. For the first time since Terry had arrived as a pup he was brought from his kennel into the house until the worst of the weather was past.

Coal shortages made it impossible for fires to be kept in throughout the house, and on the basis that it was better to have one room really warm than two or three simply aired, they all crammed into Lou's room downstairs, where a good fire was kept going during the day, and banked up with dust and wet ash to slumber through the night.

Beyond that one room, the house was given up to the frost. The aunts were fortunate in being away at work, where they were much more comfortable than they would have been at home. In their rooms at the top of the house, where John had his eyrie immediately below the roof, it was arctic. Wrapped in coat, gloves and scarf he ventured up just once, to find the panes opaque with layers of frozen condensation, and the windows locked fast by the ice outside. Scratching his way through the frost on the glass he peered out across a glacial roofscape, and down over the frosted slates to the gutter, where the upturned body of a dead pigeon, feet in the air, lay locked into the ice.

A trip to the lavatory on the far side of the yard became a test of endurance, and those whose bowel movements provided for the briefest of visits were the favourites of the gods. For others like him, with colonic arrangements designed by nature to take such matters in a leisurely, even contemplative manner, it was a chilling ordeal. It was no time to linger, as was his custom, with the *Beano* or *Dandy*.

Bedrooms were iceboxes, and preparations for the night began early in the evening. Hot-water bottles that had been gathering dust in cupboards for years were welcomed back as old friends. Great stone monsters with screw stoppers from Lou's early days; shiny, ribbed metal canisters in knitted jackets, and comfortable rubber bottles: all were pressed into service as the frost bit deeper into the house. There was no alternative to bedroom stoicism for the adults, but the children enjoyed the indulgence of changing into their nightwear in front of the fire. Then came the hectic dash through the chill of the passages, up the stairs, and the final breath-catching plunge between icy sheets to seek out the one patch heated by the glow of the bottle. Apart from the feet, it didn't take long to warm up beneath a good layering of blankets and an eiderdown.

But, as the temperature stuck remorselessly below freezing, it was the feet, always the feet, that were the problem. Pallid, waxy and icy cold, nothing seemed to restore life to them. John had been warned repeatedly and knew the risks, but eventually the temptation to nurse just a little warmth back into them was overwhelming. On the hot-water bottle at night, and surreptitiously before the fire by day, he toasted his toes, and they blossomed. On digit after digit the chilblains erupted: lustrous, angry and inflamed, each

183

ruby-red dome a colourful token of his folly and the focus of his torment. Worse than the affliction was his mother's home doctoring: two bowls of water, one unbearably hot, the other freezing cold, into which his pathetic-looking feet were alternately plunged. But it worked, and gradually the agony abated.

None of the walks of the pre-war days were resumed, but a week or so after Christmas, when the frost had been deep and unrelenting for several days, his father wrapped him up, and for almost the last time they set off together to visit one of their old haunts. Fascinated by the tales he had been told of life and work on and around the river, he had been taken to most of the local piers, steps and access points to the foreshore, and early on that numbing winter afternoon they were returning to Limehouse pier and the river stairs. They went despite the bitter weather because for the first time that century the Thames was said to be frozen over.

It was a slippery, hazardous expedition. Throughout the park, on fountain, railings, trees and swings, freezing rain had accumulated layer upon layer, sheathing them in a thick, heavy coating of ice. High in the canopy of the plane trees, boughs hung twisted and broken by the weight of the load, and upper branches, flexing in the wind, shed thin, sharp shards to accumulate in deepening layers around the trunks. At the entrance to Garford Street ice curtained the walls of the railway viaduct and hung in spikes from the girders above as they passed through towards the river and Limey Hole, one of their favourite ports of call. Once a traditional plying place for the Thames watermen, the Hole had also been the final point of departure for the unhappy cargoes of the transportation ships heading for the colonies. Now it was just the haunt of casual visitors to the foreshore like themselves.

There had never been any realistic prospect that the Thames at Limehouse would be frozen. It was too far downstream, and the regular movement of tide and shipping kept the water open. But elsewhere the foreshore and the buildings, works and machinery that lined it had been transformed by the frosts and the ice storm.

They arrived an hour or so before low tide, as the river was still flowing out towards the estuary. At the foot of the stairs, and for some distance beyond, where their feet would normally have sunk and stuck in the mud, the surface had already frozen enough to support their weight, and gingerly they walked out towards the mooring dolphins that stood off from the wharves. Great balks of timber driven deeply into the mud and tied with cross-beams, they would normally have been dripping with algae and slime. Now, up to high-tide mark, they were swollen with a thick jacket of dirty, grey-green ice. Further away, cranes, jetties, bollards, the steel latticework of Limehouse pier and its pontoon, warehouse winches and lighters at their moorings all laboured under the same crushing load.

They moved out across the walkways of the pier to the pontoon and stood watching the dark waters of the river hurrying down towards Greenwich and on to the estuary. From Shadwell, the Tower and the frozen reaches far upstream, jagged, broken sheets of ice came spinning and turning on the current to fracture and split against the piles of the pier before being swept on down the long stretch of Limehouse Reach. The deeper frost of evening was already biting through their gloves and shoes as they turned for home before river, docks and city were once again engulfed by the unrelieved blackness of the wartime night.

Britain wasn't alone in facing an exceptional winter. For some time the *Herald* and the press at large had been boosting their readers' morale with reports of the brutal weather that was savaging the enemy. Ordinary men and women were said to be dying from exposure in Germany, and in Berlin, where ice was thick on every window, day-to-day life was nasty, brutal and cold. Not a word of reportage or editorial comment appeared on the misery of life at home in London or the plight of the country at large, yet tucked away in the personal columns of the same papers there were also appeals for funds to help the poorest of the poor in the East End where the bitter weather was adding greatly to their hardships. It was all part of the propaganda/censorship battle that would be played out to the limits over the next five years.

The really deep freeze lasted for almost a fortnight, and even when it eased a little the severe conditions lingered on for weeks, but it was almost over before the nation knew any more about it than they saw from their own doorsteps. Weather news was classified, and not until the end of the month were full details released by the censor. 'Now It Can Be Told' were the headlines over the pictures and stories from across the country: the Thames frozen for eight miles and tugs breaking the ice at Kingston; the sea frozen at Bognor Regis; street hydrants supplying water to houses frozen solid; skating on the Serpentine for the first time in many years, and a woman found dead in her bath sitting in a block of ice.

But with the hard times came some compensations. Circumstances were creating a demand for something a little lighter than the usual BBC diet, and Aunty was having to loosen her stays. An extended service of broadcasting designed originally for the Forces was also adopted with enthusiasm by the civilian population. It brought with it more variety shows, an increase in poplar music and light entertainment, and for those who were developing a taste for it, swing from America. Dance bands and their leaders flourished under the new exposure, and in Carters Terrace they were slowly learning to live with Lou's passion for Troise and His Mandoliers. There was a passion too with the women for the entertainment provided by Lord Haw Haw's anti-British broadcasts from Germany. Promoted by the papers to the status of national clown and international buffoon his idiosyncratic propaganda performances had spawned a variety show at the Holborn Empire and almost achieved the status of essential listening. Phoebe in particular had a special vein of vituperative abuse which she reserved for his nasal outpourings – an attitude which lingered on into much later years whenever it appeared that a German rider might be on the verge of success in the *Horse of the Year Show*. But Haw Haw's entertainment value began to sour when events took a much more serious turn later in the year and the advice of the ministry on all such broadcasts was 'tune them out or switch them off'.

With his resumption of life in Poplar, John found that in other ways than schooling things would no longer be as once they were. Street play was restricted both by the winter weather and the continued absence of many local children, but after a week or so he did meet one old friend again, Pop-Jaw. Afflicted with a major disfiguration, possibly a birth defect, that had left him with a grossly swollen face and distended jaw, it took the innate cruelty of children to devise the unfeeling and grotesque nickname that the boy appeared to accept as readily and casually as Billy or Tom. Of his thoughts and feelings when alone or of his parents if they knew of his humiliating title they knew and cared nothing.

It was a disfigurement that made him look the hardest of hard cases, which perhaps protected him from the mockery of strangers, but it seemed not to pain him, cause discomfort or handicap him in

186

any of the children's daily activities. His mates had known him long enough to think nothing of his appearance. They accepted him in every way and he was distinguished from the crowd in one respect only, his nickname. Indeed they knew no other for him. His appearance was not a burden that Pop-Jaw had to carry into maturity. He had stayed with his family in the East End throughout the first evacuation, and unlike John's they had no bolt-hole to run to when the bombers finally came. Together with his parents and many neighbours in the same street, Pop-Jaw was one of the earliest victims of the Blitz.

Eventually a few more boys from the pre-evacuation days showed up, but they were never back to more than half their number and missed many of the activities that had previously filled their days. The Gaiety had discontinued its regular Saturday-morning cinema shows when its audience disappeared en masse, and they were not resumed despite the increasing number of children returning. Without their heroes and villains from the moving pictures Saturday mornings were a void, and their play lost much of its inspiration. Sundays, too, were a blank – no bands to follow, no hymns to parody or preachers to mock. They had no conception of the shadows that were to cross their lives in the months to come, and those changes seemed major deprivations at the time.

If there were wartime losses there were also gains. The great sandbag screens erected in front of public buildings, shelter entrances and elsewhere made for challenging climbing. The defence works in the recreation ground and the few street shelters, unused as yet, and already littered and malodorous, provided a retreat from the weather and a base for the new war games. Horses, six-shooters and above all guitars and singing cowboys were out. Machine guns, tanks, Spitfires and commandos were in.

For the weeks the bitter weather lasted it was to slides that their energies were devoted: slides of a length and efficiency as exceptional as the weather that created them. There were several, each with its own special character and appeal, but the king of them all, a Cresta run of slides, was on a narrow, wall-lined passageway that ran between two streets close to Pop-Jaw's home. With the advent of the ice and snow Pop-Jaw's performance on his home slide became legendary, and among his friends, for a few short weeks, his status was Olympian. The Fates who had dealt with him so cruelly in appearance had blessed him with coordination, a sense of balance and sureness of foot beyond his age and without equal among his peers.

They all achieved some degree of competence but the ice-bound passageway was an unforgiving environment, and they were drawn to the sport as much for the entertainment of seeing their friends go arse over tit as for the slide itself. It was as often humiliation as success that awaited them – except for Pop-Jaw. He clumped off into the distance in his battered old boots, turned, threw a look of contempt in their direction, and then accelerated gracefully towards the launch where he leapt, hung briefly in the air, landed perfectly balanced, and was away on the ice speeding between the walls.

None could compete with him, and as the days of frost turned into weeks he and the slide went from strength to strength. Inevitably others tried to follow where he led and gave him much amusement. Those that were lucky took their tumble without damage. Those that were not, made their transit bouncing between the walls, sometimes vertical, all too often horizontal. Most carried a scar or two on knuckles, elbows or knees for their pains. While his friends slipped and stumbled, Pop-Jaw was unstoppable. For week after week he was cock of the walk until the February thaw rang down the curtain on his brief but remarkable career.

When the weather finally improved almost six months had passed since the evacuation, and seven weeks since John's return, but nothing had happened that seemed to present any threat to him or his immediate world. Some food rationing had started, as he was constantly reminded, but he was happy to top up with bread, which was still available ad lib. Certainly things were not quite as they used to be. He saw less of the aunts, there was the tedium of the blackout, and many old friends were still missing, but with spring on the way there seemed to him no reason why life should not be resumed much as before. In many ways, as the weather improved, they did take up some of the old routines. He joined in shopping trips to Chrisp Street, went for a walk or two with his father, and resumed visits to the swings and roundabout in the park, but when he was allowed out by himself it was with the strict injunction not to wander too far from home, and to return at once if he heard the sound of a siren.

When schooling eventually resumed after Easter it was an irregular, uncertain affair. Almost half of John's class were still away, as was Miss Roberts, and the teachers they saw were constantly changing. Much of the time they were simply minded not taught, but there were few in the small class who were unhappy with that state of affairs. There was lots of storytelling and class games, a little reading, writing and arithmetic, and history stories of country and Empire, high in propaganda and morale-boosting content. There was no serious attempt to achieve any structured approach to their education, but considering the situation that was perhaps inevitable.

With the worst of the winter over, there were a few months when Clara and Kath, the two optimists in the family, felt that the situation might perhaps not be quite so bleak after all. Elsie, always realistic but notorious as the family pessimist, told them not to be such bloody fools and was finally proved to be right. The end of February brought an encouraging reminder of the one resounding success of the war with a great parade in London for the victors of the *Graf Spee* encounter, and a little later Clara returned home with a souvenir issue of *Picture Post* on the same theme. By the end of March seven months of war had passed and apart from rationing and other relatively minor inconveniences things at home were much as they used to be. The nation heard the news that the strength of the defences of the British Expeditionary Force in France was astounding and set off for the Easter holidays feeling much reassured. On their return they and Clara were further encouraged by a statement from the Prime Minister that Hitler had 'missed the bus' in not overwhelming the British forces before they had consolidated their defences. They were now so strong that the country could face the future with a calm and steady mind.

It was an unhappy piece of timing. Within days Hitler's troops had invaded Denmark and Norway. Within weeks they were sweeping across Belgium, Holland and Luxembourg and pushing on into France. Chamberlain resigned to be replaced by Churchill, whose 'blood, toil, tears and sweat' speech painted the first realistic picture of what the future might have in store. The cancellation of the Whit Bank Holiday helped to reinforce the message, and if that were not enough any lingering illusions were shattered as the first pictures appeared in the cinemas and papers of the floods of refugees streaming across the roads of France before the advancing German divisions.

In May the children's schooling, for what it was worth, was

interrupted once again when the family moved to Essex for a couple of weeks. The steelwork for an Anderson air-raid shelter had been delivered to Bayhurst and had to be erected. Jack and Charlie were to travel down at weekends to do the work, but the rest of them were going to stay there for as long as it took. On that visit, too, Bayhurst's long isolation was to end with the installation of a wireless. If anyone was going to be living there on a permanent basis they needed to be able to keep in touch with events.

As yet none of the preparations for war had touched Pitsea. In the warmth of early summer the station slumbered on unchanged. Ragged banks of dog roses tumbled down the hill behind the platform, their buds fattening in the afternoon sun. A breeze blew softly from the marshlands and the heady scent of hawthorn sweetened the air. Beyond the station, where the rails swept along the foot of the hills towards Benfleet, the meadows were bright with buttercups. All was as before – the same idyllic contrast to the bustle and smells of Poplar.

The gardens on the way to the crest of the hill were bright with the first flush of summer, and from their seat in the churchyard it was the old familiar scene: the silent station below them, the wide sweep of the creeks and marshes beyond, and the distant river under a sky streaked with the smoke of shipping. But in the far distance, above the tanks of the oil refinery at Thames Haven, around the docks at Tilbury, and further off in the haze of the Kent coast, clusters of barrage balloons were an ugly reminder that the summer idyll was unlikely to last.

At Bayhurst, too, everything was reassuringly unchanged. The back door, for once in perfect harmony with frame and foundations, opened at the touch and the children slipped in ahead of their mother. After a day baking in the sun the bungalow was hot and airless, and there was an extra pungency to the old, familiar, musty smells that billowed out as they threw open the doors from the passageway into each of the four little rooms. Satisfied that all was as it should be, they left the others to busy themselves with the many preparations for their stay and wandered out into an unkempt garden. Idling on the swing behind the apple trees, they watched as Phoebe dragged the bedding out to air and freshen, and Lou made a round of the house opening the windows one by one. Swinging slowly to gentle pushes from an unusually indulgent sister, John planned the days that lay ahead.

In Essex it was time, not war, that had worked its own inevitable changes, and there would be no more visits to Aunt Tot's. The fascination of George's workshop – its pungent aroma of newly worked timber, varnish and oils; the rustle of wood shavings on the floor and his soft bucolic exchanges with Joe – those were all shades of the past, as were their leisurely and indulgent afternoon teas in the cosy, domestic comfort of Aunt Tot's overstuffed front room.

Of the past, too, were Joe and Aunt Tot themselves. High on the hill, tucked neighbourly between the tumbling stones of earlier residents, they now lay together, secured by George's best joinery against the clammy hand of the clay. The elms that Joe himself had cut and shaped for so long now coffined them, wrapped their roots around them, and gave them their shade. The workshop was closed. George, a recluse in his own little world, was seldom seen, and Tot's house had been sold for what Lou said was a fraction of its real value, reflecting the uncertainty that war cast over every aspect of life.

The German's house next door to Bayhurst stood empty. Even before they walked through the gate Mrs Heard brought them the news that just a few weeks earlier, two men had called, and carrying just a suitcase the German had left in their car and not returned. The house was locked as he had left it, and no one had any idea where he had gone or how long he would be away. Everyone assumed that he had been interned and would return when the war was over, but the war and many years of peace passed and no more was heard of him.

It was a warm and sunny May, and while they waited for the weekend Phoebe and Lou busied themselves about the garden on the first extended visit of the year: Lou with enthusiasm and enjoyment, Phoebe reluctantly, as one of life's duties. From the swing or his seat in the crutch of the hornbeam John watched them at work or idled the golden days away on the paths and lanes of the countryside. Across the Channel the Germans were making their opening thrusts in an advance that within just a few weeks would carry them through to Dunkirk.

Jack and Charlie were both lucky to be on a five-day week. They arrived at the bungalow late on the Friday and after an early breakfast the following morning began to prepare the ground for the shelter. With his final chunk of toast in hand John joined them

191

and sat watching the spadework that a few years later would become so familiar to him. When the call came he would be a reluctant conscript to the home front, but as the restrictions and food shortages of the war and the years that followed bit more and more deeply, Jack's health deteriorated, and John was to be increasingly pressed into service in the vegetable plot and a closer acquaintance with a soil that could break a gardener's heart.

To every thing there is a season, says the Bible, and never was that more true than of the heavy loams of Essex where timing is all. Seemingly passive and inanimate, they have in fact a demanding life cycle of their own and to be productive must be taken in season. Work them early in the year, when the rains of winter linger in the sodden soil, and their clays coalesce into a glutinous, back-breaking mass that clings to the spade at every cut and to the boot in ever-thickening layers. Neglect them for summer sun and drying winds to do their work and they set to spade-shattering stone, or fracture into fissures wide and deep enough to swallow hope itself. But catch them and rough-dig them in their coming-on mood, just moistened and softened by the first rains of autumn. Deliver them up to the frosts of winter and the scouring winds of March, and in the warmth of spring they will crumble at the touch to a fructuous yielding tilth to gladden a gardener's heart.

He squatted alongside the workers watching them as they cut spit after spit of grass-covered soil and stacked them to one side. For rough digging the timing was good, the soil soft and yielding, and the underlying cheesy clay soon exposed. They worked in old, comfortable clothes: shirt, trousers, worn and shabby waistcoats, and boots. Sleeves rolled up, trouser bottoms tucked into their socks, they cut their way methodically from each end of the plot. The spades sliced easily into the moist clay, and soon block-shaped spits, greasy and shining, were lying in growing lines alongside the deepening hole. Tea came out from the house every hour when they stopped to roll and smoke a cigarette before they started again. By midday on the Sunday the pit was complete. A little longer than a man, about four and a half feet wide, and three to four feet deep, it was ready for the shelter to be erected the following weekend.

The halcyon weather continued and John saw little of home during the following week. There was news of intriguing new developments in the fields at the bottom of the lane and, together with Mickey and Johnny, another young boy on leave from the city, he set out to investigate. Together they made their way to the ridge of the hill, along the margins of the fields and then into Rushbottom Lane, the old green way that ran across the meadows close to All Saints' church. Whatever purpose that ancient country track may once have served was long gone and it had lain untrodden for years. On either side the hedges were tall and untrimmed, a mix of elm, ash, dogwood and sweet hawthorn tangled with wild roses. The lush growth of May was untrampled, and they pushed their way waist-deep through flowering cow parsley, nettles, stitchwort, red campion and fat, juicy grasses, dragging the stems from the base to suck on as they passed along. Swarms of midges and the pungent reek of crushed hedge garlic followed them as they turned on a narrow byway to the pond by the church, where they stripped off shoes and socks and scattered the ducks panic-stricken with their splashing in the shallows.

Mickey was in his element. In his oldest of working clothes, still fragrant with the smell of pig, he plunged and cavorted to within an inch of total immersion. His two companions looked on in envy, but hadn't the nerve to risk their decent clothing and join him. Stretched out on the pool-side grass, they dried their feet in the sun, put on their socks and shoes, and went on their way dry-shod with a sopping Mickey grinning between them. His clothing was wet and mud-stained. Water dripped down his legs into his shoes. His unsocked feet squelched in his shoes at every step and he was ecstatic.

As the new arterial road came into sight they could at last see the activity that had given rise to all the talk. Crawling slowly across the low-lying land on either side of the road monstrous machines on caterpillar tracks scarred the meadow with a deep, dark gash as they passed along. With each bite of their buckets they gouged out a hole half the size of the shelter base dug so laboriously by hand, and on each side of the deepening trench the excavated spoil extended to form a long, high ridge.

They watched the activity for some time without any understanding of what was happening or why. It was Mickey who took the initiative and edged himself forward alongside the man who appeared to be supervising the work. He watched silently, making sure that he wasn't going to be hounded away before looking up and speaking a few words. He listened to the man's reply, and then waved them up to join him.

'They're tank traps,' he said confidently.

That probably meant as little to Mickey as it did to them, but he didn't blink, and before they could ask for an explanation they were given one by the man, who had seen the puzzled look on their faces. John listened but failed to grasp the real significance of traps for German tanks in his Essex countryside. It wasn't lost on the family when he told them at the end of the day.

Mickey's pigswill round continued as before, but it was now scarcely worth the effort. Food was no longer discarded as casually as in previous years. More and more people were keeping ducks, geese or chickens either for eggs or meat, or both, and any scraps not wanted for human consumption went to supplement what the birds scratched up for themselves.

When they made their early rounds the gate to the German's had always been closed when they passed on their way up the hill, but towards the middle of the second week it stood wide open. That was enough to tempt them into an exploration of the garden around the deserted house. They knew well enough that the German hadn't returned and the house was empty, but to ease their nervousness they knocked on the front door as though on their normal call for scraps and waited for a few moments before they went further. When satisfied that all was still they moved on, but quietly and with care. Only a narrow strip of garden and a hedge separated them from Bayhurst and there would be trouble if they were spotted.

At the front and side windows the curtains were drawn, but at the back they were open, and with their chins at sill height they looked inside, scrutinising the room for the tell-tale signs they felt sure would mark it out for what it was: an outpost of the enemy, sinister and menacing. They saw a table, chenille-covered just like Lou's; chairs, upright and easy; a bookcase stuffed with books and magazines; a brass fender round the open fireplace; a sofa and a sideboard. Two large, framed portraits hung on the walls. Other smaller photographs and china knick-knacks cluttered the mantel-piece. On the sideboard a pair of handsome oil lamps, a combi-nation of brass and decorated glass, stood either side of an ugly black clock. There were no swastikas, no Nazi emblems, no framed portraits of the Führer. It was all disappointingly ordinary and surprisingly like home.

They passed on cautiously through the garden towards the shed and workshop that stood some way from the house. The door was shut and a closed padlock still clamped the hasp to the staple, but the whole fitting had been wrenched from the woodwork of the frame and the entrance was no longer secure. They pulled at the door of the shed, hesitated briefly, and then slipped into its silent warmth and closed the door behind them.

There was a workman-like, down-to-earth smell to the place: a mixture of creosote, drying vegetation, damp earth, bonemeal spilt from a bag on to the floor, and a spicy scent from the thin timber of seed boxes on the workbench baking under the hot sun. Behind the door the old boy's hat and garden coat hung waiting for him, and beneath the bench his work boots were curling at the toes in the heat. Bunches of dried flower heads and herbs swung from the roof. The bench top was littered with old seed packets, plant pots, tins, bottles, boxes of clips and ties, and other gardening parapher-nalia. Beneath the bench, piles of sacks, newspapers, and yet more pots and seed boxes, toppled over and spilled on to the floor. A heavy lawnmower, a besom and a long-handled scythe stood in one corner. Those and a garden roller standing outside were the only tools to be seen. Whoever had broken the hasp and staple from the frame and stolen away with all the other tools had not waited long before deciding that the owner might not be returning, and was only a German after all. They left as quietly as they had entered and moved on to the rest of the round.

It took only the following Saturday for work on the shelter to be completed. The corrugated-iron sections were dropped on to boards levelled off on the bottom clay and bolted together with T-irons to form a round-roofed hut. The back and front plates were fitted and that was that. But although the Anderson came with a reputation for good bomb and blast protection that was more than justified, experience had shown that in low-lying or poorly drained land it rapidly developed a secondary use as a plunge pool when surface water and rain flooded in to fill the excavation. As the two functions were generally considered to be incompatible, the prac-tice was adopted of sealing the excavation inside the corrugated iron with a skin of several inches of waterproof concrete up to groundwater level. That work was completed a few days later by council contractors. Narrow double-decker bunks made of floor boarding and other second-hand timbers were then erected on each side, duckboards dropped on to the rough concrete base, and the shelter was ready to be covered with a thick jacket of the excavated soil.

While the shelter was being erected, and the family were enjoying their early summer idyll, British forces were clinging desperately to a perimeter around Dunkirk and clustering together on the beaches to await evacuation. And just eight miles down the road from Bayhurst another evacuation was taking place as children from the Southend area were moved away from what was now considered a potential invasion site.

14

Desperate Times

They were back in Poplar in good time to hear the first public announcement that British forces were being evacuated from France, but in common with anyone living close to the affair in or around the estuary or south coast ports they had already heard the rumours of a catastrophe in the making. Within a few days came the first pictures of the scenes on the dunes and piers of the Dunkirk beaches, and from then on despite censorship and the most positive of presentations the sequence of news that reached them via newspapers and wireless was unremittingly bad.

Italy having waited long enough to see which way the wind appeared to be blowing had entered the war on Germany's coat-tails. The Germans marched into Paris. Outside London the first major air raids on the east coast and along the Thames estuary prompted a second wave of evacuations from the city, but with the threat now perceived as including invasion as well as air attack Phoebe and Jack had no difficulty in deciding that this time they would not be separated from the children. A few days later the family sat together looking through 'If Britain is Invaded', the latest in the long, long line of pamphlets, instructions, leaflets, threats and published invectives with which the country would be inundated by their government as the war progressed. Its seven rules for conduct in the face of the enemy made depressing and unsettling reading for the stoutest and left poor Clara feeling that the Hun was just around the corner. On the same day Jimmy Bellamy called in the evening to discuss the gravity of the situation with Jack. Their past political associations and activities had been such that neither was under any illusions about their future and that of their families in a Nazi-occupied Britain.

It was a time when the increasing anxiety, uncertainty and feeling of impotence felt within the family must have been shared

197

by the country at large. The overwhelming success of the Nazi Blitzkrieg in Europe, and the total collapse of resistance from the British Expeditionary Force had been in some small part offset by the remarkably benign weather that blessed the Dunkirk evacuation, but with that over the country stood practically unarmed. France had fallen, the Channel Islands were occupied, there had been serious reverses in the naval war, and the enemy was now just across the Channel. But of all the wretched news that came with each daily paper the most distressing for many was the new category of entry in the personal columns: sad little notices appealing for information on servicemen missing, last seen at, or surrounded at, Dunkirk.

In those weeks when blow seemed to fall relentlessly upon blow, news of perhaps the worst single disaster went for a while unreported. In mid-June in the port of St-Nazaire the liner *Lancastria* was bombed and sank in little more than thirty minutes taking with her almost 3,000 British troops awaiting evacuation. With the country's morale already at rock bottom, news of the incident was suppressed for some five weeks on Churchill's orders and even when published was given minimum publicity.

Churchill's record in home affairs was such that the family had little reason to welcome his succession to the premiership on that score. Aggressively hostile to the suffragette movement, to union activity and to all aspects of socialism, Churchill in ordinary circumstances would have offered a poorer prospect than his predecessor, but when it came to war and the right man as war leader the two were as bulldog and poodle. It was a time when within less than two weeks he gave his great 'we shall never surrender' and 'this was their finest hour' speeches and spoke at length to the nation on the curse of Hitler. The family read the speeches and listened to the broadcasts, and they knew that however much they detested his social and political attitudes at home Churchill, unlike Chamberlain, spoke a language and in terms they recognised, understood and endorsed when it came to the evils of fascism and the obscenity of Hitler and all he stood for.

The two children were generally there, on the fringes of the family conversations, half-listening when the news was discussed. Moira was old enough to have at least some understanding of the issues, but at John's age the implications for himself of all that he heard, were lost on him. He was certainly well aware of increasing constraints on the pleasures of the table as rationing bit deeper and deeper, but as long as he could top up and keep his belly full with bread and a scrape of something he was content. His own immediate world still seemed as secure and stable as ever, and he played away the weeks of summer while the world at large was falling into chaos.

For those children who still attended school the regime was relaxed and informal. If it didn't advance their education a jot, it was a pleasant enough way to pass the day before they were released on to side streets even more deserted of traffic than they were before the war – an ideal playground for their games of marbles, gobs or tin-can-copper. In the park the narrow, open trenches of 1939 were now shelters of concrete and steel half-buried in the ground, with wild flowers and grasses already colonising and softening the earth mounds that covered them, but the swings, roundabout and slide were all operating as usual. Even their experiences when the first air-raid sirens sounded did little to ruffle the even tenor of their lives. The instinctive, gut-churning response to that dismal, chilling wail came later, with the forging of the link between the sirens and the sights and sounds that followed.

On the streets, as in the park, the sun still shone. The milk cart, brewers' drays, and rag-and-bone men still made their rounds, and the steaming mounds of dung dropped by the horses were as keenly prized as ever in the few cultivated plots just over the terrace wall, where hanging gardens of marrows and cucumbers now tumbled down from the earth-covered tops of the Anderson shelters. Those with the gardens were the lucky ones. Sewers, gas and water mains and electrical cables made it impossible to build shelters in the terrace, and as nowhere inside the house provided any effective protection, the family bolt-hole in any emergency was to be with the Moriartys in Rigden Street. They were old friends from Lou's early days in the terrace, and their house had a solid, substantial cellar considered as good a refuge as anything else nearby.

It was not until mid-summer that air-raid sirens were heard in Poplar, and when they sounded for the first time there were only three in the house – Lou, Phoebe and John. Jack and Clara were at work, Moira not yet back from school, and Rene with the baby was visiting friends. Phoebe hesitated, thinking of Moira on her

199

way home, but Lou had no doubts. 'Come on, Phoebe. She knows where we'll be, and we can't help by staying here.'

Mr Moriarty had done a good job on the cellar. Cleared of rubbish, scrubbed out, whitewashed and with an electric light extension from the floor above, it looked almost welcoming. They settled down on old chairs and benches placed around the walls, and they waited. Phoebe put her arm around her son. 'All right?' He nodded.

Apart from a few words of greeting they sat nervously silent except for Mrs Moriarty who was murmuring quietly to herself. John listened and watched, puzzled by the few words that he could hear, and by the stringed beads that she caressed and passed through her fingers as she whispered to herself. By her side her daughter sat with head bowed and lips moving silently.

'What's she doing, Mum?'

'Shush.'

Phoebe and Lou were now talking softly to each other, but Mrs Moriarty continued with the same calm ritual.

He whispered again, 'Mum, what's she saying?'

'Shush, I told you. Ask your father later on.'

Beyond the cellar all was still and silent. Eventually Mrs Moriarty put away her beads, pulled her chair towards them, and soon they were deep in the day-to-day issues that concerned them, rationing and shortages. Shortly afterwards the all-clear sounded, and they returned home. It had been a deceptively peaceful introduction to shelter life.

Other alerts followed, but they were either false alarms or the action took place so far from Poplar that nothing was seen or heard. After a few experiences of rushing from the house for alarms that led to nothing they were treated increasingly casually and finally ignored. Mrs Moriarty's whispered words and beads were not forgotten, but it was beyond Jack's ability to explain the mystery and meaning of the rosary in terms that his son could understand.

By early July the situation was such that it was increasingly difficult to decide which was the best place of safety for the women and children of the families, London or Essex. Churchill's latest broadcast had spoken of the great air battles that were yet to be fought, of an invasion that might come possibly that night, or next week, or never, and if it did, of a London fought for street by street, and in ruins or ashes before any surrender to the curse of Hitler. All was uncertainty and conjecture and in the event it was more by default than by any calculated decision that they stuck to their normal pattern of proceeding at that time of year, and in mid-July, ten days or so before the schools formally closed for the summer holidays, the family went again to Bayhurst.

They were casual, disorganised affairs, those Essex excursions, when timing and route were left largely to chance. On this occasion pot luck meant the slow train via Tilbury – an interminably tedious detour on a long loop that followed the north shore of the Thames before sweeping past the desolate wastes of the aptly named Mucking Marshes to rejoin the main line at Pitsea. A little more than a year earlier they had last travelled that way through surroundings undistinguished but peaceful. Now the manifestations of war marked their journey at every stage: compartments crammed with soldiers and sailors who tumbled out at Tilbury, anti-aircraft gun emplacements along the shoreline of the river, bomb damage from the early raids visible in the buildings around the town, clusters of barrage balloons over the docks, and further on across the Fobbing Marshes more balloons hanging over the oil refineries at Thameshaven.

For over a month Lou, Phoebe, Doll and children remained at Bayhurst. Clara came only for the weekends with one or both of the men who arrived to put in some time on the garden. Vegetable plots and soft-fruit areas opened up a few years earlier had been kept in order by occasional visits earlier in the year. Flourishing in the warmth and sunshine of May and June and plumping up with the rains of early July, they now provided a welcome addition to the increasingly limited range of food available. Late broad beans, early peas and runner beans, lettuces, beetroots, radishes and carrots were supplemented with gooseberries, raspberries and cur-rants. In the years to follow such home production would come to form an increasingly valuable addition to the countryman's diet that was denied to those in the towns.

At the bottom of the lane the tank traps that the boys saw opened a couple of months earlier had started to fill with water from the rains of early July streaming down from the hill. The thick impermeable deposits of underlying clay made them perfect

201

reservoirs and already the water stood two or three feet deep in places. They were as yet cold, sludgy and uninviting, and it took Mickey to see their potential as future swimming holes.

Other signs of the preparations for invasion had also appeared since their May visit. At the junction of the lane with the arterial road, and elsewhere across the countryside, pillboxes had been erected as part of an extended chain of defences. Constructed of thick, reinforced concrete, with one narrow entry, and firing slits at shoulder height, some stood conspicuously above ground, others had been partially sunk so that only the firing slit and a couple of feet of concrete were exposed. They all faced up the road towards Southend. Never called upon to play any active role in the war, they did for a while perform a useful function as shelters from sudden storms, or secret places for the sexual fumblings and fondlings of rustic assignations, but inevitably, used as lavatories and dumps, they became thoroughly foul and noisome places that lingered on only because they were far too difficult and expensive to demolish. At the same time as the pillboxes went up all the signposts came down, but as the panzers didn't come it was only the occasional bemused despatch rider who was put to the embarrassment of seeking directions from the locals.

Sporadically to begin with, but then with increasing intensity the sights and sounds of war began to invade the skies above them. Initially there was little or no German activity, but at North Weald and Hornchurch there were two major fighter stations, and from those, when the skies were clear of cloud, small groups of fighters could be seen moving towards the estuary and the Kent coast, and returning at intervals a little later. Far away as they were, those sightings were the first contact they had with the events that were being reported on the wireless and in the papers. There wasn't much to see, just distant shapes moving into and out of the broken clouds, but they stood together and watched them until they were out of sight. Several air-raid warnings came and went, but they followed the same pattern as in London – the alert, a period of waiting with nothing seen or heard, and then the all-clear. As in London they were eventually ignored, although news filtered through to them of attacks along the estuary and night raids on Southend and Shoeburyness.

The reality of war, when it finally arrived, did so unexpectedly. In the silence that followed the sounding of yet another alarm everyone continued with what they were doing. The Lanes were working in the garden next door. Lou and the others were busy in the house. John and Valerie were outside on the swing, and heard the engines first. The sound came faintly, a distant hum fading and then reviving. It was different enough for them to stop their play and listen, but they had no reason to detect any note of menace, and stood looking with interest towards the sky over the estuary, waiting for whatever was to be seen.

It was Lou's old ears that sensed that things were wrong. Followed by the others she ran from the house with Moira by the hand calling to them as she came.

'Come on, you two. Don't just stand there. Into the shelter!'

They tumbled in and sat crouched on the edges of the bunks, nervous and tense as they listened for the first time to the sounds of war above them; the menacing pulsing drone of the bomber engines, short bursts of cannon fire, the crack of anti-aircraft shells and perhaps – they weren't sure – the distant thud of bombs. Remote and muffled on that occasion they were to get to know them more intimately soon enough. A similar incident occurred a couple of days later. Fighters were seen moving towards the estuary, and once again there were distant bursts of ack-ack, but nothing else was seen and the noises passed away into the distance.

On the first Friday of their stay Jack was expected to join them in the evening and stay to catch a late train back on the Sunday. He would bring news from Poplar of those who were still in town, any items needed from home, and perhaps some fish from Bill for their Saturday tea. The day started in routine fashion for them all, but would not continue so. Despite the increasing possibility of air raids the feeling was that life had to go on as usual, for the children as well as the adults. Moira took to her books, Valerie was too young to wander far from home, and John was left to his own devices subject to the instruction that he was not to stray too far and to get home immediately if the alert sounded.

Despite the early thefts from the shed in the German's garden, both houses had remained otherwise secure and untouched, but that morning Mickey brought news that the large barn on the side lane had been broken open, and they intended to have a look. From a distance the building still seemed to be secure, but as with the shed, although the padlock remained in place, the hasp had been broken from the timber and they could easily slip through the door. Inside they found themselves in a garage that had been looted and despoiled with systematic determination. Every drawer from beneath the workbench had been pulled out, and the contents strewn across the floor. Where they had been locked, the timber had been smashed to break them open. Tins and boxes lay empty on a bench strewn with their contents: assorted bolts, nuts, springs and fittings of little value. Shelves had been pulled from the walls, light bulbs smashed, and paint cans opened and poured in streams across the floor. Everything that might have been useful and portable had been carried away by those who had broken in.

But there in front of them, surrounded by litter and debris and saying 'play with me', as plainly as if it had spoken the words, was an open-backed motor lorry. It stood as the German had left it for the duration, raised a little off the floor, with its axles chocked up on thick baulks of timber. The wheels were gone, stolen with all the other items that had disappeared. One side of the bonnet was open, and anything of value that could be stripped from the engine had been taken. But the engine itself was still there behind a radiator on which a rising sun glowed softly above the legend *Albion*. Apart from the missing wheels, the lorry was as complete as any boy could have desired.

Overwhelmed and a little uneasy at such a scene of devastation they paused for a moment or two, but the temptation to enjoy a lorry of their own was overwhelming. Picking their way through the chaos and debris they pulled on the handle and opened the driver's door. The destruction visited on the rest of the garage had not extended to the inside of the cab. Clambering up to the smooth, shiny bench-seat they sat behind the steering wheel gazing at the tantalising display of knobs, dials, levers and switches stretched out before them.

Before they left they had pushed, pulled, twisted, turned and adjusted every one, but without response. The horn remained frustratingly silent, the lights unlit and the engine stubbornly unresponsive, but they were on their way. On that day, and on many days throughout the long war years to come, their battle wagon would carry them where the fighting was thickest: alongside Monty and the Desert Rats harrying Rommel across the Western Desert; into Normandy and through France with the Allied armies; and with Zhukov hounding the German divisions from Russia and into the heart of Berlin. They would be exhausting and demanding times, but they would triumph. Towards midday they closed the door behind them and headed for home light of heart, and with great expectations for the afternoon and the days to come.

When the first alert of the day sounded they trooped out dutifully towards the shelter, but already there was a growing realisation that the plotlands of Essex were unlikely to be high on the Luftwaffe's list of strategic targets. Like the Lanes, who could be seen in the neighbouring garden, they stood by the entrance to the shelter watching and listening as an entirely new scene unfolded. The throb of the engines was heavier, more insistent; the sound of many more planes than before. They were closer, too, and should have been visible, but for a while they scoured the sky in vain. Then high over the estuary, into a gap in the broken cloud, a flight of bombers emerged. Three, six, ten, and then more than could easily be counted.

They heard a shout from Mr Lane. 'Fighters,' and he pointed up towards the bombers. Then they saw the neat, compact outline of fighters flying in formation above and a little behind them, but they were German, not RAF. The progress of the aircraft appeared to be entirely leisurely, orderly and untroubled. There was no flack, and apparently no opposing fighters. They became aware of them only when they were seen breaking through the bomber formation, but they were few in number, and seemed to have little impact. As the engagement proceeded it moved into and out of broken cloud, and at such a height that it was difficult to follow the action. The bomber formation continued on its way unbroken, but running into the first puffs of ack-ack as it moved on beyond Thames Haven. A little later they heard the distant, dull thud of bombs. The fighters on both sides twisted and turned, now in view, now lost behind clouds. No aircraft on either side seemed to be hit, and before long the skies were empty again. Phoebe went to make tea and sand-wiches, and together they sat to eat them on the grass by the shelter. After half an hour or so the aircraft could be heard again, but more distantly, somewhere above the Kent side of the estuary. Then there was silence, and later the single long note of the all-clear siren.

In the afternoon there was no return visit to the lorry. Phoebe was going to the local shop and took John with her. Avoiding the lane she chose the country route through the long grasses of the cross-lane where to the eye of the casual passer-by the door of the

German's garage was still secure, past little orchards and empty plots, and finally to the general grocer's shop that in better times had supplied Mickey with stale bread for his sow. Wherever there was anyone in a garden or on the lane as they returned, the events of the morning provided Phoebe with a rich resource for conversation, speculation and surmise, and they were scarcely back at Bayhurst and unpacking when the second alert of the day sounded.

Once again they moved out to the shelter and stood close to the entrance. There was less cloud this time, and the bombers were seen almost as soon as they were heard. There were perhaps thirty or forty of them, plus a substantial fighter escort. As in the morning they followed the line of the estuary, but this time they were nearer to the Essex coast, and their progress was not so untroubled. The RAF were there in greater numbers, and unlike the morning encounter they harried and broke the formation, from which a couple of bombers became detached. One turned and was eventually able to rejoin the main flight, but the other must have been hit by fighter fire, and the family's wartime experiences were further enriched, as for the first time they stood and watched men die.

At their distance it was impossible to see in what way the aircraft had been damaged; perhaps the pilot himself had been hit. There was neither smoke nor fire as it tumbled from the sky. It was as if the air had suddenly and unreasonably withdrawn its support. One wing dipped, the nose dropped and slowly, twisting and spinning like an autumn leaf, it drifted to earth. No parachutes were seen, and however many crew it carried were still locked inside during the long spiralling descent. They watched it in silence, and nothing was said as the plane disappeared from sight. When a few moments later smoke was seen rising, it was Lou who spoke:

'Serve them bloody well right.' Recollections of the North Street tragedy of the First World War were still strong in Lou's mind.

Jack would normally have been with them by seven o'clock, certainly by eight at the latest. Whatever Phoebe's feelings were when he failed to show up, she said no more than that he would be with them soon and that the children could stay up until he arrived. Neither the family, nor anyone they knew, had telephones at home and there was no way to make contact before morning. They just had to sit and wait.

It was almost dark, and they were thinking of lighting the gas, when Jack and Charlie arrived together. They had been travelling

206

via Tilbury on a train that was held at a standstill for almost two hours as it approached the station. Many of the bombs dropped by the afternoon raiders had fallen on the docks and factories around the town causing the fires and damage that had delayed them. Before the children went to bed John joined with the others in reporting the events of the day, but omitted any reference to the discovery and exploration of the lorry.

Their first night-time alert came just after midnight. Roused by his father, John awoke, confused and half asleep, to hear the last dying howls of the siren. With top coats buttoned over nightclothes, and blankets in their arms, they came together in the little living room under a subdued glow from the gaslight. In John's muddled state the room looked strange and unfriendly, and the worried, drawn faces around him less familiar and reassuring. Their emotions, try as they might to conceal them, were contagious, and suddenly in the small hours, when he was half awake and half asleep, the foundations of his world seemed to tremble.

If the alert got them together quickly, there was no rush to the shelter which was at some distance from the house. Although it was August, the evenings were cool, and nothing had been done to make the shelter fit for a long night-time stay. The children were covered with blankets and settled into chairs where they drifted into and out of the proceedings for the next half-hour or so. Charlie went out and came back to report clear skies, a full moon and the fact that it was bloody chilly. Nothing could be heard, and apart from searchlights in the distance nothing could be seen. As soon as it was decided that enduring the rigours of the shelter would be more than the situation demanded, they made a pot of tea. John sipped a cupful, warm, sweet and milky; chewed sleepily on a biscuit; and woke up the following morning remembering little of the previous night's alarms.

The following day they carried to the shelter as many cushions, blankets and coverings as could be spared from the house. An oil lamp with matches was placed at the back, a heavy curtain hung across the entrance, and all was as ready as it could be if they were forced to use the shelter overnight. At Lou's insistence a spare jerry was left under the bunks, although how anyone was going to use it and retain a shred of dignity was not at all clear: if the worst came to the worst there might be as many as eight crammed into the shelter.

A day or two after their arrival the rains had ceased and a long, dry spell set in that would last throughout their stay. A light breeze from the north and cloudy skies kept the temperature down a little but by the fourth Saturday of their stay it was warm, sunny and, as far as they were concerned, untroubled for once by the sights and sounds of war. The morning air was soft and sweet. Over arch and wall around the house roses hung heavy on the trellis, and from the honeysuckle the low murmur of insects drifted in through the open window where the family sat at breakfast planning the day ahead. The future held nothing but uncertainty. Britain stood almost defenceless and the odds seemed overwhelming. Yet for a few hours, in their own little world unchanged from those untroubled days before the war, it was almost possible to forget the threat that hung over them and live the day as though all might yet be well.

An early dew was already off the lawn when the family moved out to take advantage of the weather. While John idled contentedly on the swing the gardeners were at work around him: Jack and Charlie, open-shirted but already sweating, hoeing or lifting early potatoes and other root crops; Lou in her old gardening apron cutting gladioli and the tall white chrysanthemums; even Phoebe assisting and picking at the still-ripening crops of soft fruit. Clara, as a working lady, enjoyed the privileges of an extra hour in bed and a late breakfast, but it wasn't long before the clack of the mower from the front lawn signalled her arrival in the garden.

John watched as his gran carried her flowers into the house, before giving him a wave as she returned for rainwater from the large butt outside the back door. When he next saw her she was reappearing from the flowering bower that screened their rustic privy.

'Charlie! Do us the honours will you, son. It's almost up to the brim.'

He looked up at her call.

'What it is to be the favourite son, Jack. Sure you don't want to oblige?'

The family interment was a revolting and distasteful chore, but one which Charlie accepted with good grace. Jack had tried it once, but was gagging and heaving before he was halfway up the garden. Charlie was made of sterner stuff and lugged the brimming bucket

208

from the privy with scarcely a grimace. Jack followed at a distance with a watering can filled from the butt for the final ablutions.

As in the cut-price cemeteries of Victorian London so it was with the privy interments at Bayhurst. They were densely packed together in one designated plot, and although the final rites were always decently carried out, and the corpse buried at a reasonable depth, it was an area that otherwise remained untouched through all the years of family occupation. For those who followed later the soil's unusual fecundity may have come as a pleasant surprise.

Later in the day Mickey called for John. With so many people out and about in the lanes enjoying the fine weather, they decided against another visit to the lorry and turned instead to the extensive area of bush, scrub and grassland behind Mickey's cottage where he had a hide for the few treasures he had acquired in what seemed to John to have been a remarkably enterprising childhood. John took with him some matches from the scullery at home and, under Mickey's apparently knowledgeable supervision, had his first experiment with fire.

After four weeks without rain and a few warm, sunny days the undergrowth was tinder dry and the long coarse grasses snatched at the lighted match. They flickered into a bright flame which a gentle breeze soon fanned to a blaze on a wider and wider front. With a conviction belied by subsequent events, Mickey pulled a couple of old sacks from his hide and demonstrated that by using them as beaters it was a simple matter to control the fire as they wished. Initially things went well. Following Mickey's theory they thrashed away at the flames on the fringes of the fire and held it on a nice tight front for some time.

It wasn't clear which of them made the mistake. A thin tongue of flame reached out to touch the base of a clump of brambles and blackberry bushes dead for a year or more and eager to embrace their final consummation. There was a momentary pause as dead leaves and grasses shrivelled in the heat before the whole bush exploded into a blaze that confounded them. Suddenly flames were dancing high above their heads, lifting still-glowing ashes and tiny, blazing shreds that dropped threateningly into the dry grasses around them. Fortunately their burning bush was well away from any other large clumps of scrub, and some hope remained that they could contain their demon and keep it to themselves. They danced around it like dervishes, beating at the foot of the blaze to stop it spreading further. But as they dealt with that emergency, the original front of the fire in the long grass was expanding and gathering strength. Sweating and desperate, they dashed from one challenge to the other, hurling at the fire the worst invective they could invoke while beating frantically at the flames. The air was thick with fine, black dust from the crushed ashes. It fell on their clothes and into their hair. It blew into their eyes and ears and penetrated their socks and shoes. Fragments of still-hot ash borne aloft in the swirling vortices of air fell back on to their skin, stinging and burning.

Finally the last flame was beaten into submission. They stood triumphant, but it was a pyrrhic victory. John looked at Mickey and despaired. His arms and legs were streaked with sweat and dust, his face smeared with ash, his eyes red from the smoke, and his hands were black. Knowing that he could look no different John left him and trudged towards home. His shirt was dirty and pocked with burns from the ash; his hair was tangled, and his heart was in his boots. He thought it might perhaps have been better if they had returned to the lorry after all.

Phoebe and Lou were outside the back door running sheets through the mangle when he turned the corner and stood before them. Lou saw him first.

'Oh my God, John! What have you been up to?'

His mother spun round, and he resigned himself to his mortification. Stinging from a couple of slaps and a torrent of recrimination, he was dragged up the garden to his father working on the vegetable plot with Charlie.

'Jack. Will you just look at the state this boy's come home in.'

Jack looked up from his gardening, gave the scene before him a few moments earnest and serious consideration, and burst into laughter.

'Well, if you think it's that bloody funny, I'll leave you to clean him up and get on with what I'm doing.'

As John was washed and tidied in the scullery his father teased out of him a full account of the adventure and sent him on his way with a few words of advice on the dangers of meddling with fire.

On the fine evening that followed the conflagration the family locked the house and took to the lane for a stroll together as far as the arterial road. Jack and Charlie wanted to see the tank traps and other defences for themselves, and at the junction with the lane there was a pub where they could rest and have a drink before the walk back. John was once again in good odour with his mother, but knew well enough that if forgiven, his transgression was not forgotten: she had an elephantine memory for such things.

Before they left Lou cut a few flowers from the garden for Aunt Tot's grave. When they reached Mayfield it looked much as it did in Tot's time; the garden neat and tidy, and the orchard trees heavy with fruit. While the others walked slowly on Phoebe and Lou lingered awhile recalling the old days of trips to Tot's before the Great War, when Lou was in her prime, Phoebe a young girl, and Tot with her pony and trap collected them from the station.

Climbing the stile on the lane below the church they turned on to the footpath that had been Tot's short cut to her favourite retreat on the ridge above. The grain harvest was under way, and while the others strolled along the hedgerow beneath the elms, John made sorties into the sharp stubble, stuffing his pockets with gleanings of corn to take back for Mickey's sow. Beyond the narrow gate in the churchyard wall thistles, nettles and brambles grew tall in a corner where the graves were old and neglected. They pushed their way through to the patch that was still well tended, and Lou laid her flowers on the grave where the headstone had been in place for less than a year. Cut from the same source as the older stones around, it was as yet unstained by weather, its lettering crisp and clear. Unlike its companion stones, it stood as yet upright, with no bias towards any of its neighbours. A little of Aunt Tot's spirit in that: it kept itself to itself.

Moving on past pond and farmyard, they turned back down the lane towards the tank traps. Despite the growing chill of the evening there were already a few boys splashing knee deep in the water of the traps, but it would take the rains of winter to fill them deep enough to swim in.

Once past the pillboxes they headed for the Harrows Inn. In Tot's album she had kept a photograph of the old country pub which had once stood on the spot. It showed an inviting, tidy little hostelry tucked under the shade of a grove of elms on an unmade country lane. It must have been standing there for a century or more, but shortly after the arterial road carved its way through the countryside within a few yards of the door, the old place came under the hammer, metaphorically and literally. It was soon demolished and replaced by a monstrous 1930s gin palace designed to catch the holiday trade that would be passing to and from London and the coast. The handsome elms were toppled to create space for a surrounding coach and car park, but both now stood utterly deserted and would do for some years to come. Petrol rationing would see to that.

They sat on the benches at the front where the building was well out of sight behind them. Jack and Charlie came out with beer for themselves, port and lemon for the ladies, and a drink for the youngsters. Beyond the concrete of the carriageways the countryside stretched unbroken on either side of the lane. On the arterial road nothing moved, and the only sound that broke the silence was the regular thud of a heavy mallet swung by a labourer driving fencing stakes a couple of fields away. It was still and peaceful as they walked back in the gathering dusk, and so it remained throughout the night.

Alerts on and off throughout the Sunday kept the children in the house or garden at all times, but they saw only defending fighters crossing high above them until late afternoon when a large formation of bombers moved inland from the east to pass almost overhead. Intense bursts of ack-ack fire, apparently quite ineffective, followed them, and they crammed into the shelter as much for protection from the shrapnel as the threat of bombs.

The raiders moved on, and when nothing more was heard they went in for tea and to talk over the various plans and ideas that were being considered for the weeks ahead. No one liked the existing arrangements with the families separated, some in Essex, some in Poplar and meeting only on occasional weekends. There had been no major raids on London, and there seemed no reason to think that any were imminent. More significant was Churchill's recent warning against believing that the invasion threat was over, and that was considered to be the more immediate danger. Eventually they decided that Jack and Charlie would return to London as usual later that evening, and unless there was any immediate change in circumstances they would all go home to Poplar during the following week.

15

Last Days in Poplar

The following day was relatively quiet. So it remained on the Tuesday as they left to return to London, but when they climbed the hill on their way to the station thick columns of oily black smoke could be seen above Thames Haven marking an earlier raid, and in the distance across the river high above the Kent shore the sky was smudged with a dark haze from still-burning fires. From then on the news was of air attacks elsewhere in the country that came with increasing frequency and intensity culminating in reports that in one day of raiding more than a thousand bombers had been engaged. Contemporary reports of almost 150 German aircraft downed on that one day may have overstated their losses, but it was always clear in whose favour the balance was tilted when the engagements took place over home ground.

Clara's laundry office at this time served as a sort of clearing house for gossip and local news that included some of the details that the papers omitted, and she returned home day after day with news of continuing attacks along the estuary and on Thames Haven, Hornchurch and Tilbury. But apart from one or two false alarms Poplar remained peaceful and undisturbed, and to the children it seemed almost as though they were resuming the old routine. For the first time in many months Elsie and Kath were together on the Friday evening for one of their rare weekends at home, and the household was up to complement again.

An early start in the kitchens was the rule in the schools where they worked, but at home they relaxed, and it was a while before they were down for breakfast. As usual the children were there to greet them, but times were harder, short commons increasingly the rule, and there was nothing savoury or fancy about their breakfast to tempt John into joining them. Satisfying the parrot's pestering for his sop of sugary bread he listened to them discussing the

213

reports in the papers and their plans for the day. Eventually came the invitation he had hoped for and his mother's agreement. 'Glad to see the back of you if they don't mind.' Always very happy to have his aunts to himself, he was more than satisfied when Moira declined an offer to join them. Less than half an hour later, after a quick scrub, brush and polish from his mother he joined them, and they set off together for the rest of the morning.

Whenever and whoever the aunts were visiting they took no little trouble with their appearance. In their make-up they exercised the discretion of middle age. A little rouge here, a touch of lipstick there, a thin veil of powder overall, and a dab or two of a light and delicate perfume was just enough to counter the wear and tear of long days in the heat of the kitchens. Their perfumes were the best they could afford, and somehow they had built up a supply that would last them well into the years of war. Gloved, hatted, wearing light summer coats, and perfuming the air around them, they seemed the embodiment of earlier, happier days as they moved through the drab, grey surroundings of wartime Poplar. A conscious gesture of defiance perhaps at a time when it seemed that things could only get worse.

They were off on the short bus ride that would take them to visit Clara Dent, a childhood friend of Elsie's schooldays. After so many years of friendship Clara was almost one of the family, and whenever they were at Bayhurst for an extended stay Clara was one of the regular Sunday visitors. Catching one of the earliest trains from London and knowing the uncertainty of the Sunday bus service, she often walked all the way from the station, but still arrived in time for a late breakfast. The aunts set out the deck-chairs, and for the rest of her stay Clara divided her time between pottering in the garden, and lazing the day away with the others. Apart from Lou, she was the only really keen gardener among the women. Phoebe, a town girl through and through, had no eye for the country; Clara was too fastidious to go 'mucking about with a lot of dirt', and Elsie and Kath reckoned that they worked hard enough in the week to be excused gardening. So with her sleeves rolled up, and wrapped in one of Lou's aprons, Clara worked away with trowel, hoe or secateurs, responding with a laugh or comment to the encouragement or advice, invariably ill-informed, she received from the deckchairs. At regular intervals pots of tea were brought to the garden, and then she was willing enough to give in to their call, 'Come on, Clara, give it a break, girl. You've done enough.' In early evening she left for home laden with flowers and thanks for all the work she had done.

Unremarkable in appearance, Clara had a voice that should have won the heart of any man. It certainly won John's. He had grown up surrounded by the voices of the women around him, attractive enough when they were singing, but when they spoke it was with the brittle, aggressive edge of cockney. An excellent vehicle for the challenges of day-to-day life in the East End, but not in itself a thing of beauty. For many years he was unable to understand how Clara, an East Ender like his aunts, came to have a voice of such a special and distinctive quality, but whatever the reason he fell in love with its sweet-sounding and gently modulated music. The explanation came later, when he learned that until she was six or seven Clara had lived in Lavenham, and her many years in London had done nothing to efface the soft Suffolk tones or her passionate love of country and garden.

Placid, matronly and loving, she was of all his single ladies the one most designated by nature to be a mother, but like his aunts and perhaps for the same reasons she remained unmarried. Small wonder that John, his sister and their cousins were spoilt and indulged as they were, when there were so many like Clara around them. Eva, Clara's older sister with whom she lived, he saw seldom, and knew little. Together they ran a couple of those convenient neighbourhood shops that were once scattered throughout the streets of the East End, but have long since passed from the scene. One they lived at, the other was a lock-up shop a short distance away.

Their guiding principle for stock selection was to have on hand a few of those everyday items most frequently in demand, subject only to certain mutually exclusive lines. It did nothing to stimulate the sales of best shag pipe tobacco if the adjoining shelf was stacked with bars of carbolic soap. Their market was mainly children and smokers. For the children the window and counter carried an array of screw-top glass jars filled with the varied and colourful delights on offer. Bullseyes, farthing toffee sticks, hundreds and thousands, gobstoppers, liquorice sticks and allsorts, nut rings, acid drops, sherbet dip, lollipops, humbugs and many more stood on display alongside packets of chocolate and fancy sweets in the form of cigarettes, cigars and animals. In the shop window a

215

few cheap toys or gewgaws were tucked in with the sweets: tops, whips, a selection of marbles (large or small, plain or rainbow-flecked), skipping ropes, coloured chalks and pencils, diabolo, tiddlywinks – anything in fact which was cheap and eye-catching. Inside the shop a small collection of more expensive items, beyond the range of their clients' usual pocket money, were kept for special occasions: jigsaws; lead figures of soldiers, cowboys and indians; storybooks; cut-out dolls with paper dressing-up outfits for girls; and cutlasses or six-shooters for the boys. That was the pre-war range of course. As the war developed the bombers disposed of the lock-up shop, and the other just faded away as stocks diminished.

For the smoker the window displayed the usual assortment of lies and enticements: here an advertisement for 'Craven A Cigarettes – So Good for Your Throat'; there a bucolic portrait of some crusty old codger sucking his pipe outside the village inn, and the legend 'Hale and Hearty Billy Mears, Smoked Wills Fine Shag for Sixty Years'; and everywhere the promise of satisfaction and flavour beyond the smoker's wildest expectation. A few yellowing display packets of Woodbines, Player's Navy Cut, Senior Service and Gold Flake, together with a bowl or two of dried-up pipe tobacco, were a token reminder that fresh and fragrant supplies were available within. There was little expectation of passing trade, and the regulars knew that they would have no reason for complaint.

Inside the shop the goods were kept in a range of jars, bottles, glass-topped display counters, and multiple racks of tiny drawers. A little pipe tobacco was kept shredded, but generally it was cut as required from one of three or four large blocks of the most popular blends, and as the ounce or half-ounce was sliced away, the rich, enticing aroma of fresh tobacco scented the shop. In addition to the sweets, toys and tobacco goods, they kept a few domestic items that were either packeted, boxed or tinned to ensure there was no contamination of the tobacco. The aromas from the tobacco and sweet products lived quite happily together.

Despite his damaged lung, Jack had been a smoker from youth but stopped about twelve years before he died, as soon as the first hints of the cancer link were published. Most of the time he smoked cigarettes, where economy dictated that he roll his own, but for a few years he also puffed at a pipe using a special Ogden mix from Clara's shop. He kept the shag pressed into a small, polished wooden bowl, like a miniature Ali Baba jar with a tightly fitting lid, and over the years the fragrance of the tobacco slowly permeated the wood. After his death the bowl was found tucked away at the back of a bookshelf, and when the lid was lifted Clara's corner shop lived again as the sweet and heady bouquet of Ogden's Old, Rich and Mellow drifted from the wood. It finally passed away from overexposure after the bowl had been opened time and time again to allow John to indulge in bouts of olfactory nostalgia.

Clara was always prepared for the arrival of children with her visitors, and it was understood that they would be allowed one indulgence and no more. She had it ready for John when he arrived; a neat little package containing a choice selection from her jars. That got the problem out of the way for the rest of his visit.

Behind the shop were the living room and scullery, and beyond, the garden into which Clara poured all her frustrated love for the countryside. Narrow and confined, hemmed in by walls of flaking bricks, and cursed originally with an exhausted, unproductive soil it had revived and flourished under Clara's caring hands. Not a foot was uncultivated, no patch of bare soil could be seen. She campaigned for dung from passing horses as keenly as any of her male competitors and had her pack of young scouts and retrievers for the latest contribution from the streets. They arrived with steaming sack or bucket and were rewarded with a sweet or two for their pains. At the end of the garden, neatly screened away behind a trellis of climbing plants, was the compost box. Into it went the dung, cardboard, paper and anything else she could obtain that was capable of decomposition. From it in season came the rich compost on which her garden blossomed and flourished.

Utility and production were her guiding principles. The only permanent plants were those neatly trained against the walls. There was no lawn, and no path apart from a few bricks trodden into the soil to form a narrow footing down the centre. Close to the house carefully tended patches were planted with summer vegetables and salad greenery. Towards the back a few winter crops were developing. In between the vegetables, wherever there was a space, she planted her summer flowers. Propped on a few boards and bricks against the wall by the house some old windows formed the cold frame in which her earlier crops had been started. Clara brought four chairs to the one uncultivated part of the garden just outside the back door, and while the ladies sat with their tea in the morning sun, John sucked his few last sweets. They left for home with beans, peas, lettuce and a bunch of cut flowers for Lou. That August visit to Clara was to be the beginning of the end for their days in Poplar.

They knew there had been heavy bombing elsewhere and had seen reports of the savage aerial battles high above the fighter stations around London, but there was no general understanding at that time that it formed part of a calculated strategy to knock the RAF out of the sky and give the Germans control of the air for an invasion. From Essex news filtered through of repeated and increasingly intense raids in or around Southend, on the airfield at Rochford, and on Thames Haven, Tilbury and Horndon, but there had been no sustained bombing of London, and there seemed to be no reason to regret the decision to return to Poplar.

During the afternoon an air-raid warning sent them scurrying to the Moriartys' cellar for an hour or more, but it passed quietly and they returned home. That night an alert in the small hours brought them all together with the same bewilderment and uncertainty as before, and the operations of war came one step closer to their door. In faint moonlight they made their way up the terrace to the Moriartys' where, white-faced, sleepy and initially silent, they sat and waited. In the garden shelter at Bayhurst they had been able to hear the approach of the bombers while they were still at some distance. In the cellar, sounds from outside were muffled, and it was the thud of distant explosions that were heard long before the bombers arrived.

'Bloody fine time we picked to come home for the weekend, Ma.'

Elsie was the first to speak above a whisper. It broke the tension and earned her a laugh all round and a wry grin from her mother. The hammering of ack-ack and the intensity of the bomb blasts increased as the raid moved closer.

'We'll be alright in here, won't we, Jack?'

He wasn't sure the question was well timed, but gave the answer Clara wanted to hear.

'Oh I think we'll be safe enough.'

The bombing came no nearer and after a short while ceased altogether. When the all-clear came they walked back, still in near darkness, with nothing to indicate where the bombs had fallen or what damage had been done. Rene's baby, who had slept through it all, was put back to bed, but no one else could sleep. Even their customary comfort in times of need was denied them: strong, sweet tea was already a luxury of the past. A pot was brewed of course, but with both tea and sugar rationed, it was a cup which cheered just about as little as it inebriated.

'Oh my God, Ma. Gnat's piss.' Elsie's comment summed up the general feeling.

As they sat over their tea the sky was brightening, and Jack went up to the windows on the top floor. He returned to say that no signs of damage could be seen close to hand, but that he thought he could see smoke rising in the distance where the bombs may have fallen. In the course of the Sunday both Charlie and Bill called to report and see how things were, but otherwise everyone was more than content to have a quiet time after the alarms of the night. Late in the afternoon Kath and Elsie left to return to their schools. It was to be a long while before the family saw them next, and they would never again meet in the old Poplar house.

When, a couple of days later, it was announced that the RAF had bombed Berlin it was generally welcomed as some good news for a change. Even John could appreciate the *Boy's Own* message, 'You bomb our capital city, we'll bomb yours.' There can have been no one then who saw the action for what it was later considered to be: the first step along a very short road that would lead to the devastation of much of central London.

That night was quiet, but from then on night alerts were more common, some of them lasting until dawn. Better arrangements had now been made in the cellar for those all-night vigils. Bedding of sorts was put down for Moira, John and the two Moriarty daughters. They were taken to the cellar at their usual bedtime and Phoebe, Rene and the baby joined them later for the night. Jack and Clara, who were still at work, decided to stick to their beds for a decent night's sleep unless things got too hot, and Lou stayed with them out of sheer, cussed determination not to be put out. In the event, although there were many alerts, and planes were frequently heard passing overhead, no more bombs fell within their hearing.

During the day things seemed almost normal. If there was an occasional alert nothing was seen or heard and all their activities went on much as usual. Jack and Clara went off to work, Phoebe and the others carried on with the domestic round of shopping, housework and cooking, and John met up with his friends to play in and around the streets. The weather was good so they visited the park, and there was even the treat of an afternoon trip to the Hippodrome cinema where the alarms and excursions of *Gunga Din* were shown to an enthusiastic reception from the local youth. Full of stiff upper-lips, derring-do and heroic sacrifices in a noble cause, it fed their imagination for the few days that were left to them, and in the streets they played at nothing else.

16

Black Saturday

There's a lot to be said for a nice cup of tea! When it came to Londoners the old song had got it absolutely right: tea was their sovereign remedy, their balm for troubled spirits, their comforter in times of trouble. Bad news about aunty – put the kettle on. Feeling a bit off colour – put the kettle on. All-clear sounding – put the kettle on. And in Carters Terrace they were choosy about their brew. They liked it often, and they liked it hot, strong and sweet, but when it came to tea things were starting to get tough. By September rationing had been in place and biting increasingly deeply for eight months. It might have been easier to pool rations for the whole house, but old habits died hard so Phoebe and Lou continued to manage their own housekeeping, although it was generally Phoebe who did the shopping. They were united however in their complaint that it wasn't so much the rationing as not knowing from one week to the next just what the allocation would be. Butter had been up and down like a yo-yo from 4 to 8 to 4 to 6 to 4 ounces a week. Bacon had not been much better. When sugar dropped to 8oz for all purposes it was bad enough, but when tea was rationed at 2oz a week in July it was as though the very fabric of family life had been threatened. Nor did they dream for a moment that it would be five long years almost to the day before they would enjoy a niggardly increase of half an ounce.

Their belt-tightening wasn't helped by the knowledge, well publicised in the *Herald*, that for those with the money, though perhaps not the same taste for hot, sweet tea, there was no shortage of luxury foods in expensive restaurants: at prices well beyond Dockland pockets of course. But that was a familiar story about which they could do nothing, and so the old routine continued with Phoebe doing the shopping for rationed goods in Chrisp Street every Saturday afternoon while keeping her eyes open for any little

221

extras that might be going on the side, an exercise that became increasingly frustrating as everyone came to do the same.

She was there with John a couple of weeks after the visit to Clara Dent, and despite rationing and general shortages the stalls and shops were bustling with activity in the late-summer sunshine of a benign September day. Her essential shopping was soon done, but she was in an unusually obliging mood that day and it took little special pleading for her to be persuaded to add a comic to her basket and divert to the recreation ground for a few minutes on the way home.

Towards the end of that golden afternoon it was almost possible to forget about the war. The gentle warmth had tempted many people out to relax and enjoy themselves. A few were picnicking on the grass with sandwiches and flasks of tea. Others lounged on the park benches studying the news in the day's papers, or simply basked lazily in the sunshine. John headed for the howls and shouts of the playground where the swings, slide and roundabout were all busy. Phoebe sank on to a seat, closed her eyes for five minutes, and left him to his own devices.

They were just ready to leave when the sirens sounded. The daytime alerts up to then had been few, and as nothing had come of them the response of the visitors to the park was at first uncertain. Some carried on as if nothing had happened; a few hurried away heading for home; and the rest drifted towards the entrance to the public shelter. Phoebe said later that she had thought for a moment of making a run for home, but decided against it.

They ended up in the shelter with about thirty or so others, mainly women with their children, and just three or four men. The interior was dank, dark and dirty, the air stale and fetid. Long and narrow, with walls and ceilings of bare concrete and steel, it contained just a few rough benches. Faint sunlight filtering in through the narrow, sandbagged entrance provided the only illumination. At one end a couple of canvas curtains hanging from the ceiling concealed a separate recess. By comparison the Moriartys' cellar seemed almost luxurious.

A few people stayed for a short while only and then left. Those who remained settled on the benches, smiled uneasily at each other, and exchanged a few words about yet more false alarms and time wasted. Phoebe took John's hand, pulled him closer to her, and they waited. From just outside the entrance one of the men called that he thought he could hear the sound of bombs. That silenced any talk. It was going to be a daytime alert quite different from those that had gone before. Within moments the men were back inside, and no one needed to be told what was happening outside: it was all too apparent.

In later years John found it far from easy to recall and analyse with any certainty the feelings that he had then, as he watched the events of the war unfold around him, some at a distance, others closer to hand. It was said that of the children who were not personally and intimately caught up in the action many survived the sight and sounds of bombs, destruction and fire at least as well as the adults, and that others only on the fringes of events often experienced nothing but excitement and interest. John was one of the lucky ones. He saw the aftermath of conflict, and there were times when it raged around him, but he suffered no physical injury, endured no personal trauma. The buildings over his head some-times trembled, but never collapsed, nor was anyone close to him injured or killed in the action. In one sense he understood perfectly well the sequence of cause and effect when exploding bombs and people were in close proximity. In another he never grasped the immediacy of the danger for himself and those around him. The child's world in which he lived was still a world where to be surrounded by parents and family was to be secure. It was enough to be with his mother, who was doing a good job beside him concealing the anxiety she felt, for no one at home knew where they were or what might be happening to them, and she had no idea what might be happening at home. Those were not thoughts that occurred to John as events unfolded.

For almost ninety confused, terrifying and interminable minutes they were fortunate in seeing and understanding nothing of the full savagery of the storm of destruction that the bombers were unleashing around them. Their world shrank to the narrow, dirty slit of shelter and the battery of sound that hemmed it in. There was a little but not much crying from the children. By the entrance the two men sat occasionally talking softly together, and if the women spoke it was in hushed suppressed voices. Mostly they sat silently, cuddling their children to them, with their heads lifted and turned, as though listening intently to identify in the general tumult some special sound which never came.

The assault on their immediate area varied in its frequency and severity. Some blasts were so close and powerful that the walls trembled and a thin rain of dust fell from the roof, and sometimes, from far away, they heard explosions that seemed far greater than bombs alone. There were brief periods of relative calm, but always near or far there was the incessant thud of bombs, and the sharper crack of gunfire from the anti-aircraft batteries in and around the docks.

The ordeal was not without its diversions, and the Luftwaffe bore no responsibility for John's personal crisis which was unexpected and humiliating. During a momentary pause in the bombing one of the men walked through to the end of the shelter. He pulled aside the canvas curtain, stepped inside, drew it back behind him and remained there for a few minutes. When he reappeared the explanation for the noisome atmosphere that had embraced them when they entered was clear for all to see and smell. Tucked in behind the curtain was a rusty lavatory bucket the existing contents of which must have been simmering gently in the heat until they were fomented into a vigorous and malignant assault on their noses by the latest reinforcements.

The stench which thrust itself up his nostrils had an alien aggression. It lacked the homely familiarity of Bayhurst's rustic privy and was unabated by the chemicals that sweetened its air. It took just a breath or two for his gorge to rise. He opened his mouth to speak, but immediately threw up on to the floor. Combined with the smell from the bucket that was too much for some of the other children, and his response triggered a chain reaction of gagging and heaving. Perhaps in its own way this served a purpose as a diversion from the raid which continued around them. While they were being cleaned up the world fell silent almost as suddenly as it had descended into tumult. The throbbing of engines passed away into the distance, and they waited for the all-clear.

Less than two hours earlier they had entered the shelter from a tranquil world of blue skies, gentle sunlight, afternoon picnics and the laughter of children on swings and slides. The world to which they returned was brooding, harsh and uncompromisingly hostile. Dark billowing clouds from untold fires rolled across the sky, obscuring the sun and filtering its light to a sullen, sulky bronze. High above the tower of St Matthias' and the roofs of the High

Street, swirling columns of smoke and flame climbed above a general conflagration that seemed to be raging unchecked. Further away over Bugsby's Reach, where only a day or so earlier he had looked out from home to watch the mastheads of shipping moving peacefully down the river, a pall of smoke flickered red, crimson and orange, marking the passage of the bombers over docks, factories and homes. The air was a choking cocktail of sweet and acrid fumes from the hundred and one products stored in the factories and warehouses being consumed in the holocaust. On the shores of the south bank, meats, cheeses and fruits were reducing to ashes alongside the blazing furnaces that had once been the timberyards of the Surrey Docks. In the bonded vaults of London and St Catherine's upriver bursting butts and tuns of wines and spirits spewed out their rums, brandies and liqueurs to feed the flames. And a few hundred yards from them, into the inferno that marked the docks of West India and Millwall, tumbled all the goods that had been the very lifeblood of the merchant venturers and the focus of Empire: spices, waxes, fine Persian carpets, resins, sugars, hides, furs, ostrich feathers, molasses, dates, dried fruits, hogsheads of tobacco, rubber, fine teas from Serendip, ivory, gums, myrrh, frankincense and probably gold.

Beyond the railings of the recreation ground the even line of the terraced houses was now broken, where mounds of bricks, timber and shattered furniture lay burning or smouldering in place of the homes that had stood there a couple of hours earlier. Many other buildings, little damaged by blast, were burning fiercely from the showers of incendiaries. In the centre of a sweeping amphitheatre of fire and destruction the shelter, the church and the park stood untouched.

All of that they absorbed in the few moments when the little group from the shelter stood just beyond the entrance, stunned by the sight of their city transformed. A few cried. John choked on an emotion which he did not understand, perhaps the dim recognition that those two hours marked the passing of his world of childhood. But beyond his own narrow and personal vision they also marked the first in the long and irreversible chain of events that would bring about the final destruction of the spirit of the old East End and the dissolution of its communities. Even as the group stood looking about them, Phoebe had turned towards the East India

225

Dock Road. On the far side, never looking more welcome, the solid substantial pile of the Board of Trade stood untouched, with no sign of damage or fires around it. They set off for home.

More than three hundred medium-heavy bombers, almost two hundred light bombers, and a supporting force of some six hundred fighters had passed across the East End in the space of little more than ninety minutes. There was to be no counting the hundreds that would follow in the six hours of night raids that were to come. It was to be the start of many weeks of intensive, unrelenting raiding during which the Germans sought to raze the area to the ground.

Apart from the all-pervading smoke haze and the stench of burning, the two streets through which they passed showed no obvious sign of the events of the past two hours, but above the rows of tightly packed, back-to-back houses that extended to the Limehouse Cut and beyond, more smoke and flames marked where bombs had fallen to the north. Others like themselves, caught by the raid in the open, were also hurrying anxiously home. Those who had sat it out in cellars, stair cupboards or, if they were lucky, Anderson shelters, were stepping outside and looking around, struggling to take in the scale of the devastation and relieved to find that their own streets had so far been spared.

As they turned the final corner they saw Lou standing at the entrance to the terrace where she had been waiting and hoping ever since the all-clear sounded. She looked back to the house and called out, and within seconds Jack was on his way up the terrace to meet them. They sat drinking tea together as the story of the afternoon unfolded. Colour returned to faces that had been drawn and grey with anxiety when they returned home, but there was still concern about Clara. It was one of the alternate Saturday afternoons when she was at work, and she should already have returned home.

After the events of the afternoon none of them had much of an appetite, and it was simply from force of habit that they had turned to laying the table for a meal when Charlie called to report that he and the family were safe and to see how things were in the terrace. He brought the first news of damage and death in the community about them. A stick of bombs had fallen the length of one of the narrow lanes running off from Chrisp Street, bringing down most of the terraced houses on one side of the road. The street was blocked

226

with rubble, and as Charlie passed wardens, ambulance men and other helpers were starting to look for survivors and bring out bodies. Having satisfied himself that the terrace was untouched he left to see if he could give any help on his way back home. In the terrace he would have passed Clara, who returned having suffered no more inconvenience than a long delay and detour because of an unexploded or delayed fuse bomb that had fallen alongside the main road and which was being dealt with by the army.

As the credits roll at the beginning of each episode of *Eastenders* the camera pulls slowly back to show an aerial photograph of the Thames as it makes its great sweep around the Isle of Dogs. A distinctive feature, it is immediately recognised by its television audience worldwide. In 1940 it was just as familiar to the pilots of the Luftwaffe. Today it would be called ground zero: the Germans knew it as Zielraum G – the target area, or 'goal-room', for their bombs. One of their own intelligence photographs presents the area in fine detail. Taken from several thousand feet it shows a Heinkel 111 silhouetted over the Surrey and Commercial docks. On the Isle of Dogs the docks, wharves, warehouses, roads and marshalling yards are clearly visible, and above them Poplar High Street, the recreation ground and, just faintly, Carters Terrace. Crisp and clear, it had been taken on that fine, sunny afternoon of 7th September 1940 just moments before the first bombs fell.

Many of the raiders who came in the daylight found their target area by following the river, that oldest of highways to the heart of the City, as it ran in from the estuary between the Kent and Essex shores. The squadrons that came after dark needed no such guidance. The incendiaries of the afternoon had touched off a conflagration that raged unchecked through dusk into the night, providing a beacon that blazed out to light the bombers in from the coast.

In the terrace they did not need to hear the evening alert to know that they were on their way again. The howl of the sirens preceded them in from the coast, passed on from district to district as the raid made its way inland. In the backyard Terry's ears pricked up at the distant sounds long before they could be heard in the house, and with canine anticipation of what was to come he set up a howling that was caught and echoed by every dog in the neighbourhood. He alerted them well in advance, and after the events of the afternoon they knew that there was no hope that the bombers would be passing over and beyond them, as they had in the past.

No one stayed at home that night, and by eight o'clock the Moriarty's cellar was full to capacity. There was by then some sort of seating for everyone, and just room for the very young and old to stretch out on a rough mattress on the floor, but it was cramped, stuffy and claustrophobic. The experience was much as it had been in the afternoon. They could see nothing and had no knowledge of what was happening beyond what they could hear. The bombing was not continuous, but came in waves that increased in intensity and then subsided before the next formation of bombers flew in.

While Mrs Moriarty and her daughters sought comfort in their rosaries the others made a half-hearted attempt to distract themselves with a few day-to-day activities. Phoebe had her knitting, Lou her crochet work, and the men a newspaper or book. During the lulls in the bombing their knitting or reading had at least some of their attention, but as it increased in intensity and the thud of explosions moved closer, their work dropped into their laps and they raised their heads, waiting anxiously until it eased again.

There were occasional periods of respite in the small hours when, overwhelmed with tiredness, the children dozed fitfully until the next assault arrived, but few of the adults had any sleep that night. After many hours, in one of the interludes of relative calm, Lou decided she had had enough. 'Oh come on, Mary, let's make some tea for God's sake. '

In the kitchen the last few pints of water ran from the tap and down the sink before they realised that the mains had been cut. It was the same with the gas when Mary put her hand to one of the taps on the cooker. No tea, no drink at all until the night was finally over, but at least the electricity was still with them and they had a light in the cellar. While they were making their discovery in the kitchen, Mr Moriarty, Jack and Dick stepped outside to stretch their legs and see how things were. They returned to report many more fires burning in the docks and elsewhere, but that in the streets immediately nearby they could see little damage.

It was between four and five in the morning when the all-clear sounded and they emerged from their refuge. Only later in the day, when they saw what had been happening elsewhere, did they realise what little purpose it would have served had a bomb fallen close to hand. They should still have been in darkness, but in all directions around them rolling clouds of smoke glowed with the glare of the fires raging beneath them, and above the furnace that was the docks the sky blossomed into fiery golds and reds as the flames rose, faded away and then surged again in an explosion of sparks, burning embers and ashes as they were fed by the fall of another wall or floor in warehouse or factory. Explosions continued at random, not of bombs, but of drums, canisters, ammunition and explosives caught up in the blaze.

As they turned into the terrace and looked up beyond the roof of the Board of Trade towards the Isle of Dogs and the Thames, it seemed as if the river itself was on fire from Hay's Wharf to the Royal Albert Dock. It made a nonsense of any pretence at black-out, and it would have mattered little if they had thrown on all the lights when they stumbled down the steps and into the house.

A breakfast of sorts was thrown together as they talked things over. They had no gas, but a fire was soon lit in the old range, and no one offered any objection to a cup of tea made with water from the butt in the garden. No decisions were to be taken until it was light when Jack and Dick would go out to see how things looked further afield and get some information on the events of the night.

As they waited for sunrise, Charlie arrived with an early report: many more houses totally destroyed or severely damaged by blast; some streets completely blocked by fallen rubble, and no sign of fire engines at any of the many buildings where fires were raging unchecked. The ARP were out and assisting, but all other services seemed to have been completely overwhelmed by the intensity of the bombing and extent of the devastation.

As daylight strengthened the three men went in separate directions into the local streets. When they returned it was with the news that damage in the immediate area had been greater and closer than was thought. A number of houses in Duff Street were in ruins. Just off Grundy Street a whole row of terraced houses had been reduced to rubble and was burning fiercely. Fires started by incendiaries on the roofs of the Board of Trade and the Queen Victoria Seamen's Rest had been quickly put out. A little further off, the Town Hall had been destroyed, but inside the docks it seemed as though warehouses, buildings and ships were being immolated in one all-consuming firestorm. What they saw from their own particular location in Poplar would have been true for an observer in or near to any part of the Docklands that morning.

Wherever he stood, he would have appeared to be at the centre of an arena closed off from the world and normality by towering walls of smoke and fire.

Careless of rapidly disappearing rations they sipped yet more tea as they listened to wireless reports on the events of the previous twenty-four hours, and were astonished to hear that there had been an overnight warning of an invasion with German troops landing on the south coast. It had been a false alarm of course, and one which they were happy to have missed at a time when they had more than enough on their plate. It would eventually become clear that chaos, confusion and the need to preserve morale as far as possible meant that most of the news they heard that morning was grossly distorted, but even the fact that the BBC was still broadcasting was in its own way reassuring.

Not until later did they become aware of Hitler's speech of 4th September made in response to the bombing of Berlin at the end of August. Accusing the RAF of murdering innocent women and children he concluded his long, hysterical rant with a promise to return the British bombs a thousand-fold, and raze their cities to the ground. Knowledge of his words would, in any event, have added little to the appraisal that was being made of the family's situation and prospects. The terror bombing of Wielun, Warsaw and Rotterdam left no one in any doubt that the previous twenty-four hours had been just a foretaste of what was to come. It took them little time to decide on their course of action. It was summed up in one word: Bayhurst.

Their decision had been made by mid-morning. Regular visits to the terrace would be made by one of the men until something could be done about the family pets, but that apart the house was to be closed down and abandoned for the duration of any intensive bombing campaign. Charlie returned home to organise matters there, and for the next few hours the old house was alive with activity for the last time as they packed cases and bags for their journey. Priority was given to clothing and whatever was going to be needed for day-to-day living, but there were also a few items of value and others with strong sentimental associations that were not going to be left behind for the bombers.

Carrie had been sharing the cellar with them during the raids and, once the decision was made to evacuate to Essex, she was asked by Lou if she would like leave the terrace and join them. On that point Carrie was absolutely clear. She had no one else to be worried about and wasn't going to be moved. She had spent most of her life in Poplar, seen out the Great War there, and no German buggers were going to stop her living out the rest of her days there come what may. There were many like her, who not only couldn't, but wouldn't be moved. They said goodbye to the Moriartys, who were themselves thinking about leaving if they could do so. They knew about Bayhurst and understood that it could not possibly house them as well as Lou's family. When Jack next returned to the terrace they had gone and, like so many, were never to return.

By late morning Charlie and family were back laden with cases and bags, and accompanied by Doll's father who said that he would stay with them until he was satisfied that they had found transport out of Poplar. He brought the news that the railway line was reported to be blocked near to Stepney and that no trains were running out of Fenchurch Street for the time being. Like so much information on that morning the report proved to be false and was to cause them a lot of unnecessary trouble. Failing Stepney, the nearest station was Barking, but from the terrace to Barking was about five miles.

Nothing had been heard from Bill, but it was going to be impossible for anyone to get to Stepney and back to find out how things were there. If he called, he would almost certainly guess where they were, but a note was left for him with Carrie, who would also be looking in to see how the animals were until Jack, Charlie or one of the others returned.

A final drink was made and a bite to eat taken. Terry, Mick, the cat and the goldfish were given a good helping of food. The fire was raked out and doused, and then they were ready. The door was locked, and with a final few words to Carrie they turned their backs on home. Most of them were never to see it again.

17

Goodbye to the Terrace

No one, not even the children, left the house unladen. Despite continuing fine weather they were swathed in clothing, wearing winter coats as the easiest way of carrying them. In addition to bags and cases, Jack, Dick and Charlie had bundles of extra bedding, tightly rolled and lashed with string, slung across their shoulders. They had no idea whether buses or trams would be moving on the main road, or whether the trains would be running when they arrived at the station, but at least they were on their way, and fortunately it was to be a day free from raids.

On the East India Dock Road they were not alone. Other groups were also on the move looking for somewhere, anywhere, away from the fires that were still burning, certain markers for the next wave of night bombers. With cases, bags, sacks and bedding rolls, some with laden prams, and some with their goods piled high on coster barrows, they were making their way to the east, away from the docks, away from the city. Some like Lou and her family would have left their homes still intact and would have had a definite haven with relatives or friends in mind. Others, having lost home and everything but the few items they carried, would be relying on what provision the authorities could make for them. In the immediate aftermath of the raids this would all too often prove to be uncertain and inadequate.

After fifteen minutes at the stop with no sign of tram or bus and no real expectation of one, they set off on the first stage of what would have been a long, hot and exhausting walk. They were on familiar home ground, a road that the oldest of them had walked a thousand times and more, but on that bleak morning it could not have seemed more alien and hostile. A haze of stinking smoke hung over everything. In side street after side street, and here and there along the main road, the tumbled heaps of rubble and still-smouldering remains of houses, shops and workshops bore witness to the intensity and indiscriminate nature of the nine hours of sustained bombing endured since the afternoon of the previous day.

There continued to be no sign of public transport, but at Poplar police station they were told that although no trams had been seen, some buses were moving, and as far as was known, the road to Barking was passable with care and a few diversions. At the next stop they dropped their loads and settled to wait for a bus. Only a stone's throw from Poplar hospital, where he had been thrust so unwillingly into the East End world, John sagged on to one of the cases and waited tired and disconsolate to make what was to be his final departure from it.

'My God Jack, I'm glad Pappy didn't live to see this. It would have broken his heart.'

No one replied to Lou, but Clara began crying quietly. Nothing more was said, and they stood looking hopelessly at their world utterly transformed by the bombers that passed in the night. Towards Rotherhithe the sky was shrouded in darkness from the smoke, ashes and soots of fires that were to burn for a week in the sheds and timberyards of the Surrey Docks. In front of them All Saints' churchyard was an isolated enclave of normality. In the graveyard the trees stirred softly in a light breeze. The fabric of the church was unscathed, its glass unbroken, but above the tower the spire rose up a stark and desolate marker against a backdrop of ugly, sullen clouds still rising from an arc of devastation that swept from the West to East India Docks, where it seemed there could not be a building that had escaped the blasts or a warehouse that would survive the fires.

When neither bus nor tram arrived they took up their loads again and made their way a little further along the road. Past the tunnel entrance, and past the chaos behind the curtain wall of the East India Docks, to join the dejected groups of refugees that were trudging over Bow Creek and into the lower end of Barking Road. On such a morning comparisons were meaningless but, if it were possible, conditions were even worse there than in Poplar. Towards the river, Silvertown, Custom House and Canning Town were ablaze. In and around the Victoria, Albert and George V docks, bond stores, rubber works, sugar refineries and fuel depots spewed their contents on to the flames, and in the heart of it all, fats from

233

the meats in the cold stores, oats and barley from the grain silos, dried fruits and tobaccos stoked fires that were utterly beyond control and could only be left to burn themselves out. From a burst main, water that might have gone to moderate the blaze surged out and ran to waste in a torrent that flooded the road and the basements of the houses alongside.

House after house lay in ruins, burning or too badly damaged to be a home again. Along the Thames, barrage balloons swung like grey ghosts in the heavy pall of choking, oily, black smoke that reached out downriver towards the estuary, where miles away at Hornchurch it still hung heavily enough to cloud the skies above the fighter station. By good fortune, a little beyond the bridge, they found public lavatories and a church that had been opened as an emergency and reception centre for the area. Inside they were able to drop their loads for a while, rest and have a cup of tea before they started for Barking once again.

At the bus stop they waited with two or three other families hoping like themselves to get to the railway station. On the opposite side of the road a bus passed half-empty travelling west, but nothing moved to the east. When at last a bus appeared, there came not one but two together, with a third coming into view in the distance. It was a trivial, insignificant incident, but it provided the first opportunity for a long time for a laugh. It was reassuring to see that at least one old London tradition had survived the onslaught. They waited for the second bus which had more room. The bedding rolls and as many cases as possible were stuffed under the stairs. The women went inside, but the men climbed up to the top deck, and from there, as the bus made its way slowly eastwards, they looked out at the wasteland the bombers had left behind them.

From buildings demolished by the blast, tiles, bricks, timber, furniture, shards of glass and other debris spilled out across the pavement and into the road. Around some the bus could pass; elsewhere a detour into the side roads was the only way through. The destruction was random: without pattern and without sense. Of one building nothing identifiable would be left, just a mound of bricks, timber and rubble where a home had once stood. Of another, when all else had been blown away, chance would have left one small feature of the house untouched, or a few tokens of family life clinging to their customary places. Here, a broken staircase led up to vacancy or to the jagged remains of half a floor still giving precarious support to a bed and its debris-strewn bedclothes. There, high up at second-floor level, a family photograph hanging on a wall and a clock below it, still balanced on a mantelpiece, were all that remained.

At one house in a row of three-storey buildings, where the freak and unpredictable effect of blast had operated with dramatic and bizarre results, the driver slowed to a crawl as they passed and every head turned. It was as though a knife had sliced its way down the centre of the building carrying one half away, and opening the other half to view like a child's doll's house.

On the right, floor, walls, roof and contents had collapsed to the ground in a tangled heap of rubble. With them they had carried away the internal walls between the rooms. On the left, apart from one floor running at a rakish angle, the structure stood as before. Except at ground-floor level, where debris blocked the view, the rooms and contents were virtually untouched, and with the disappearance of the internal wall stood like a stage set with every intimate detail open to the casual gaze of the curious.

In a cramped little room under the eaves, the end of a bed, two occasional chairs and a small table stood just a few inches from the void. On the floor below, the back panelling of a wardrobe and chest of drawers obscured the rest of the room. On the first floor a kitchen cupboard listed a little on the sagging floor, but boxes and containers still clung undisturbed to its top. Clothes on an airing rack standing alongside it were flapping and drying in the breeze. On the top floor blankets and sheets were draped across the end of the bed. Hats and coats hung from hooks on the backs of the doors, and in every room all the trivial, personal articles of day-to-day life stood exposed to common view. They looked on in silence until the bus started to pull away when one woman choked and burst into tears, thinking perhaps of the sight of her own home stripped open in the same way.

When, some three hours after leaving home, they walked into Barking station it was a relief to see no signs of bombing there or in the immediate area, but above them the drifting pall of smoke was a constant reminder of what they had left behind. They passed through the ticket hall and down to platforms choked with families

235

like themselves striving to be away from the East End before dark. There was absolutely no doubt in anyone's mind that London would be in for another night of the same.

No information about the trains could be obtained beyond the welcome news that the line from Fenchurch was in fact open, that the track to Southend was undamaged and that trains were running. Timing and routing were to be a matter of patience and luck however. Having in mind the daytime raids that had already been made along the estuary, and the juicy targets at Thames Haven, nobody fancied the Tilbury route unless it was absolutely unavoidable.

On the crowded platform every possible resting place was occupied, so cases and bedding rolls were used to make seats for Lou and Rene with the baby, and they settled down to wait. Because of the crush John was not allowed to wander the platform as he usually did on their Essex trips, but a visit to the chocolate machine was sanctioned so that he could satisfy himself that it was empty. He did and it was. Soon the loss of sleep, the tensions of events and the sheer frustration of the day began to catch up with him, and he did not find it difficult to fall asleep when his gran pulled him down on to the bedroll beside her.

When he was shaken awake an hour or so later, the waiting crowds had already surged to the edge of the platform for a train that was spotted approaching from the city. A groan of disappointment followed it into the station as it was realised that the carriages and guard's van were already stuffed to capacity. A few people without children were able to cram in here and there, but for the rest it meant more tedious waiting.

The crowds eased back from the platform edge. The bedding and cases were packed up once again, and Lou returned to her seat. The engine huffed lazily, the guard was nowhere to be seen, and as the delay continued with nothing to indicate imminent departure Lou was stirred to action. She stood up and took John's hand.

'Come on, John, we'll see if we can find out anything about Uncle Bill and Leslie. All right, Jack?' He must have guessed what she had in mind and merely nodded his head.

They set off together towards the head of the train through a ruck of cases, bags, children, prams, parcels and people of all ages and conditions. Crowded and stuffy, each compartment had its window down, and starting behind the engine Lou worked her way along the carriages.

'Anyone here know The Swan at Stepney?'

There was no need to mention that The Swan was a pub, that would have been taken for granted, and the mumbled negatives from the cramped compartment made it clear that she had been heard. On to the next compartment, and the next, but before they were at the end of the first carriage she got the answer she wanted.

'My local. What about it?'

'Do you know the fish shop just over the road from The Swan?'

'You mean Bill Lagsding's?'

That was better than Lou could possibly have expected, and within a few moments the disembodied voice from the far corner of the compartment had become a face at the window.

Yes, he knew Bill. Drank with him from time to time, and could reassure Lou with the news that he had passed the shop that morning. It wasn't open, and he had seen no one, but he could say that the shop was undamaged. More news from that area came as they talked: many houses destroyed in Ratcliffe and Limehouse, Rotherhithe Tunnel closed causing traffic chaos, and destruction and fires throughout the factories and warehouses around the river. As the delay continued they chatted on until the train at last drew slowly away, and they returned to the others. Lou told them her news, and once again they settled down to wait.

When a train was seen approaching from the Southend direction little interest was shown until it stopped at their platform and was seen to be empty. Its destination was not announced. There was not a porter to be seen, and there was a general reluctance to act for just as long as it took the crowd to realise that the engine was being decoupled. At that moment the ranks of refugees rose as one with their gear and belongings and surged into the compartments. Happily their assumption was the right one, for it would have taken a brave, perhaps foolhardy, station master to disembark them.

There was little waiting this time. The engine shunted round from the London end, coupled up, and within moments they were moving away from a deserted platform dotted with abandoned prams and a few other items too large to cram into the bulging carriages. Fractious, cramped, tired and hot they were at last on their way. There were enough seats for all the women, and Phoebe pulled John on to her lap in the corner. Within moments languor, warmth and the monotonous clack of the crawling train had overwhelmed him, and he was asleep.

When he awoke they were at Laindon. The carriage had half-emptied, and there was room for him to move on to a seat and recover from his sleepy stupor as they travelled on to Pitsea. All his well-known landmarks were there: the field with the cut-out men carrying a mock ladder advertising Manders paints, the frayed rope dangling from a tree-swing over a stream, and the strange tower observatory on one of the houses where they crossed the main road. He marked them all off as they progressed those few, last miles, but the anticipation and excitement of earlier visits was not there.

At Pitsea they tumbled out with their belongings and settled on a seat to consider the next part of their journey. The train pulled away on the long sweep around the water meadows towards Benfleet Creek, and other fugitives from the bombing trudged up the stairs and over the bridge, and dispersed on their way to whatever refuge awaited them. No one spoke. A warm breeze blew in from the marshes. There were no sounds of war, and only the distant barrage balloons and smoke clouds hanging over Thames Haven intruded on the old familiar scene. It was little more than twenty-four hours since they had scampered into the park shelter, and the silence now around them seemed as profound as the tumult of recent events had been overwhelming.

The brief reverie over, the journey to Bayhurst had to be faced. The main-road buses late on a Sunday afternoon were likely to be irregular, and with the amount they were carrying the thought of walking all the way was barely considered. Even if a bus was available, there was the walk from the station and finally the long haul down the lane. They moved up from the platform to the booking office and settled to wait with their belongings, while Jack, Dick and Charlie put their heads and the contents of their pockets together and set off to see if transport could be arranged.

A short distance from the station, where the lane from the main road ran out towards the marshes, there was a garage and hauliers which also operated a few coaches. On a Sunday afternoon the business yard was empty and the garage closed, but the owner lived at the back and was soon found. The case they presented to him was persuasive: the events of the last twenty-four hours and the previous night's raid, a tiring, time-consuming journey, a baby, children, an old lady, cases and bags to carry. He stopped them before they were far into it. Yes he would do what he could, but of his three coaches two were out for the weekend and the third under repair. The best he could offer was the back of an open lorry. Would that do? Wouldn't it just! How much? Call it his good deed for the day!

They walked back to tell Lou and the others of the arrangements, and within ten minutes the lorry was in the station yard. Rene and the baby joined the driver in the cab. With a little pulling, pushing and laughter the ladies were hauled on to the back. Cases and bedding rolls became seats, and they were off. Exhilarated by the wind in his hair, the bouncing ride, and what seemed to him not only a novel but desirable way to travel John thought the day was at last beginning to show promise.

Their driver refused to set them down at the bottom of Clarence Road. The ground was dry and hard, and he was determined to take them to the door. It was a generous thought, but under the lush growth of summer the ruts and hollows of the previous winter lay hidden, and for those in the back it was a draining, bone-shaking conclusion to a long and exhausting journey. As soon as the lorry stopped, Nora and the boys were out to give them a hand, and while the driver was pulling up the hill to reverse at the cross lane, Lou dug into one of her bags and came up with a half-bottle of Scotch which he was happy to accept for his trouble.

The sound of the engine died away, and on a tranquil, late-summer evening they turned in at the gate with their goods and gear. There were twelve of them: Lou, Clara, Charlie, Doll, Valerie, Rene, Dick, the baby Janice, Phoebe, Jack, Moira and John. There were two bedrooms with three beds. It was going to be a tight squeeze.

18

A Pause in the Journey

The bungalow was as sulky as it always was after a short period of neglect. The door stuck, the familiar odour of slow decay filled the air, and in the narrow passage the floorboards now sagged perceptibly where dry rot was relentlessly eating into the joists below. It was still light enough for windows to be thrown open, however, and the stale air was soon swept away by the fresh scents of evening.

It took little time for the allocation of sleeping quarters to be decided. Lou and Clara would share the double bed in one room with Moira on the floor. Doll, Rene and the baby would have the room with the two single beds. In the front room Valerie and Phoebe would be on the two convertible bed-chairs with John on the floor. Jack, Dick and Charlie would do as best they could on the floor of the living room.

All this seemed fine to the two younger children: safe from the bombing, free from the rigours of school, and with their usual make-do country beds to sleep in. They looked forward to the weeks to come in the autumn countryside, and were happily unaware of their true situation and a threat more grave and pressing than the bombing that within little more than a week would see them abandoning the perceived haven of Bayhurst to become refugees on the road once again: destination unknown.

They set about making their preparations for the night at once, and there was much pushing and pulling around of furniture before the sleeping arrangements were finally organised. The three feather beds were stripped from the bedrooms and brought into the living room. It meant a harder night's sleep on the under-mattresses alone, but it gave those on the floor something between their bones and the boards. It was dusk before the arrangements were completed. Curtains and blackout were closed and the gaslamps lit. Then the siren sounded. All their arrangements went by the board.

They knew that the risk from any raid had to be minimal. The only target near them of any possible interest to the Germans was Thames Haven with its oil installations and refinery, where the bombers had already made their intentions clear on a number of earlier visits. Fires from those raids were still burning, but more than four miles of wasteland and marsh lay between Bayhurst and the refineries, and apart from Thames Haven there was nothing around but plotlands, farms, hamlets and a few villages.

They were twelve in all, including a baby and an old lady, and although there may have been little to choose between night after night spent in a cold, damp and unhealthy shelter, and the remote prospect of a stray bomb dumped at random by a bomber anxious to get home, no one at that time was willing to take any unnecessary chances. The scenes from their journey were too fresh in their minds for that.

They were clearly too many for the shelter, but with three small families plus Lou and Clara there was initially some reluctance to suggest who should go and who should stay. Appropriately it was Lou, quite impartial and with an equal interest in all of them, who resolved the matter after a few words with Clara. Neither of them were going to be turfed out of bed again come what may. As for the rest, Rene, the baby and the children should be fitted up in the shelter, with Phoebe and Doll joining them on alternate nights. The three men would stay in the house with her and Clara.

There were no alternative proposals, so that was how it would be. One of the feather beds and the bedrolls the men had carried were added to the cushions and blankets set aside on the previous visit, and as quickly as possible the shelter was made ready for the night. When the children finally crept inside an oil lamp was burning, an old carpet runner had been thrown down over the duckboards, and to young and innocent eyes it looked almost comfortable and an exciting adventure. The September night was cool so they wore night clothes, dressing gown and top coat, and inevitably it would be hours before they slept.

For that night, and the ten that followed, Lou and her family would be witnesses to the passing of just a few of the waves of bombers that for fifty-seven nights without respite carried fire and destruction into the centre of London. By the time it was over they

241

had come close to tearing the heart out of the city and killing the spirit of its people.

Although there was nothing on the plotlands of strategic interest to the Luftwaffe, there were targets not very far away that received their constant attention. From early on in the year there had been mine-laying and attacks on shipping in the estuary. Throughout the summer, raids on the docks, factories and oil refineries of Tilbury, Gravesend, Thames Haven and Coryton had been countered by the RAF with fighters from the airfields at Hornchurch and North Weald, and in the weeks prior to the first great London raid those airfields themselves had been on the receiving end in the German campaign to knock the RAF from the sky and gain control of the air. With tactics and target changed, Bayhurst would now be under one of the major flight paths for those squadrons homing in on London and using the Thames as their route marker.

From inside the shelter they could hear voices from the direction of the house where the others were standing by the back door watchful and attentive for the first sign that the bombers were on their way. No one had any doubt that they would be coming. Doll had taken the early watch in the shelter and soon lost an unequal battle to keep the children from peeping out. The lamp was extinguished, the curtain pulled back, and they crammed into the entrance to look up at the sky. The night was silent and tranquil. It wanted seven days to the full moon, and only the palest of light filtered through the hazy clouds above them. They paused in their struggle for vantage points in the entrance and listened again. A second siren was heard, but faintly in the distance, and then once again there was silence.

There is a moment of stillness in the film *Zulu* when the little garrison at Rourke's Drift is waiting, tense and uneasy, for the approach of the Zulu impis. A murmur of sound is heard but fades away; nothing perhaps but the stirring of the breeze in the scrub. The soldiers stand breathless and turn their heads to catch at the sound. It comes again more strongly, but fades once more. Then gathering strength it increases in intensity to roll over them wave upon wave: the rhythmic beating of spears on shields.

So it was with the bombers. At first a distant hum, only half-heard before fading into silence. Heard again the sound was still faint, but more importunate. Then, as the squadrons rolled on, it

242

swelled to the relentless, pulsating drone that had been the precursor to slaughter and destruction across Europe. Born out of the wail of the sirens it was, like theirs, a sound which even after a lifetime could chill the hearts of those who had stood helplessly listening to it throbbing in the night sky above them.

By now those in the house were standing outside the door looking towards the estuary where the searchlights were coming on in sequence as they struggled to follow the raid in towards the city. Frustrated by the cloud they swept the sky seeking to find a break. Perhaps somewhere they found it, for the ack-ack was soon hammering away, and everyone returned to cover from falling shrapnel.

High above, in the light of the half-moon, the bombers would have seen beneath them a grey sea of broken cloud stretching away to the west where it glowed warmly over the still-burning fires of the East End marking the target for that night and many more to come. The first wave passed over, leaving them undisturbed and unmolested in their shelter. It would be followed by many more but by then the two cousins, tucked in head to toe in their narrow bunk, would be fast asleep.

They had an early, chilly and damp awakening with the smell of clay and earth in their noses. Alongside them the ribbed, corrugated-iron sheets were greasy with condensation, and the top layer of bedding was damp with drips from above. It was barely light, but in the house they had long been on the move. Jack, Charlie and Clara were preparing to leave for the station to travel back to town if at all possible. Life had to go on, and they needed to find out whether they still had jobs to go to, and if so what possibilities there would be to get into and out of London on a regular basis. There were also more personal items and some food to be brought back from Poplar . . . if the house still stood. The children walked with them to the bottom of the road and watched until they passed out of sight around the bend at the top of the lane before returning to their breakfasts. They were allowed their freedom during the day on much the same basis as before; no wandering too far from home, and an immediate return if the siren sounded.

The uncertainty of their situation was such that no thought had been given to the business of education, and it came as a dampener to John's plans to find that all the local children were back at school. For twelve months now that aspect of his own affairs had

243

proceeded on such an erratic, hit-and-miss basis that he was surprised to find that elsewhere life, including the unfortunate necessity of school, had carried on more or less normally.

His options for companionship for the day were limited. Moira was too old and would in any event wish to dictate proceedings, if she deigned to accept his company at all. Valerie was tolerable as a devoted acolyte about house or garden but, despite her willing engagement in the more robust activities of boys, was too young for the interests he favoured when roaming at large. Forced by necessity into his own company, he found that there was in fact some pleasure to be got from his solitary wanderings in the lanes and fields. It was the time for seasonal pickings and in the hedge-rows beside the road the blackberry bushes were heavy with fruit. He chose only the fattest and sweetest from the very tips of the brambles as he dawdled his way to the top of the hill. They were at their best then, but only to the end of the month when, as George had once confidently informed him, the devil piddled on them and they became tasteless.

At the top of the hill the road petered out into a field of stubble falling away to the patchy development around Tarpots. Corn had been grown there for years, but now the ground nurtured an alien crop. From hedge to hedge across the field, in parallel, disciplined lines, rank after rank of tall metal poles sprang from the soil. Into the field beyond, and further still, they stretched until a barrier of woodland intervened. From top to top of the poles thick ropes sagged across the fields and into the distance. Yet another anti-invasion device they were calculated to be invisible from the air – a lure to snare and destroy any gliders attempting to use the fields as landing strips.

For the rest of that week when he wandered beyond the garden he did so by himself. The dispensation 'not too far' was stretched to the limits and beyond, but fortunately the daylight hours were free from alerts until late afternoon and he was always home in good time. In the orchards on the cross-lanes the trees were already laden with apples. The cottages were scattered, the orchards hidden from view. The fruits were old-fashioned varieties long since out of favour, but early-ripening. The ground was already littered with windfalls and those that remained on the trees commanded attention.

His early introduction to scrumping had been from Mickey who was an authority on such matters, and it was simplicity itself to slip under or through the few strands of barbed wire that formed the only barrier. In a matter of moments he had helped himself to as many apples as he wanted and returned home triumphant, his pockets and jumper stuffed with the spoils of his crime. Pock-marked and waxy, the greenish/yellow skins of the apples hid a luscious, soft white flesh that sprayed the nose and face with a shower of juice when bitten. A little sharp and acid in flavour, they were sweetened by the knowledge that they were forbidden fruit. As he spilled his loot on to the table in the scullery, Lou shook her head, clucked disapprovingly, but put them on one side to be used later.

Tea was over, and it was very late afternoon when the alert sounded and they headed towards the shelter. Through light, broken cloud the bombers could be seen clearly as they moved steadily from the east in neat, compact formations. To the onlook-ers it seemed as though it would be another unchallenged progres-sion like the one they had watched just weeks before, but they were unaware of the squadrons from the Essex stations already high in the sky above them and waiting. Only when one formation of bombers broke and scattered did they see the RAF fighters sweeping in to harry them. As enemy support fighters joined in the melee, all order was lost, and they watched mesmerised as the sky became a confused tangle of con trails and smoke from aircraft spinning, twisting and diving in hot pursuit or striving to escape.

'Making a basket' was a phrase Aunt Tot had used to describe the wild aerobatics of rooks rolling and tumbling in the air over their nests in the elms. The basket woven by the birds had been a celebration of flight, life and freedom. Now, in their wild manoeuvres high above estuary and marshes, young men, still little more than schoolboys, made a basket of bitterness, destruction and death. In very few moments the skies were clearing. Of the bombers many continued on towards London, but more than a few had lost their relish for the mission and peeled away to north and south as the pursuit continued. Some trailed smoke behind them as they disappeared from sight, but they saw none destroyed.

Clara returned from London as the all-clear was sounding. Jack and Charlie arrived later, after meeting in Poplar to call at the house. The news they brought was mixed. Clara's laundry and her office was still undamaged and functioning. The same was true of

245

Charlie's job, and they would both be travelling to work in London on a daily basis for at least the time being. Jack's job had survived the first night's raid, but not the second. High explosives and incendiaries had left the ROP depot shattered and burned out, but there was a prospect of work elsewhere, and he would be going back to town for at least a couple of days to check and to call at the house again. Carters Terrace and the buildings immediately around remained undamaged, as did Charlie's house. Carrie clung on in the terrace and intended to stay, but the Moriartys had gone, as had many others. In Poplar at large, in the docks and on Commercial Road, the destruction was extensive.

Having satisfied himself that Terry and Mick were still thriving, John tucked himself away to listen to the talk, but the places, people and incidents meant little to him, and when they were all crammed into the one small room after dark, life seemed restricted and frustrating. Events left him little opportunity to mope, however. The evening alert sounded, and once again the children made their journey to the night shelter.

When John passed the German's house a few days after their arrival he noticed that the front door, previously closed and locked, now stood slightly ajar. The next time out he checked more closely: the house was clearly open. He was not by nature a bold, investigating child without a companion by his side, but curiosity and the thrill of exploring drew him in through the gate. In the front garden the grass was now rank and running to seed, the flower beds overgrown with weeds. On the front of the building one large pane of glass in the windows was shattered, and the door frame was broken and splintered where entry had been forced. The door swung back at his touch. Inside it looked much like Bayhurst, a narrow passage running from front to back with two rooms off each side. The passage was empty, and the doors closed apart from the one to the back room he had peeped into four months earlier. Treading quietly he moved cautiously forward to the one open door.

The room had been pillaged and despoiled beyond belief. Anything that was portable and of value had been stripped from the place. The loose carpets had been taken and the floors were bare. The clock, oil lamps, china and small chairs had disappeared. The little bookcase had gone with them, but most of the books remained, scattered over the floor with some old, yellowing maga-

246

Louisa and Pappy

The author and associate

Elsie the accidental suffragette - Hyde Park 1913

The plots - early days

Doll, Moira, Phoebe, Author

The palace on the plots

Men at work   Front elevation

Louisa (seated, second from left) and family

Lillian, Clara, Phoebe, Katherine, Irene, Elsie - 1924

William   Charlie

Irene, Lillian and Phoebe

Moira - bitten by the acting bug

Elsie 'dressed up to the nines'

Bathing belles

Country holiday jaunt

Bayhurst: A home for all seasons

Em, Phoebe, Louisa, Clara, Dick, Rene, Clara Dent

Doll, Valerie, Clara Dent, Moira, Clara, rustic privy at rear

Bayhurst

Kath and Elsie with their surrogate children

The swing - Moira and Valerie

Just before Dunkirk

Jack, Dan and Gilmore

Black Saturday 7 September 1940
Heinkel 111 over Isle of Dogs at the start of the raids

Home was top right just above the docks

Image courtesy IWM C5422

St Matthias' Church,
erected by the East India
Company 1766

In the dock's heyday

The new commercial vision

Poplar recreation ground

Poplar Outrage Memorial

IN MEMORY OF
18 CHILDREN
WHO WERE KILLED
~BY A BOMB~
DROPPED FROM A
GERMAN AEROPLANE
UPON THE L.C.C.
SCHOOL~UPPER
NORTH STREET~
POPLAR~ON THE
13th OF JUNE 1917.

ALFRED H. WARREN O.B.E.
MAYOR.
J. BUTEUX SKEGGS.
TOWN CLERK.

zines. The sideboard, which had been locked, was broken and shattered where the doors and drawers had been forced. Nothing had escaped the attention of the intruders. What they hadn't taken they had vandalised. The fabric on the sofa and easy chair was slashed; the curtains torn from their rails. Among shards of broken glass and shattered framing the portraits from the walls lay with other photographs trampled underfoot on the floor. He remembered his aunt's words about anti-German attitudes and actions during the Great War. This, then, was a taste of what it was like.

In the years that followed he would himself be guilty of the same sort of vandalism. Once the German's properties were seen to be standing open, neglected and already vandalised, the children appropriated them as playgrounds and games got out of hand. They were careless and thoughtless, no one intervened, and so accidents happened. Windows were broken; ceilings were brought down, and fires were started. Within a few years the buildings were little more than shells.

He picked his way through the debris looking over the books and magazines. Apart from their pictures they meant nothing to him, but the images in the broken-backed albums and loose photographs scattered on the floor could have been those he looked through with his aunts: formal wedding groups, snapshots taken on the street of a local town, holiday photos, young children, and faded images of older relatives, long since dead. Four or five packs of commercial snapshots lay almost unmarked. Not much larger than cigarette cards they were perhaps a souvenir of holidays taken when the wife was still alive: Ypres, Brussels, Bacharach. A thicker pack contained images of 'The Romantic Mosel': quaint Gothic buildings around the marketplace at Bernkastel; vineyards above Trier; castles and churches at Beilstein; and the bridges at Trier and Koblenz through which the Americans were to fight their way in the dying weeks of the war. He picked them up and put them in his pocket. Hidden away until much later, they eventually joined the magpie collection of mementoes he carried with him from those years. In the passage he tried the handles on the other doors. At every room they opened on the same scene of theft and destruction.

Each of their days followed much the same pattern. Mornings were invariably undisturbed. Starting around mid-afternoon, attacks would begin to build up, but they would be spasmodic, often just a few planes pushing up the estuary. When the larger formations came by day they spawned the same spirals and webs of vapour trails from the high-altitude dogfights, and for the first time they heard reports of bomb damage locally. Often it was nothing more than a deep hole blasted into the clay, but even this drew the curious who had seen nothing of the damage in the city for themselves. Webb's farm, which lost a barn and windows and slates from its roof, was the centre of attention for two or three days, and bomb shrapnel was eagerly sought after.

There were times when they saw and heard nothing of the incoming flights and were only aware of the action when the raiders turned for home. It was from one of those homing flights that they saw their second bomber shot down. Already damaged, it was flying much lower than the others when it received another burst of fire from a fighter that came in from behind. For a few seconds it flew on level and unchecked, then, as a thin curl of smoke began to trail from one engine, it rolled slowly onto its back and began a long, gracefully curved but ever steepening descent that carried plane and crew into the dark waters of the estuary. Within just a few months they would be joined there by one of the nation's flying heroines when Amy Johnson was lost on what had seemed a routine flight for the Air Traffic Auxiliary, and before those encounters were at an end the mud and ooze of the river would have swallowed the remains of many men and machines, enemies and friends.

They saw only a few planes destroyed, but knew well enough from news broadcasts and the papers that those that came in the daylight were paying a heavy price. Only much later did it become clear that the figures fed to the public were often grossly over-stated, but in essence it was true enough that the exchanges were running heavily against the Germans, who were undoubtedly getting a hiding.

Not all the raiders passed on to London. There were extensive attacks the length of the estuary and throughout Essex. The results of some they could see for themselves in the thick plumes of oily smoke that poured out of the stricken installations at Thames Haven. News of others came to them from the local markets which acted as clearing houses, often well informed, of incidents not otherwise reported: a major incendiary attack on Brentwood, repeated and heavy attacks on the docks at Tilbury, and occasional raids on Chelmsford, Rochford and Southend.

248

Of the raiders that came after dark they saw little. The September weather was indifferent and the planes often passed far above the heavy cloud base, but even on a clear night, under the brightest of moons, the planes could not be seen unless caught by the searchlights. Their pilots on the other hand would have had the most impressive of views: the waters of the Medway bright against the dark mass of the Isle of Grain marking the start of their flight path, and then the Thames silver in the moonlight guiding them to the city in the distance, still glowing from the earlier raids.

On either side of the river, from Sheerness and Shoeburyness to Southwark, batteries of searchlights followed the progress of each formation as it moved in from the coast. Their search was a restless, random scouring of the dark sky, until one of the raiders was caught in a beam when two or three others would sweep across to fasten on to the same target. Invariably the bomber pressed on regardless, sometimes fixed at the centre of the web of light and passed on from battery to battery, at other times slipping from the limelight into cloud and welcome obscurity.

Without effective night fighters, the RAF could mount no serious challenge to the hundreds of bombers that came in the dark and slipped away before dawn. The only deterrent was the gunfire from anti-aircraft units that were never silent when raiders were passing. Whatever the weather they blazed away, and in the dead of night, when they were the only defence, they were a great morale booster. Under heavy cloud little could be seen, but when the skies were clear on the nights of the full moon the ack-ack response to the bombers was spectacular, dramatic and, as those who watched it learned much later, largely futile. Its shrapnel was more of a hazard to the friends on the ground than the enemies in the air.

19

On the Road Again

The Monday morning a week after the flight from Poplar saw
Phoebe and Clara in tears. There had already been much talk over
the weekend about Churchill's broadcast a few days earlier, and
news reports of the scale and ferocity of the raids and air battles of
the Sunday had provoked yet more discussion on the same theme:
what should they do next? Neither Charlie nor Clara had left for
work, and there had been long arguments over breakfast and
afterwards that led to the tears.

In his broadcast Churchill had referred to the impending threat
of invasion:

> *This effort of the Germans to secure daylight mastery of the*
> *air over England is of course the crux of the whole war. So*
> *far it has failed conspicuously. It has cost them very dear . . .*
> *Herr Hitler is using up his fighter force at a very high rate . . .*
> *On the other hand, for him to try to invade this country*
> *without having secured mastery in the air would be a very*
> *hazardous undertaking. Nevertheless, all his preparations for*
> *invasion on a great scale are steadily going forward. Several*
> *hundreds of self-propelled barges are moving down the coasts*
> *of Europe, from the German and Dutch harbours to the ports*
> *of Northern France . . . convoys of merchant ships in tens and*
> *dozens are being moved through the Straits of Dover into the*
> *Channel . . . Behind these clusters of ships or barges there*
> *stand large numbers of German troops, awaiting the order to*
> *go on board and set out . . . no one should blind himself to*
> *the fact that a heavy full-scale invasion of this Island is being*
> *prepared with all the usual German thoroughness and method,*
> *and that it may be launched now . . . If this invasion is going*
> *to be tried at all, it does not seem that it can be long delayed.*

The background to the decisions taken at that family discussion and their outcome is best described in the letter Jack sent to Elsie just a few days later. Fortunately it was one of many she preserved.

Bayhurst
Clarence Rd.
Sept 20th. Fri.

Dear Elsie,

Your letter came yesterday, and knowing that it was from you, I thought it best to open it as I could not immediately send it on to Phoebe.

To answer your questions about evacuation first, the state of affairs in London is such that schemes for evacuation are in a state of chaos. Children have been waiting a week or more to be evacuated, and women and children are being sent to such places as Wanstead Flats, Epping, Ongar and the outer suburbs. 300 and more women and children billeted in a school at Hayward St, Silvertown, after having been bombed, awaiting evacuation, were bombed again on the following night only five escaped alive. This is not a rumour, but is absolutely true. In London yesterday I found no schools open to receive registrations, and we couldn't take the kids back there to await the chance of being sent perhaps to Woodford or somewhere like that.

Poplar is half deserted, whole streets of people have cleared out. Even the Seamen's Rest is shut down and closed. Those still in Poplar, go out to Becontree and other places to escape the bombing, trips are being run to Epping Forest where some go to sleep. So much for that, now for the news of everybody about whom I know you will be anxious.

If I compel them to take drastic measures you must try to believe that I am trying in very difficult and dangerous times to think ahead for the safety of them all and not to look merely for an escape from immediate dangers.

The thing that is most obvious to-day is, that the best chances of escape are afforded to those who take a chance and clear out to some place of safety, or comparative safety, without waiting to be sent. You should know that I compelled them all in the first place to come here immediately on that

251

Sunday morning, warning them at the same time that they must only think of Pitsea as a temporary refuge.

I had good reasons for not wishing them to stay here, I talked it over with Charlie and explained to him how if invasion took place on this part of the coast, they would be caught like rats in a trap, and not allowed on the roads. None would have got away, while we would have been powerless to help them. I have continually urged them to clear out from here. You must realise that Clarence Rd lies between two main roads and two main railways, the consequences were not comfortable to think about. I could have sent Phoebe and the kids to Oxford and dumped them on the billeting officer there, he would have been compelled to find them somewhere to go. However I told them all that I would see them all sink or swim together, and that I would not be satisfied until I saw them all away from here, all together where I can keep my eye on them, and where they will still have some chance of moving about.

I know how you are worried, but you should imagine how it has been to dread every day longer that they stayed here wondering if the next day would be too late. They have talked of taking Ma to you, but while I did not persuade them not to, I did not encourage the idea, for frankly I don't like your part of the country either. Apart from all this, the place here is not getting more comfortable. The planes pass over here all night long in a continuous procession, more and more guns arrive and get nearer to us, the shrapnel bursts right over the roof, and the German planes circle round trying to drop bombs on the gun positions. Last night a bomb dropped on Alcocks farm at the bottom of Clarence Rd. On Wednesday there was a fight right over our house. Six Spitfires shot down a bomber, which seemed to be coming on top of us all. You should have seen them all run. It was falling directly on to the houses at the bottom of the garden when suddenly it flattened out, skimmed over the roofs and crashed at the other side of the main road.

Well they are no longer here, and for the moment I cannot tell you how they are placed. On Wednesday evening, I went to Campbells, hired a 14 seater and packed them all off to Dunstable in Hertfordshire. They left yesterday (Thursday morning). I told Dick to go with them and take care of them all, I told him to go to the nearest railway station there, dump the luggage, or find a place to dump it, and find a bed first for Ma and for Rene and the baby. I told him to go to any billeting officer or to the police station or if possible find beds. Then they were to try to find a house to let, or a furnished house to let, in any case as they were all women and children billets would have to be found for them, as they could not be left to roam about, neither could they be sent back, as I told them to say that they had come from London.

However it turns out, I know that I must accept responsibility for what happens to them all, for I persuaded them all together to go. There they all are, mine yours and ours and each one just as precious and me trying to help the lot of them and hoping that I can scheme ahead to keep them safe. Dick is to return here to let me know how they get on, as letters take so long. Whether they will get settled down or whether they will come trooping back I don't yet know, but I am hoping that they will not come back.

Charlie has tried to get his cards, but cannot get them, he goes up to London, and I am staying here to get his food, until we know how they have all got on. I was in London yesterday. Carrie is the only one left in the terrace, Moriarties have gone, and most of those in Rigden St and round about, every day more leave. There are notices in the Labour Exchange telling men of many firms that they must return to their jobs.

I fed the parrot, the bird, the cat and the goldfish. All are still alive and well. I took Terry to be destroyed last week, so he is gone. They asked me to ask Carrie to mind the parrot but if they get settled down I will take him to wherever they are.

Don't worry any more than you can help. I shall leave no stone unturned to keep them all safe. Clara is not at work and is with them as it became very difficult to get from here to London, every day some part of the line is blocked. Yesterday it took me 4½ hours to get from here to Barking.

I told them to try and get a place not in Dunstable itself but in the village or countryside outside. Dunstable lies to the north and west of Luton, and north of Whipsnade near to the

Chilterns, and is about twice as far from London as St Albans,
but more to the west, they would have to pass through St
Albans to get there. As I receive news of them I will let you
know how they are getting on, and of course if they get settled
down they will write to you. I hope you and Kate are both
well and I wish that you could also be with the others. Ma
suffers of course, but is a bit of a brick, some of them had a
bit of a row with me yesterday before they went, but Ma said,
never mind Jack boy, I know you are doing it all for the best,
and that cheered me up I can tell you, because I am trying to
do what is best for them all.

Those gone to Dunstable are Ma, Clara, Rene and the
baby, Phoebe, John and Moira, Doll and Valerie, and Dick
to help them along and be responsible.

Good luck to you both.
Don't show this letter to anyone.
Jack.

They knew very well just what had happened to the buildings
and people of the villages and land through which the divisions of
the Wehrmacht fought their way across Europe. The cinema
newsreels had shown it all dramatically and in detail, and the
thought of experiencing the same at first hand was not a pleasant
one.

Jack's analysis of their situation at Bayhurst in the event of an
invasion was essentially an accurate one. They had already seen
many of the anti-invasion defences constructed in the countryside
and lanes around them: the pillboxes, the tank traps and the anti-
glider installations on the fields. From those who had travelled into
Southend they also heard how the town and its environs were
being turned into a fortress. There were multiple lines of anti-tank
defences, gun emplacements, barbed-wire barriers, pillboxes, concrete barriers and, allegedly, minefields. The first line of defence,
centred on the pier and stretching out to east and west, was an
unbroken anti-tank barrier over three miles long. But it was also
clear that once those defences were breached the way to London
was wide open apart from the lines of tank traps and pillboxes at
vital junctions.

When the threat of invasion arrived it was thought as likely to
come from the east as from the south, and the countryside of Essex

254

to the north of the Thames might have been designed for Blitz-krieg. The flat beaches around Southend were ideal for an initial landing, and the pier was a ready-made utility for unloading support troops once a beachhead was established. Between South-end and London miles of flat meadowland offered comfort to gliders, and the open, gently undulating countryside was largely free of heavy woodland or any other natural features that might hinder the deployment and operation of armour.

Through that countryside two roads opened the way to London. At the top of Pound Lane the old A13 ran parallel with the river to the East India Dock Road, their Poplar home and the City. Two miles away at the bottom of the lane the dual carriageways of the A127, the new arterial road, offered a wide, fast, open route into the north-eastern suburbs that would serve the German tanks just as well as it did the East End charabancs. On either side of the roads, forming the icing on the cake for an invader, two railways ran from Southend into Fenchurch Street and Liverpool Street stations. For a Panzer commander it was the stuff that dreams are made of. For defending generals it would have been a nightmare.

The fog of war is a concept covering everything from confusion and simple error through to concealment, disinformation, lies and propaganda. As real in 1940 as it is now, it was a major factor in the reporting of the Hallsville school bombing referred to in the letter. It happened in Silvertown on the night of 10th September, when the school was being used to shelter people whose homes had already been destroyed by the raids of the three preceding days. The few photographs taken immediately after the bombing show a building in utter ruins. No official account of the incident exists, but anecdotal evidence from those who helped at the scene and other eyewitnesses make it clear that the devastation was complete and survivors few. The estimates of deaths range from 79 (the number officially acknowledged) to over 400, according to those who helped with recovery and others who watched the refugees passing on their way to the school and saw the aftermath of the bombing. It seems probable too that the number sheltering in the school before the bombing would not have been known with any accuracy. The site was turned into a mass grave without any recovery of individual remains being attempted, and the truth now lies buried under the tarmac of the new school playground. Only the immediate location of the incident was misreported in the telling. The school was in Agate Street; there was no Hayward Street in the area.

When eighteen children were killed in the bombing of North Street School in 1917 it was appropriate to the public mood and general circumstances to publicise it extensively as the 'Poplar Outrage'. In 1940 when tragedy followed hard on the heels of tragedy, and the public mood was black, the Hallsville incident was effectively and understandably suppressed.

The final line of the letter is puzzling. Censorship was part of the fabric of wartime life, and it seems unlikely that Jack was unaware that it extended to the Post Office, which had authority to open letters at random so that its censors could check that information of possible use to the enemy was not leaking out intentionally or otherwise. Possibly having regard to the generally bleak tone of his letter the comment was aimed at preventing any unnecessary or gratuitous display of its contents by Elsie, and with some reason. Following Dunkirk, spreading alarm and despondency had been made an offence carrying a month in prison and/or a £50 fine. Local magistrates had seized on the opportunity with such mutton-headed enthusiasm that the home secretary had found it necessary to intervene to reduce excessive fines and prison sentences for comments that were little more than trivial or an expression of honest opinion.

There is little doubt either that the course the family had decided to follow would not have been looked on kindly by officialdom. In July, not long after Dunkirk, when the thought of invasion was uppermost in all minds, public notices from the Ministry of Information appeared in the papers. 'What do I do if I hear the news that the Germans are trying to land or have landed? ... I Stay Put ... I think 'Our chaps will deal with them.' I do not say 'I must get out of here.' I do not go on the road. I just stay put. Fighting men must have clear roads.'

Sadly it had been made all too clear during a few weeks in May just how ineffectively the Germans had been dealt with in France. Since then the situation had worsened, and few had any doubt that if an invasion came at that time, and with the same effectiveness as the Blitzkreig on the way to Dunkirk, the results were likely to be no different.

Only after many years was it disclosed that Churchill and his military advisers had taken much the same jaundiced view of the country's capacity for conventional defence, and had seriously considered the first use of poison gas on invading German forces when they came ashore, as a way of redressing the military balance.

There was a double irony to the timing of their departure. The air battles they had witnessed on the Sunday before they left had marked the turning point in the Battle of Britain. From that day there was never any prospect that the Germans would succeed in wresting control of the sky from the RAF, nor would they, after the losses of that day, embark on daylight attacks on such a massive scale as those of the preceding week. That failure to achieve control of the skies meant that only two days before their departure from Essex, Operation Sealion, the Nazi invasion of Britain, was postponed for the second or third time in circumstances which meant that it had effectively been abandoned. Of that the country at large knew nothing of course, and for some time to come the threat of invasion seemed very real.

More than fifty years passed before his father's letter came into John's hands. During that time he had seen and read more than enough about the war, the sufferings it inflicted, and the emotional impact on those in any way caught up in its coils. But it was not until he read the letter that he began to grasp something of the personal torment of those who had to make decisions and accept responsibility for the lives and futures of those they loved, in circumstances which were in every sense a matter of life and death.

For the younger children who had been witnesses to the arguments and tears, it was a confused and unhappy time. Bayhurst for them was a second home with many happy memories, and they could not understand why they were leaving again so soon. Only Moira perhaps had some vague grasp of their situation or the circumstances in which they were setting off into the unknown with no idea where, when, or how they would finally come to rest.

At the bottom of the road the coach waited for them, and laden once again with bags and cases they made their way down the cinder track while the Lanes looked on in puzzlement. Their journey took them first a short way down a deserted arterial road before they turned off on to minor roads to Brentwood and beyond. From then on it was a slow and tedious passage through villages, towns and countryside that were foreign to them. They had no interest in the passing scene, and overcast skies with occasional showers reflected a mood of tension and despondency felt as much by the children as by the adults.

Incredulous that they did not know for certain where they were going or when they would get there, John's second enquiry brought a response from his mother which made it clear that it would be unwise to press the matter further. There were delays, detours and a couple of longer stops for lavatory calls. Their sandwiches and drinks were consumed with no prospect of replenishment, and still they travelled on.

It was late in the afternoon when they stopped outside a police station in Dunstable. Dick went inside and within a few moments returned with a policeman who gave the driver directions. They travelled on another half-mile or so and then stopped again. They had a longer wait this time before Dick emerged with a man who climbed into the coach, looked them over with hostility and suspicion, and stayed with them until they drew up at what they were told was the Town Hall, where he left them in the coach and went inside.

Weary and anxious they sat waiting for his return desperately hoping that their wanderings were over for that day at least. There was little inviting about the building in front of them. The dirty, crumbling stonework of a mean depressing facade presented a sad contrast to the metropolitan splendours of their own public buildings now falling before the Blitz, but if it offered a meal and a bed for the night it would be a palace.

To their relief he was soon back to give them the nod, and they followed him behind the wall of sandbags, through a pair of clattering swing doors, and into a large, but cluttered entrance hall. The floor was piled high with boxes, blankets, folding beds and a jumble of domestic gear. The walls were plastered with public notices and war-effort posters. There they were left to wait while Dick and Lou went off with the official who arrived to attend to them. Hungry and thirsty they dropped their bags and cases and collapsed on to the upright benches which were the only seats available. When Dick returned it was with the news that the Town Hall itself was to be their billet for that night.

For the last time that day they took up their loads and were ushered along a narrow corridor into a large high-ceilinged hall sectioned off with moveable partitions. Inside there were perhaps two dozen other women and children whose situation seemed to be the same as their own. At one end there were tables and chairs; at the other rows of camp beds. After an hour or so a meal was provided, and then, miserable and homesick, John settled down to spend the night under the unsympathetic eyes of the turnip-headed county worthies of the past whose dim and dusty portraits lined the walls around him.

PART THREE

20

The Promised Land

Tucked away in a secluded, wooded valley hanging below one of the ridges of the Chiltern Hills is Promised Land Farm, and it was to the Promised Land, as it seemed to John, they were taken on the morning after the night in Dunstable. Not to the farm itself, but to Loosley Row, a hamlet on the crest of the hill above. There, for the next nine months, Clare and Ted Williams would provide Phoebe, her children and eventually Jack with a refuge, a home and friendship. Lou and the others all ended up in the same village, within easy walking distance.

The bungalow in which they settled was roomy, but plain and undistinguished, yet for the children it would remain the acme of convenient and gracious living for many years to come. It was modern, having been built just before the outbreak of war. It had a separate bathroom with a permanently fitted and plumbed bath, and a flushing toilet self-contained in a little room of its own. Both were indoors – an entirely novel concept in their limited experience. There was a large kitchen, a separate sitting room, and three bedrooms. As the Williams had only one very young son there was ample space for all.

To John's young eyes the Williams seemed about the same age as his parents. In fact they were younger by a few years and had married late. In character Ted could have been Joe Harrod's son. Gentle, deliberate and patient, he was a shy man who seemed on first acquaintance to be a listener rather than a talker, but when he had something to say the old Bucks dialect was as sweet to John's ears as Joe's Essex burr had been. To his wife most often it was no more than 'If you say so, Clare,' or 'If that's what you think, Clare.' He was the most amenable of husbands and richly deserved by his wife.

Clare was as unlike Tot as Ted was like Joe. Physically she was the utterly original personification of every hackneyed portrait of the ample, rosy, country wife found in the pages of popular pastoral fiction. In character she was another Clara Dent, as loving and as generous, but with the husband and child denied to Clara. The Williams opened their doors to Phoebe and her family as though they were old friends, and if they had to be away from their own home nowhere could have been more welcoming.

At dusk on the evening of their arrival the blackout was put in place, the lights turned on, and the silence and normality of the night was almost unnerving. No sirens, no bombers, no ack-ack, no disturbance or threat, and at the end of the evening a proper bed to sleep in. The promised land indeed for them, while little more than thirty miles away those left behind in London could do no more than endure the continuing nightly onslaught.

Their first full day was a Saturday, fine and sunny for late September, and while Phoebe and Clare sorted out their arrangements for housekeeping, ration books and other domestic matters, the children were free to wander the garden and pronounce judgement on their new surroundings. A town/country divide that would increase with the years separated them even then. Within Moira the call of the stage was already stirring. With like-minded friends in 1939, and during the Phoney War when theatres reopened, she had climbed her way up to the gods in the London theatres. Olivier, Gielgud and Ashcroft were already stars in her firmament. If she could not get to the theatre, cinema was an acceptable substitute, and in the pages of *Picturegoer* and *Picture Show* she followed the fortunes of her idols and the gossip that surrounded them.

They stood together in Ted's garden on the edge of a ridge in the heart of the Chiltern Hills. Before them the land fell away towards Promised Land Farm and the Saunderton valley.

It was an idyllic country scene: woods and isolated coppices; rich pastureland and arable fields; low hedgerows and trees hiding sunken lanes; sheltered farms and smallholdings; and beyond the valley the land rising again to tree-covered Bledloe Ridge, and the scrub and coppices on Lodge Hill. Condemned, as she thought, to a future divorced from all that civilisation had to offer, Moira looked it over with a jaundiced eye.

'Oh my God! The back of beyond, and for how long?'

She turned back to the house, leaving her brother to wonder at the blind folly of a sister oblivious to the potential of the new world stretched out before her just waiting to be enjoyed.

Ted's garden, even larger than the Bayhurst plot, was a living, breathing, growing testament to Dig for Victory and self-sufficiency. Neither bloom, shrub, nor decorative tree had any place in a scheme dedicated to maximum productivity and efficiency. On the house side of a dividing fence he kept a good-sized kitchen garden and a patch of land growing fodder for the stock in his livestock paddock. Apart from pigs, which Clare would not tolerate, Ted kept, or had kept, pretty well every type of livestock that the land was capable of supporting. Hens scratched and clucked contentedly inside their own high chicken-wire compound. Despite their bright inquisitive eyes they were, as John was to learn, the most pathetically stupid of birds. Two goats were tethered on lengths of chain, and half a dozen geese wandered at liberty over the whole of the paddock. In the corner by the gate a small battery of hutches housed the domesticated rabbits. It would only be a matter of days before John had received his first country-craft lessons from Ted and was scouring the hedgerows to bring home his contribution to their rations.

Despite the wicked-looking eyes and lethal horns of the goats, he was satisfied that their chains were stout and felt it safe to introduce himself. The geese had ignored him and were quietly pulling at grass on the far side of the paddock when he went to the gate. It was a tranquil, pastoral idyll: warm and sunny, the background clucking of the fowl, goats lazily pulling at the shoots of a hedge just within their reach, and the geese contentedly grazing in the distance. But at the sound of the gate-latch the geese lost interest in the grass, and six heads and beaks on stiff, outstretched necks swung as one to focus on John as he entered the paddock. He took a step forward and as one they began to move. Their manner was determined; their formation compact and organised. Very like the pattern of the German squadrons over the Thames, he thought, and probably with the same aggressive intent. He hesitated. They accelerated. Heads down, wings beating, and furiously honking a challenge, they swept towards him. Their intention was unequivocally hostile and he had no doubt as to their target.

It was an ignominious and humiliating retreat: a panic-stricken scramble over the fence and down the garden pursued by honks of triumph from the geese: lesson number one – know your country livestock. It was a few days before he learned that they could be faced down, and much longer before he had the nerve to try it.

The rest of that weekend disappeared in a round of visits to see where the others had ended up and to explore the main village, little more than half a mile along the road at Lacey Green. As they learned about their more distant surroundings Moira was relieved to find that she was not after all to be quite out of touch with her idols. The village shop already had orders for *Picturegoer* and within a week she had the latest copy. Princes Risborough, about two miles away, boasted not one, but two cinemas satisfying the overwhelming national demand for escapism, and a few more miles took them to such wartime delights as High Wycombe had to offer. The only restraining factor on a life of utter dissipation was transport.

Two options were available. There was a reliable, comfortable, tolerably modern bus service that ran to a timetable seemingly designed to be of the least possible use to anyone in the village. This generated regular accusations, probably true, that the bus company thought only of its customers in Risborough and Wycombe.

The alternative was a local institution known as Farmer's Bus, which the family soon discovered was as much a form of entertainment as transport. They never established with any certainty whether the name denoted the owner of the vehicle, or the occupation of the original public it was intended to serve, some of whom by 1940 must long since have lost all interest in any form of temporal transport. Speculation as to its age was confounded by the fact that over the years, the many years, of its operation, the vehicle had apparently enjoyed extensive modifications and renewals at the hands of its eccentric operator. With an intimate knowledge of his customers' requirements he published a timetable the admirable intentions of which were marred only by a performance erratic, flexible and uncertain in all respects but one: he was never early.

Farmer's reputation preceded him, indeed at his usual cruising speed it would have been hard pressed to stay behind, and when they met him for the first time they were deterred neither by the spartan, unsprung seating, nor by the distinctive smell of farmyard that travelled with him. Not that this was attributable to Farmer personally. It was simply a natural consequence of his operating

266

maxim: 'If you can get it through the door, I'll carry it.' In a rural locality that could make for interesting fellow travellers.

The nervousness attendant on that initial trip with Farmer was a little like the fear of flying for the first time, but they allowed the obvious faith of the locals to overrule any doubts engendered by the highly individual qualities that the bus and Farmer displayed on arrival. For the bus, a simple explanation was to be found in age, overwork and multiple modifications. For Farmer it was a more complex combination of food, beer and lack of physical activity. His size would have been memorable under any circumstances. That he was able somehow to tuck his vast bulk around the gear lever and behind the steering wheel made it all the more remarkable.

On their maiden run to Risborough they were impressed and encouraged by the impatient note of enthusiasm sounded by the engine when it set off on the journey. It was explained, as they soon discovered, by the fact that the run to town was all downhill. For their return journey the bus was full to standing, and had a diffident air about it even before they started. On the gentle gradients out of town it was patiently coaxed from gear to gear and then optimistically into top just as the hill to the Loosley Row ridge reared up before them, when it seemed to lose all heart.

As the climb to the ridge steepened, and the corresponding slow descent through the gears began, Farmer's grip on the wheel tightened, his arms tensed, the veins in his forehead pulsed and his torso began to oscillate gently from the waist as he added his own physical effort to that of the straining engine. The accompaniment from the local jokers began softly at first – 'Push, push, push!' – but increased as Farmer's struggles intensified, to burst into a crescendo and round of applause as the bus finally crawled over the crest of the hill. Farmer's torso came to rest, its work done, and he collected his fares impassive and utterly unmoved by the performance of his passengers. One of the great journeys of the world: Farmer's Bus, Risborough to Loosely Row, circa 1940.

The wandering life John had enjoyed for so long came abruptly to an end on the Monday after their arrival. In Lacey Green, as far as education was concerned, day-to-day activities proceeded much as before the war. The school was operating as usual with its full complement of teachers, and Phoebe presented him a little early so that any necessary formalities could be completed. By morning

267

break he had formed a first tentative judgement on his teacher: probably quite acceptable, but not a patch on Miss Roberts. The village children were not the problem they might have been with some incomers bringing with them the vernacular of the East End. He was good-sized and weighty for his age and could take care of himself with any of his classmates.

Compared with the bleakly functional, multistoreyed institutions of Poplar, the little village school in Lacey Green was an educational establishment a boy could almost come to love. There were just a few high-ceilinged, well-lit rooms on the one floor, and after the long corridors and rambling stairways of North Street it felt comfortable, cosy and child-sized. Externally, the dirty, slab-sided face of the Poplar barrack was replaced by warm russet-coloured bricks framing panels of flint and mortar reaching up to decorative gable ends. Best of all, behind the building, beyond the playground, instead of the confining fence and walls of the North Street buildings, the fields stretched away to a distant horizon of beech woods. When he returned to Clare's at the end of the day, it was generally understood from his comments that he had settled in.

From then on every moment of his activities out of school embedded him deeper and deeper into the country way of life in the Chilterns and moved him step by step further from his origins. His guides and mentors on that journey were Ted and the Barhams. Ted not only reared stock, he also went out with his shotgun to take whatever the countryside had to offer, and was happy for John to go with him. Generally what he took was within the law, rabbits and pigeons, but if the circumstances seemed appropriate, and bounteous Nature thrust some other opportunity at him, he was never so churlish as to refuse. They all tasted pheasant for the first time courtesy of Ted and the local squire. During the week, apart from tending to his livestock, he had time for nothing else before he started work, so his foraging expeditions were at the weekend and John had to rise early to join him – no great problem thanks to Jack's training.

Happily Ted detested the cruel use of snares, a view John shared with him as soon as he saw the bloody tormented messes that they left behind. Always soft-hearted with animals, even Ted's expert killing with the shotgun disturbed him, but the opportunity to be out and about with him was too great to resist. Ted followed a regular round and had a number of patches that he particularly favoured for rabbit. One of these was the east-facing slope of a steep-sided valley quite isolated from roads, and unoccupied except for a middle-aged couple living in the run-down remains of what had once been a fine house. On that sunny slope rabbits could always be found scurrying and bustling around from the crack of dawn, as could the lady of the house. She was not looking for rabbits though, but for Ted, and between them they played out a not unfriendly, but highly competitive contest in which the stakes were the rabbits – dead or alive.

An advocate of animal rights long before they were ever so defined, she knew Ted's routine, and at weekends kept close watch on her valley. Ted's approach, made under cover of the wood that ran along the ridge, was stealthy and silent, and the result was always a close call, but during John's time with Ted it was probably the lady who had the edge in their early-morning encounters. As Ted broke cover and steadied himself to let off two barrels in decent order, the lady burst from the house hammering a couple of saucepan lids together. If Ted got in first, one, or possibly two, rabbits died; if the lady, they scattered before he could take a clean shot. In either case Ted raised his hat to her, and she returned his salute with a wave of her pan lids. They never spoke, and John could never confess to Ted that his heart was always with the lady. Although Ted assured him that when hit cleanly the rabbits felt no pain, John was always stricken when they lay on their sides with legs still kicking and thrusting in an instinctive but terminally hopeless urge to escape.

Back in the kitchen when preparing the rabbits for the pot Ted stripped the skin from the flesh with a few deft movements as quickly and easily as he might have pulled off a sock, and few other creatures could look quite as thoroughly humiliated and vanquished as the scrawny, pathetic, fleshy carcasses that Ted left to be transformed by Clare's attentions. Rabbit pie, rabbit stew, rabbit casseroled, baked, roasted, potted: they had them all, and what they did not consume went into the produce-exchange chain which made wartime life so much easier for the countryman.

During the nine months or so that John spent in Bucks the novelty of watching and being instructed in Ted's smallholding routines never palled. It was only for the occasional slaughtering that he made himself absent. To John, Ted's stock became old friends, and he could never witness their passing. Otherwise under

Ted's instruction and guidance he mucked out hutches, faced down the geese, prepared rations for the livestock, sowed his own seeds, and just had time to see his first harvest maturing before they left. Goat milking he considered, attempted and abandoned in disgust at his own incompetence, the pathetic yield and the effort involved. Only when he tasted a dish of Clare's ambrosial goats' milk custard did he realise that out of those evil-eyed, malodorous and cantankerous beasts there flowed the milk of paradise.

In the following summer, not long before they returned to Essex, he went with Ted to the separate paddock that he rented to cut hay for winter fodder. They left early, while some dew still remained on the grass. Much better for cutting, Ted said, if there was still some moisture on it. His hay field was a small, irregular-shaped patch unsuitable for mechanical cutting and Ted had been scything it for years. On that fine June morning the long grass smelt sweet as it dried in the early sun, and John tugged at a few fat stalks to chew on as he sank back into the verge to watch the labourer at work. The yard-long blade of the scythe, dark with oil from its overwintering, sang a bright, crisp note under a few strokes of the whetting stone, and the haymaking began.

Planting his feet slightly apart, Ted swung the blade back and then forward; advanced a step, and then again, back and forward. So he proceeded, swinging the blade from side to side to the rhythmic sway of his body and the regular steps that followed up each stroke. So effortless and casual it looked, but after ten minutes his shirt was open to the waist and marked with sweat, and after half an hour he stopped and walked back to sit with John and swig some of the cold tea he had brought with him.

'Looks easy, don't it? But it's hard graft, John.'

He returned for another half-hour stint, another break and so on into the morning. John wandered back to the house for breakfast and returned with more tea and a sandwich for the worker. By late morning, with the sun high and hot, the cutting was over and they walked slowly back together; Ted with the scythe over his shoulder, John alongside but well away from the blade, the time-old picture of youth and the grim reaper.

He first became aware of the three Barham boys as a gale-force surge of noise on the other side of the hedge where he was collecting fodder for the rabbits. Something had been found and there was a dispute as to ownership. The debate started with a

270

word, moved to a word and a blow, and expanded swiftly to a violent three-way assault and battery accompanied by a rich and seamless exchange of obscenities and profanities. Like all maturing young boys John prided himself on the range of his London expletives to which Mickey had added a few rustic treasures, but the Barham boys completed his education until such time as he moved to National Service and looked into that bottomless well of prurient and profane invective from which all drill instructors draw.

When through a gap in the hedge he met them, he realised that he had already seen them in the playground at school. Peter was in the class above, David and Tony in the class below. Mrs Barham had apparently enjoyed a short but profligate burst of fertility which by some means had been reined in just as it looked like getting out of hand, and there were no other children. They exchanged the customary boyhood incivilities to establish a pecking order. Although Peter was older, John was bigger, and they were evenly matched. Mutual respect was established, and for the rest of his time in the village he and the Barhams formed a self-sufficient quartet, and most of his spare time was spent with them.

Dick had returned to Essex on the Monday that John started school, carrying news of their journey and comfortable settlement in Bucks. It was in early October, more than two weeks after their arrival, that a letter from Jack at last reached them. They knew from the wireless that the bombing raids on London had continued unabated, but otherwise had seen and heard next to nothing of the war since their arrival. The couple of alerts that sounded in the Chilterns were soon over and were virtually ignored. Jack's letter brought them their first news of Poplar since they had left Essex and contained a separate note for Doll.

In the late afternoon Phoebe, Lou and the rest of them got together in Clare's kitchen to hear the news of home. Inevitably it was of more chaos and destruction. Southend, Tilbury and other towns in Essex had been bombed. It seemed that daylight raids on London were being abandoned as too costly to the Luftwaffe, but night attacks had been continuous and heavy since they left. In Poplar major fires still burned throughout the docks, bomb damage was widespread, and a direct hit on a large air-raid shelter had killed and injured many people. Of family, friends and property the information was far better than they might have expected from the news reports they had heard. Bill and family were safe and well. After sitting tight in the thick of it for a while they had moved out to Bayhurst, and Bill was travelling up early each day to get to Billingsgate and keep the shop going. All the family houses were still in one piece. Astonishingly, despite the devastation around it, the little block in which Carters Terrace sat was untouched by the bombing.

Jack and Charlie had spent several days moving furniture, clothing and other household goods from Carters Terrace to Essex. The Campbell's lorry that served them so well for transport on the Sunday they fled from the bombing had made a couple of trips to Poplar, and Bayhurst and the garden shed were stuffed to capacity. The rest was in a corner of Mrs Heard's barn under tarpaulin. The pets were safe and well and had all made the trip to Essex on the lorry. The truth concerning Terry was not broken to John until some time later, and by then the cat, with whom he never had the same intimate relationship, had also gone missing from Bayhurst. Jack still had no work and Charlie would soon be finishing. Then they would join their families in Bucks, and look for work in Princes Risborough. Letters had been received from Else and Kath, who were both well, and the Bucks addresses had been sent to them. Relieved and reassured by the news in the letter, they all settled down in Loosley Row content to wait for the time being to see what the next few months would bring.

With the Barhams, John crossed and recrossed the land and villages in an introduction to a countryside and country way of living quite different from anything he had met before. After the self-effacing undulations of the Thames valley the seven-hundred-foot ridges and higher tops of the Chilterns seemed Alpine. The deep, dark beech woods that ranged across the hills were forests compared with the modest coppices and hedgerows that harboured the Essex elms. And the villages perched high on the spurs and hilltops, the farmhouses clustered with their barns in the wooded bottoms, and the ancient earthworks of Grim's Ditch all exuded an air of stability, age and permanence quite absent from the scrappy, insubstantial developments of the plotlands.

Even the names had a sweetness, romance or humour that promised much and invariably delivered: Flowers Bottom, Pyrtle Spring, Turnip End, Lily Bottom and Promised Land Farm. During his time in the Chilterns he visited them all, and the fields, the woods and the green lanes that surrounded them. He lived through one passage of the seasons on the hills and in the valleys, where he met a world of wildlife and plants quite different from the flat lands of Essex, and with each season and each new experience he took one more step along the road from Limehouse Pier and his Poplar roots.

In the local village those changes that the urban world accepted quite readily had been only slowly and cautiously assimilated into the existing pattern of life, or perhaps rejected. Of the shops, one was still no more than a private house with a few items in the window and a front door standing open. At another the owner had unwisely invested in the installation of two petrol pumps to mark his leap into the twentieth century, only to find that the village still seemed to be happy with the nineteenth. By the time John saw them the pumps looked curiously old-fashioned affairs, one capped with an elaborate, ornamental glazed Shell emblem, the other fitted with a large glass container through which the petrol had been delivered in visible and measured gallons. Both stood dirty and defunct. It was the shop with the pumps, however, that they favoured with their orders for *Picturegoer*, *Beano* and the few sweets they could purchase, but inside it was a dull and colourless affair after the aromatic delights of Clara Dent's little world.

Elsewhere signs of commercial activity were discreet and self-effacing. Behind a low, railed fence the post office stood modestly away from the road at the back of a yard paved with rustic bricks and cobbles and fringed with flowering shrubs and trees. The door and windows of the office, and the small cast-iron postbox itself, had been cut into the walls of a longer range of buildings of mixed age, construction and use. Oak-framed brickwork, partially over-hung with timber cladding, merged irregularly with panels of flint and mortar pockmarked with multicoloured brick and stone. After the noise, hustle and commercial efficiency of Chrisp Street it was a sleepy, relaxed and easy-going world.

The Barham's house was almost a mile away, on the fringe of an extended, deep wedge of beech wood that ran for several miles to the north-east of the village. The boys walked to school by one of the footpaths that ran to the villages from Lily Bottom lane, and on the Saturday after John first met them he set out across the fields to find them. The path took him close to the old mill that stood on the top of the ridge by the crossroads. As windmills go it was a forlorn and neglected specimen even for those days when rescue and refurbishment were unknown. Of the sheathing, which was fragmentary, some sections hung loose, others had fallen to the ground. The capping was broken and decayed. Just two skeletonic arms remained, one hanging in despair, the other raised imploringly for the loving care and restoration that would eventually arrive after many years of peace. Just enough of the structure remained to support a Home Guard lookout post in the upper levels.

The Barhams' father worked on the farm a little further along the lane from their home, which, from its age and appearance, may once have been the farmhouse. An uncompromisingly bleak exterior of grey rendering was matched by spartan, sparsely furnished rooms within, which offered few comforts outside the vast kitchen where they lived, ate, washed, and conducted every other function of their lives apart from sleeping and visits to an outside privy of basic, rustic design. In any but the warmest weather, a log fire blazed throughout the day on the kitchen's open hearth. Mr Barham's farm work included woodland management, and the log store was always well stocked. The flagstone floor was bare apart from one pegged rug under a couple of old easy chairs by the fire. There was a large sideboard, a couple of wooden tables and a scattering of simple chairs.

Just behind the house on one side of the plot, a brick-and-timber barn served as log store and general workplace. Eccentric in appearance, full of character and much older than the house, it may once itself have been lived in and retained a friendly, welcoming character that the house lacked. In the upper level the timbers had warped and twisted with such enthusiasm over the years that the peak of one gable end overhung the base of the wall beneath by two or three feet. At the other end the gable sagged inwards to the same extent, as though some giant hand had pushed the whole upper section out of line.

The garden was at least as big as Ted's and as well tended, and like his it supported a mixed collection of livestock. At the bottom of the plot, in one of a number of ramshackle old huts, the boys had their den where Peter kept his own special menagerie. The heavily wired and reinforced hutch in which it was housed, and the sound of manic activity within, was enough to inhibit any natural curiosity on John's part to be more closely acquainted with the residents engaged in such frenzied movement behind the wire.

Despite his natural affinity towards most animals there was not one aspect of Peter's ferrets that commended them. He disliked the smell, the taut, wiry body, the sneaky, vicious face, and most of all the use to which they were put. Peter had described their most recent outing in graphic terms that left John resolved that ferreting was one country pursuit too far for his urban sensibilities. The better to illustrate his skill in the art, Peter took one of the things from its cage, and backed John into the corner of the shed, feeling perhaps that this gave him some measure of revenge for the patronising display of knowledge about docks, bombing and aircraft recognition to which he had been subjected.

John's nose had already directed him to an offshoot of the ferreting activities. Tacked on to a board, two rabbit skins were being cured, but with palpable and nauseating lack of success. The boys received no pocket money, and to earn a few pence picked up what jobs they could in the village and on neighbouring farms. Peter had seen cured rabbit skins as a possible additional source of revenue, but having made a close inspection of progress by eye and to John's disbelief, by nose, now seemed to have some doubts. These were resolved by Mrs Barham who had originally authorised the experiment and now arrived from the house to inspect progress. Her judgement was given in terms and tone of voice that brooked no denying. Fate had already done her down that morning it seemed, and she was looking for a confrontation. John recognised the tone, and the thought crossed his mind that Mrs Barham and his mother may both have been graduates from the same school of child rearing. The skins were ripped from the board, thrown over the hedge, and the boys followed her sulkily into the house for their lunch. An invitation was not extended to John, nor in the sullen, brooding atmosphere would it have been welcomed. He made his way home over the fields to the usual warm greeting from Clare.

Despite all that the Williams did to make them feel part of the family, it was in the lengthening evenings that the loss of their own home was most felt. As only the living room was heated, it was there they spent their time together. The only diversion was the wireless, and as guests it was natural to defer to Clare's choice, which was always light music. Moira had no difficulty losing herself in a book. Phoebe and Clare took up their knitting and chatted undisturbed despite the wireless droning on in the background.

Ted spent some time with the paper and then the rest of the evening with a number of gardening and stock-rearing books. They were the only books in the house, and the only books in which he had any interest.

The monotony of those tedious, never-ending evenings was eventually relieved when the usually self-effacing Ted revealed a side to his character quite unsuspected even by Clare: given the right subject and a willing audience Ted loved to talk. Quite by chance it was John who prompted this disclosure. During an early visit to the Barhams Peter had referred to the ferret shed as an old bodger workshop. That had puzzled John. He knew nothing of bodgers and was certainly not going to betray his ignorance to Peter by asking, and so the moment passed. He thought of it again during one of the long, tedious evenings.

'Uncle Ted. What's a bodger?'

Ted pushed his book away and looked up with evident delight.

It must have been fifteen minutes before the answer to the question became clear. A direct and simple reply would have been that a bodger was a man who earned his living turning chair legs out of beech wood, but as they were about to learn, direct, simple replies and Ted were strangers. If he had opened with the ending of the ice age, moved through the subsequent afforestation of Britain, and on to the ultimate establishment of the Chiltern beech woods, his answer would have been no more circuitous and pro-tracted than the one he gave. He rambled off into the highways and byways of country crafts, the character of the beech woods, and the Risborough and Wycombe furniture industries before finally coming home to bodgers with a gleam of satisfaction in his eye. Before he had finished they were all listening to him, Clare with a look of some surprise and admiration.

Born to be an itinerant bard and storyteller in the halls of the bronze-age settlements that had once clung to the Chiltern hilltops, Ted was a man who had missed his age and vocation. The soft Bucks dialect sat easily with his leisurely, discursive style, and he told his tales with half-closed eyes as though dreaming what he was describing. His memory for the detail of the local ways of life was remarkable, particularly when talking of his own youth and recounting tales of earlier days told to him by his father, and having once made a start he lightened many of their evenings with his nostalgic narratives of past life and times in the Chilterns.

276

It was mid-October when Lou and Clara, out for a walk on the road overlooking the valley, saw two figures they recognised toiling up the hill from the main road below them. Jack and Charlie had arrived in advance of the letter they had posted more than a week earlier to say that they were coming. Within a few days they had both got jobs at a factory near to the station, and life began to settle down to a pattern that was almost normal.

Every couple of weeks there was an expedition to Risborough which included a trip to the cinema. If the weather was fine they took the footpath over the fields. Starting with views across the town and over the valley to the sources of the River Thame, the walk also passed Pyrtle Spring, one of the few places where surface water was to be found anywhere near to the village. Despite their greenery the Chilterns seemed as dry as a desert after the ponds, streams, rivers and creeks of Essex. Even the spring produced no more than a thin trickle, and in autumn the hollow where it rose was deep, not in water, but in leaves and beechmast from the trees that overhung it. Their return to the village was made on Farmer's Bus, primarily to avoid the long haul up the hill, but also for the entertainment the journey provided.

John had already been deep into the beech woods with the Barham boys. Their aim was to collect beechmast for the pigs, but it took a lot of time and effort to build up a worthwhile haul, and the trees themselves were a constant challenge too tempting to be ignored. Many rose frustratingly smooth with neither handhold nor foothold for ten or fifteen feet: trunks that were sheer and inaccessible even to the craftiest climber. Others divided just above head height into thick boughs that embraced, twisted and writhed like contortionists. For one boy standing on another's shoulders these provided a way into the canopy. And here and there were trees of bizarre individuality and character where some adolescent trauma had shocked them into a thickening or swelling at the waist, on which age had inflicted a scabrous mass of bosses, knobs and whorls. In between their branches rain-filled crucks and bowls created aerial water-worlds teeming with their own minute life until the next extended dry spell brought apocalypse, and there too the boys could find comfortable niches to drop into while they shelled and chewed on the tiny nuts from the beechmast.

With such diversions to occupy them the beechmast collection generally amounted to little, of which even less went to the pigs. A large cupful was kept back which they slowly and patiently shelled. The accumulated kernels were roasted on an iron plate over the fire and sprinkled with salt before they ate them. Beechmast, like winkles, gave great returns for just a little extra effort.

Indulging a taste for solitary wanderings that had been born in Essex, John found in the beeches a presence both profound and overwhelming. In the very heart of the woods the dense canopy filtered out life and sound as it did light, and little grew in the shade beneath the beech. Trunks rose a cold grey-green out of a litter of dead, decaying leaves from earlier years and the silence was profound. It was perfect food for a melancholy disposition to feed on. The rest of the family had seen nothing like the beech woods before. Criss-crossed by footpaths, rides and green lanes they made for easy, level and open walking, and whenever the weather was fine, and while the autumn colours held, they visited them as often as they could.

At the beginning of November they were directly touched by the events of the war for the first time. A letter was received from Doll's father reporting the result of one of the latest raids:

2nd/11/40
not 4 Scurr St
but 98 St Leonards Rd,
Poplar E 14.

Dear Dolly and Charley,
We are finished at 4 Scurr St. only your front room and front room upstairs left after a bomb dropped on the house on Friday night at 9 o'clock, but no stairs left to get up to top room, all our other 4 rooms are in a heap but the dug out is still there not touched.

I left your letter what you sent Jim on the shelf on Thursday not opened, so that is buried with the other things, as he had not been back yet since he went with Marie on Tuesday to her mothers place in S Wales, he said he would be back on Thursday but I expect he is stopping for the weekend so he has not seen the letter.

I went home this morning and found the place all in this mess, but thank god nobody killed only Mrs Jones and Mr got a shock as they were home. I managed to get Mr Wakeham to prize some of the stuff up and got the poor parrot out but

278

*still alive, then we pulled some more ceiling and wood away
and got the canary out, cage all smashed but still alive. Mrs
Downes daughter lent me a wicker cage until one of you come
up and take them from her house. I don't know what has
become of the goldfish I could not find them.*

*Dear Doll I went over to Bow Town Hall this morning
from there to Wade St School for immediate help and got it
for clothing, boots, shaving gear etc and have to fill in this
form the same as I am sending you one for all your furniture,
clothing and what you have lost in the home. The gentleman I
spoke to told me to fill them in as soon as possible and send
them off, so come up when you can and see what you can
save, your beds in front room are there but covered with
bricks and mortar but can be saved. I went to Charlies mothers
house but could not find anyone there or next door I expect
they were out so can't do anything about bird or parrot till
you come.*

*I am going to Ilkley in Yorkshire on Thursday next the 7th
for 2 weeks from Mr Dicks to a convalescent home so will
have to see the BO people again when I come back. Please let
Annie know and anybody else as I cannot write any more
now and am so queer myself.*

*From yours affectionately (Dad)
a few xxxxxxxxxxx for Valerie.*

Although they were always aware that such or similar news
might arrive with any post, the anticipation did not soften the blow,
and it was a sad time for them all. The house held all the personal
belongings that Doll and Charlie had built up so slowly since their
marriage and was the only home their young daughter had known.
On the day the news was received Charlie travelled to London to
see whether anything could be salvaged from the debris. In a
remarkable footnote to the letter, Valerie recalled that he found
the goldfish bowl intact with the two goldfish still alive. Just one of
the many freak survivals that came out of the Blitz. What the Nazis
started, the post-war reconstruction finished however, and Scurr
Street itself disappeared from the London map.

With that news they began the run into the winter and
Christmas of 1940. For the family and for the country at large it
was one of the darkest periods of the war. With the dying year had

come a succession of depressing events that quite overshadowed the good news from North Africa where the Italians were in retreat in the desert. The expected German invasion had not so far materialised, but apart from that there would be little reason to celebrate the arrival of the New Year. At the end of October London suffered its longest night raid of the war. In mid-November their papers brought them stark pictures of the cathedral gutted and in ruins after Coventry had endured its night of agony in a raid which ripped the heart out of the city. The Boxing Day Bank Holiday had been cancelled and rationing was biting harder and deeper into everyday diets. Even with the benefits that came from the wild and home-grown resources of the countryside, the daily meals had fallen into a regime that was monotonous, unappealing and often tasteless.

It seemed to John that his mother had now devised an endless range of responses to any moaning at what appeared on the table, all of them variations on the themes of 'There's a war on you know' (news to him of course) or 'If you're really hungry you'll eat it,' which invariably he did. Memories of the pre-Christmas shopping trip to Chrisp Street in 1939 now assumed a dream-like quality: a fantasy of candied fruits, bonbons, cakes and sweetmeats that dissipated like dawn mist in summer before the austere displays on the shelves and in the windows of the Risborough shops.

Early in December there were changes that made the prospects for Christmas look even bleaker. Bill wrote to say that they had moved out of Bayhurst into a bungalow they had bought in Pound Lane. That was news marking a major departure from a commonly held East End and working-class attitude of the time that viewed the concept of home ownership with suspicion, even if it was financially viable. The legalities involved, and the thought of owning a house with all the attendant responsibilities for insurance, upkeep and repairs, was enough to deter most of those who were in a position to think about it. A cheap holiday shack on the plots was one thing; a home was another. As they learned from Bill's letter he was still firmly of the old school of thought. It had been Em who persuaded him to take a chance at a time when the outcome of the war was very much in the balance.

Although Bill's success in business had left him better breeched than anyone else in the family, such a purchase might have been beyond him in normal circumstances, but two exceptional factors combined to make it possible. The war and threat of invasion had dramatically depressed house prices (it took some nerve to buy at a time when most people were wanting to sell), and Bill had long-established contacts at Billingsgate that ensured supplies when they were available. Unrationed throughout the war, fish was always in short supply and prices were high until controlled in 1941, but even after price control the business flourished.

The news triggered a whole cascade of decisions and changes reflecting the uncertainties and differences of opinion expressed before they left in September. Bayhurst was empty again, and Lou decided that she wanted to return there. She missed the occasional visits from Elsie and Kath and at Bayhurst would be able to spend time with them in her own home. Clara would, of course, accompany her. Dick had received a summons to the army and was somewhere in the north of England, so Rene decided to join them with the baby. A couple of days and a few discussions established that with a little give and take there would also be room for Doll, Charlie and Valerie, and ten days or so before Christmas they were all gone.

Phoebe viewed the developments before Christmas with all the enthusiasm that might be expected of a woman who had spent her life, including many years of marriage, sharing a house with her mother, sisters and brothers, or having them and their families just around the corner. The prospect of returning to Essex herself was considered a score of times from all perspectives, but living for any length of time with her own family added to those already squashed into Bayhurst around all the stored furniture was clearly impossible. They would be hard enough pressed to accommodate Elsie and Kath for a few days when they were on leave, and so for Christmas and the immediate future Phoebe and her family were to remain in Bucks.

21

A Chiltern Christmas

Christmas 1940, unlike 1939, brought no courteous appeals from the government for fair play and restraint from Christmas feasting, nor were they needed. For more than a year the rationing screw had been tightening and those looking for feasting now had to have deep pockets and turn to the West End, still on the receiving end of complaints about luxury eating off-ration for the rich. In general, where it existed, it was conducted with the discretion that might be expected, but La Coquille restaurant in St Martin's Lane apparently saw nothing insensitive or unpatriotic in their advertisement, 'Oui, oui, savez-vous que? Hitler does not interfere with La Coquille restaurant 79 St Martin's Lane. Lunch, dinner as usual. Nothing missing.' Scott's restaurant advertised an apology for telephones out of order, but were happy to remind clientele that 'their excellent oysters, shellfish and grills are always available and more appreciated than ever'. Christmas lunches were still available at Marshall and Snelgrove, or for the stay at home Prunier's restaurant offered a selection of 'happy little extravagances' by post: *homard à l'americaine* 5 portions for £1.15s, or *civet de Lièvre*, 3s 6d a portion.

For the country at large amid general shortages of such basics as onions the weekly rations stood at tea 2oz, sugar 8oz, butter 2oz, and from the Ministry of Food the 1940 festive message had more in common with Scrooge than Wenceslas. From now on even plainer living would have to be the rule. It wasn't quite Hitler's 'guns not butter', but the effect was the same: for the future bananas were off, imported tinned fruit was off, fresh fruit imports were off, the Boxing Day Bank Holiday was off, Christmas church bells were off, and just one week before Christmas the meat ration was cut again to 1s 10d. But if tea could lift the hearts of the nation there would, for one week only, be an extra two ounces of tea with an extra four ounces of sugar to sweeten it.

In Loosley Row on the Saturday before Christmas Phoebe and her family were persuaded by Clare and Ted to join them at the dance in the local hall. Allowed to stay up late, and with recollections of Poplar parties in mind, John went along full of anticipation. In the event it proved to be a disappointing and deeply depressing affair. The timber hall, not much more than an oversized shed, was a cold, bleak construction that wore its few Christmas dressings with an air of utter dejection. Coloured crêpe paper pinned around the light shades strove for intimacy, but achieved only an air of sepulchral gloom. Faded bunting sagged along the walls between a few nondescript swags of decoration, and bunches of mistletoe drooping from dusty beams looked more funereal than festive. Over a temporary platform at one end of the hall a couple of strings of coloured lights glowed patriotically, faintly illuminating a portrait of the king tastefully framed in berried holly but looking about as optimistic of the success of the evening as John already felt.

Most patrons arrived expecting little of the promised refreshments and bar and were not disappointed. John had seen and heard his mother giving Clare a hand that afternoon preparing sandwiches for the evening.

'Easy with the marge, Phoebe. Just a scrape in the middle or it won't go round.'

Memories of past splendours had filled his head with thoughts of jellied eels, wallies, his gran's mince pies, salt-beef sandwiches and his mum's iced cake. He looked at the reality before him and despaired: sandwiches, filling uncertain; pies of provenance and content unknown; some dry-looking fancy cakes; and tarts discouragingly presented as 'mock mince'. Behind the table the bar offered sherry, gin, rum, an anonymous orange liquid as a mixer, and Mann's brown and pale ales, both noxious brews said Jack to all who knew and loved the real thing. It was not to be an evening when John would be supping the dregs from the glasses.

The Toreadors (a three-piece band of pensionable age and appearance) strove against the odds to inject some life and vivacity into an assembly where the women outnumbered the men, callow youth and age were dominant, and the few boys in blue or khaki had the pick of the choicest blossoms. With the exception of one or two light-footed and accomplished performers, quickstep, foxtrot or waltz were danced to the same rustic shuffle, and only the arrival of the 'Palais Glide' and 'Hokey-Kokey' lifted the proceedings into something approaching gaiety.

Clare's sister Doreen, determined that John should enjoy himself, dragged him to her bosom, pressed his nose to a corsage reeking of Californian Poppy, and to his disgust exhibited his incompetence on the dance floor not just once, but on three separate occasions. She said that he was light on his feet, but even that was unable to relieve his heavy gloom. It was not Christmas as he knew it, and no amount of 'There's a war on you know' was going to make him feel any better about it. Only when the band had droned its way through the National Anthem and they were on their way home did his spirits revive.

The gaudy decorations that had been such an important part of the London Christmases had no place in the Loosley Row arrangements. A tree would be coming in from the woodlands, but of paper chains, balloons, Chinese lanterns, tinsel, hanging bells and stars, and all the multicoloured frippery that had adorned the house in Poplar there was no sign. For their country Christmas Ted would be using his local knowledge to introduce them to older, more deeply rooted customs, and on the Sunday morning after the dance, well wrapped and shod, Moira, John and Jack set off with him on a country foraging expedition that would be providing their Christmas garlands and decorations. Over his shoulder he carried a long, stout pole to which a saw blade had been fixed. They carried rolled sacks, an old sheet, a pair of secateurs and a pruning saw.

Ted knew exactly where he was going, and it was a long walk towards Wycombe over fields and footpaths before they finally stepped into the tree-lined lane that he had in mind. Turning from beech country they now had before them an avenue of tall and ragged limes festooned to their tops with tresses of grey-green mistletoe. From the lower branches a few scrappy, scrubby clusters hung close to hand, but Ted was after choicer returns for the effort of their walk. Higher up in the crown canopy of the trees, and seemingly out of reach even of the pole-saw, the mistletoe drooped in great, swelling chandelier-like globes, its milk-white berries glowing against the foliage.

Still fit and agile, with all the experience of his boyhood years in the woods behind him and just a little help from Jack, Ted was soon into the lower branches. Handed his pole-saw he hauled himself slowly within reach of one of the most attractive clusters. At the foot of the tree, carefully positioned by Ted, they stood with sheet outstretched to break the fall of the mistletoe as Ted sawed the cluster from the tree. Caught with the loss of just a few berries it was put to one side and the operation repeated until they had more than enough at their feet. By the time Ted clambered down they had two or three clusters gently nestled in each sack, and like rural burglars with their swag bags over their shoulders they left the site to the other foragers still busy around them.

Their return followed a different route through beech woods once again, and then by lanes and old walls where holly and ivy was plentiful and well-berried. With pruning saw and secateurs their Christmas harvesting was soon completed, and with full sacks, bulky but not heavy, they turned back towards the village.

Early in the afternoon while Ted was out, Clare twisted strands of ivy and holly on to a wire frame to make a wreath for the door, made a swag to hang below the mantelpiece, and draped other fragments from their collection on window sills, over door frames, around the light shade, and wherever her ingenuity could find a suitable space. Some of the mistletoe would be finding its way into the rural exchange economy later in the day, but the best of the bunches were soon swinging over their heads, with a few sprigs tucked into the swag and wreath.

Ted came back from the forestry plantations with the top cutting from a spruce as their Christmas tree, and that at least they were able to deck out with a few brighter baubles that Clare had kept from previous years. By the time berried sprigs of holly and mistletoe and smaller presents were tucked into the branches here and there, it looked quite festive, even if it did lack the flashy glitter of home.

Later in the afternoon Clare left for a gathering of the ladies of the village, not so much a bring-and-buy sale as a bring-and-swap meeting. She took with her a sack of well-berried mistletoe, a few duck and hen's eggs, some potted rabbit and, as Phoebe's contribution, a knitted two-piece baby outfit. When she returned it was with two bottles of homemade country wine of pre-war vintage, some brawn and, for the top of the Christmas tree, a fairy cunningly fabricated out of pieces of card, some old lace handkerchiefs and a few sequins.

When evening came Ted insisted that everyone had earned a

285

drink that day and opened a bottle of the country wine. The label was elegantly written and precise: 'Elderflower – Gathered at Parslow's Hillock, 10th July 1937.'

The vintage spoke of a remarkable restraint by the brewer, and many would argue that their bottle was past its date, for elderflower wine is best drunk young, but when the cork was drawn on that damp and depressing winter evening in the darkest days of the war, their world was briefly transformed. Warm, golden and limpid, the wine streamed from bottle to glass filling the room with the honey-sweet fragrance and aura of summer. Bees buzzed around their heads, and the sun was hot on their backs. John breathed in the perfume of the blossoms, savoured the wine in his mouth, swallowed and glowed with the distilled warmth of that far-away summer's day. What a master brewer that Chiltern man was.

Christmas itself could not have been worse than the dance, and despite the ghosts of Christmases past hanging over them the day went well. Home produce, and the barters and deals struck on the rural exchange, meant that they were well provided with food, unlike the millions in the cities getting by on the short commons of war. Chicken, potted rabbit and brawn formed the centrepiece of their meals, but they were topped by a cake and pudding as delicious as they were unexpected. Lou, with the wisdom of her years, a reckless disregard of the law, and perhaps remembering rationing at the end of the Great War, had made other shopping expeditions in 1939, stocking up with items that she could keep for special occasions. All of this Charlie had brought to her from Poplar in the weeks before the move back to Bayhurst was contemplated. When, before Christmas, she finally decided to return she left Phoebe a choice selection of dried fruit, candied peel and nuts – the foundation of their Christmas indulgences.

Present giving was almost an incidental feature of the day. There was as little money to spare as there was choice in the shops. Books, annuals, soap, hand tools for the garden, cigarette tobacco, cheap toiletries, seeds, a pack of cards and a draughts set were exchanged with all the conventional expressions of surprise, thanks and delight, but soon forgotten apart from the games.

Jack introduced John to the rules of draughts, and together they played out a few exchanges closely watched by Ted to whom the game was new. When Jack turned to something else Ted stepped in to take his place, and so began a tournament between youth and

286

age that they played out regularly until Jack and his family returned to Essex. They were both novices and, despite the disparity in age, proved over the months to be fairly evenly matched. John was constantly surprised that one so wise in all practical and country matters should fall so regularly for the simple little traps that he laid for Ted on the draughts board. Ted on his part was constantly astounded when he was huffed, delighted with his victories, and never at all perturbed that he lost as often as he won against his junior opponent.

The cards and draughts helped to transform the long, dark evenings of winter, and added variety to the usual diet of night-time entertainment from the Home Service and Forces Programmes. With the cards John graduated under Ted's instruction from Snap and Strip-Jack-Naked to Pontoon, where he could soon hold his own, and Solo and Nap, where he could not. Ted's innocence with draughts did not extend to cards. He gave no quarter, and under his guidance John learned a little of the wiles and deviousness of card players.

During the war years the King's afternoon broadcast on Christmas Day was as much essential listening as were Churchill's broadcasts throughout the rest of the year. Children, separation and hope for the future were the themes, and they heard it out in silence, immersed in their own thoughts. Jack's were possibly of his brother Dan somewhere on the Atlantic. Phoebe perhaps thankful that her family was still safely gathered around her, and not broken and scattered. Clare and Ted maybe reflecting on the chance of war that placed them in safety and able to play a helping role. Of the King's sober confidence in the future and the path to victory they could not judge, but only hope that it would be so.

Then, as now, Dickens was a Christmas regular with the BBC, and to sips from the second bottle of elderflower wine and nibbles of Phoebe's cake they sat through a double ration of *A Christmas Carol* and *The Signalman*. With a little game playing and music from the wireless the rest of that Christmas evening passed pleasantly enough, but it was clear that each of them at one time or another was thinking of the rest of the family together at Bayhurst, with Elsie home for a few days and knocking out on the piano all the old songs of which they were so fond. Yet they were lucky, there were many across the country having to live with absences and losses that so far had not touched them.

287

In the early years of the war only the briefest of diversions from the war effort were allowed for public holidays, and many were cancelled. When, after a couple of years, this was seen to be counterproductive most were reinstated, but in 1940 both Jack and Ted were back at work on Boxing Day. School holidays ran on as usual, however, and as the cards and draughts were still popular they were all up and about later than usual in the evenings following Christmas. A couple of nights before New Year's Eve one of Ted's friends on Home Guard watch in the old mill knocked on the door. He spoke to Ted who then had a few words with Jack, and together they went into the garden. They soon returned for the others, and well wrapped up against the cold they went out into the night.

There was no moon, and light, high cloud veiled the stars. In blacked-out Britain it should have been pitch-dark, but to the east, beyond the valley, and further still, on the far horizon beyond High Wycombe, the clouds glowed softly in a slowly changing pattern of red and gold and crimson over the flames of a thousand fires. There was no need for questions or speculation. When the papers were published after the holiday they had been relieved to see that Christmas had generally been raid-free in London: now they knew at once that it had started again more savagely than ever and that more than thirty miles away the city was burning. They watched in silence thinking of Poplar, and friends perhaps still in the thick of it. It was the East End that was uppermost in their minds, and they had no idea that in and around the city under that warm, almost cheery glow, part of the heart of old London was being consumed as the firestorm raged.

As they looked towards the burning city that night it might have given them some grim satisfaction had they known that in little more than a year, just down the road on the way to High Wycombe, Bomber Harris in his underground bunker would be setting up the Air Command that would take a terrible revenge on the cities of Germany. 'They have sown the wind,' he said, 'Now they are going to reap the whirlwind.'

Neither the BBC nor the papers were specific in reporting the events of that night. There were references to many buildings destroyed, and damage to a museum and famous Wren church, but little detail. Perhaps it was not the time of year to disclose just how much had been lost in the firestorm, but those who stood outside that night, and looked at the furnace glow in the sky above London, knew well enough that something quite exceptional had happened.

After the events of the year, and with the night of 29th December still fresh in mind, New Year's Eve was a sober cheerless affair, but to abandon the traditional formalities was too much like admitting defeat so they went through the motions. Ted went out and came in with a piece of coal. There were handshakes and kisses, a drink for everyone, and the hope expressed that the next year would bring better things: it would be hard put to it to bring worse. Just after midnight they stepped outside briefly, into bitter cold and utter darkness. Neither light to be seen, nor sound to be heard. Church bells, blasts of ships' horns on the river, the sound of singing from the Seamen's Rest, factory sirens, neighbours calling in for a drink: all of them shades of the past, and never to return. Welcome 1941.

January was dull and cold, with strong and biting easterlies. It would have been a thoroughly miserable month anywhere, but life in Loosely Row was aggravated by its position high on the Chiltern ridge. Beyond the protection of the house an icy wind sucked the warmth from exposed or underprotected flesh in seconds. Water for the livestock was quickly frozen and had to be changed two or three times a day. The walk to and from school became a hateful, chilblain-tormenting ordeal, and when the snow arrived it came horizontally, stuffing the eyes and filling the deep lanes with drifts.

In those conditions the long two-mile walk to work, but more especially the steep, unrelenting climb back up from the valley at the end of the day, soon proved too much for Jack's lungs. Little more than a week into the New Year he returned from work breathless, exhausted and ashen. Clare heated some soup for him while hot-water bottles were prepared, and he went to bed. By morning he was delirious and bronchitis was diagnosed. Thrashing about in a delirium which lasted almost three days he frequently threw back the bedclothes, so someone had to sit with him at all times. Although his bed could be kept warm by a supply of hot-water bottles, the room itself could not be heated and was like an icebox. A bed-watching rota was the only answer, with each watcher on duty well wrapped in jumpers, coats, gloves and even hat. John although young wanted to play his part and was allowed to do so except during the nightwatch. Clare, and Ted when he was home from work, insisted in joining in, so the duty wasn't onerous. Wrapped up like a mummy against the cold, mostly in company with an adult, but occasionally by himself with strict instructions what he was to look for and when he was to call his mother, he took his turn in the sickroom, fascinated and half-frightened in turn by his father's wild, nonsensical ramblings. A wardrobe mirror draped with an old curtain because it had been giving Jack the horrors was then transmuted in his mind to some even more threatening figure and had to be turned to the wall. Clothes were repeatedly thrown from the bed. Attempts to administer medicine or refresh him with a wash were violently opposed, and in long outpourings of meaningless, ranting abuse John heard obscenities which by then he certainly knew but had never heard from his father at any other time. His mother explained to him just what was happening and that in a few days it would all be over, but it was a relief finally to enter the room and see normality in his father's eyes and a weak smile on his face.

That episode was the first step in a deterioration of his lungs that within little more than a year would stop Jack from working again and lead eventually to TB. It was almost three weeks before he returned to work, and soon afterwards John wrote to his aunts. Elsie, of course, kept the letter.

Dear Elsie and Cath,

I thoght I would write you a letter. Have you had any snow at your place We have had a fall of snow today I have past up into std 4 from std three Mumy told me I was better in my spelling. I hope I will be seeing you soon

Jimmy Bellamy came today to see daddy and brout my a big pure sillver A.R.P. Bage

I went to wuthering Heights yesterday It was the Best picture I had ever seen. Daddy has started work again down at the same old place.

The great Dictater is on next week in risboro I may take the wednesday afternoon of. I went to the barbers to have my hair cut and did not come home till half past nine and mummy was worried over my.

with love from John xxxxxxxxxxxxxxxxxxxxx
pl pto
xxxxxxxxxxxxxxxxxxxxxxxx

Despite wind, weather and family separation, life looked sweet enough to him at that time. There was inevitably a firm parental correction to the sturdy independence of mind on school attendance revealed by the letter, but his love affair with the cinema went unchecked and flourished. His spelling, alas, suffered relapses, but his mother's optimism was not entirely misplaced. The ARP badge from Jimmy he kept through the remainder of the century. Sadly the alchemy of the years transmuted silver to base metal, but it was an innocent deception and readily forgiven.

Jimmy had arrived late on a Saturday afternoon with a bottle of whisky and the only detailed, first-hand news of the state of affairs in London to reach them since they had left Essex. Although Jack and Charlie had occasionally returned to Poplar, they had gone with a specific purpose in mind and had no opportunity to look further afield. Jimmy had been in the thick of things throughout, either at home or at his ARP centre overlooking the Limehouse Cut. He had also been into central London since the great raid and fire after Christmas. Ted and Clare offered to find him some bedding and a spot to kip down for the night if he wished to stay over. He had clearly arrived hoping for just that. Kate would not worry, he said, if he were not back that night, so they had a meal together, the whisky was opened, and a long evening began.

Despite the dramatic changes that had taken place it seemed to John almost like old times at Carters Terrace: his father with one of his friends, a long evening of talk, whisky and smoking, and a chance to tuck himself away in a corner and do what he most enjoyed – watch and listen. Clare and Ted, although they knew only a little of the background, were just as interested in the eyewitness account that Jimmy brought with him.

The news that most concerned them, of fortunes and homes of family and friends, was reassuring. In the eastern half of Rigden Street there had been extensive destruction, and four lives lost, but Carters Terrace and the area immediately around still stood almost untouched; a few windows broken, some blast damage and a small fire on the corner of Jeremiah Street, but apart from that all was well. He had made a point of calling in to see Carrie, who was still going strong and bent on sitting it out, but many of the houses were now deserted, the families having fled to safer ground. The fish shop was still standing, and Bill had been seen behind the counter recently when Jim passed by on a bus.

When he moved on to the situation further afield it seemed astonishing that anything was left undamaged. Docks, wharves, factories, warehouses, gasworks, power stations and whole rows of houses, so many it seemed had been destroyed by high explosive or gutted by fire or both. Time and again Jack would mention a building or landmark well known to him, to learn more often than not that it was gone. Jim didn't dwell at length on the detail of the worst that he had seen in the course of his ARP work, but from time to time his voice dropped to a whisper and John could hear nothing that was said.

As they worked their way through the whisky, the men taking it neat, the ladies in cups of tea, his listeners became more animated themselves and there were questions from Clare and Ted as well as Phoebe and Jack. When Moira chipped in with an enquiry about her old school and the People's Palace, it seemed to John that it was time to learn a little of the fate of his personal East End world.

The Gaiety Cinema? Still there and still functioning Jim thought. The Seamen's Rest, the Board of Trade and North Street School? All unscathed so far. Jim was unable to speak from personal acquaintance of the swings and drinking fountain in the recreation ground, but the old church was still standing, and he didn't think the park had been bombed. John managed to satisfy himself that all was well with the pier, Limey Hole and the Limehouse Cut before Jack intervened to forestall any more questions. He said he thought that John could pride himself on the fact that his personal interest in any potential target had clearly been enough to secure it a special dispensation. John couldn't see why this was considered to be so very funny.

Jim's trip into central London had been made on foot, and he was able to give Phoebe and Jack a street by street, almost building by building, description of areas they had known since they were children. John knew nothing of most of the places he described, but briefly, as Jim moved west beyond Fenchurch Street Station into Leadenhall Street, where many of the offices of the shipping lines had been crowded together, he was on holy ground as far as John was concerned. In pre-war trips to the West End with his mother or the aunts he had gawped from the bus at the resplendent models of great liners gleaming behind the plate glass on the ground floors of those offices. Cunard, Orient Line, P & O, Union

292

Castle, Royal Mail, foreign and smaller lines: all had on display their biggest, best or most luxurious of ships, and just once a little special pleading had brought him the indulgence from his aunts of a broken journey and half-an-hour or so on foot in front of his maritime shrines. At pavement level they were overwhelming in their splendour. Five, six, seven feet long or more, and under a blaze of lights, they shone out in company livery, bright with the glint of burnished brass or bronze, and the gleam of polished woods. Moving slowly from window to window he pressed his nose to the glass in worship before *Orontes*, *Viceroy of India*, *Mauretania*, *Queen Mary*, *Stirling Castle* and many of their sister ships.

In St Mary Axe and Billiter Street, in the modest window displays of lesser companies, he found models of the latest and best of the nation's freighters and merchant vessels. Every feature was there to scale and in immaculate detail: propellers, portholes, funnels, deck cabins, lifeboats, capstans, derricks, hatches and masts. They were the very perfection of model making, the torment of the youth of the city, and he lusted after those models as he lusted after nothing else. The thought that they might be lying crushed and shattered in the rubble of the ruins that Jim described was more than he could bear, and it was with relief that he heard him move on further to the west.

The scale and enormity of the destruction that Jim described during that evening was quite beyond John's grasp. It was only immediately after the war, when he made the same walk for himself and gazed at the burned-out ruins of the Guildhall, the gaunt remains of block after block of buildings, and the open tracts of wasteland that surrounded and bore witness to the remarkable survival of St Paul's, that he began to understand the impact Jim's descriptions would have had on those who knew the city well. But already by then wind-borne seeds sown on the rubble had flourished and bloomed for three or four seasons, softening the scars with a covering of wild flowers, buddleias and the shoots of a few optimistic young trees. Jim left early the following morning and it would be several years before they saw him again.

22

Winter Sports

As another harsh, white, wartime winter established itself across the country, seasonal sports arrived on the slopes of the Chiltern Hills. All along the Lacey Green ridge, snow-covered fields fell away in long sweeps to the valley below, and within a few days the snow had been compacted by the youth of the village into a hard, icy surface across which anything would speed with ease.

There were two runs. The first fell away evenly and smoothly, levelling out slightly just before the hawthorn hedge dividing the field from the one below. Halfway along the hedge the gate into the lower field had been opened. Through it the lucky few with an amenable sledge and the skill to steer it could sweep on to an extended run down the lower slopes to the valley bottom. The majority went no further than the deep drifts at the foot of the hedge where the hawthorn was a needle-sharp and unforgiving billet for anyone dumped into it at speed. The second run was shorter but steeper and broken by three low escarpments where sledge and rider were briefly airborne before thumping back on to the icy ground.

Their sledges were home-made, in an imaginative and inventive range of designs which worked with varying degrees of success. The bog-standard model consisted of a few boards nailed to a pair of roughly shaped runners. With many fathers away on war service, and others working throughout the daylight hours, the workmanship on the sledges was generally that of the boys themselves. They laboured to the best of their ability, and on the first slope their crude and simple constructions were not seriously tested. The challenges presented by the stresses and strains of the steeper, stepped run were of an altogether different order and could tax the basic models beyond endurance. Two, perhaps three runs might be survived without mishap, but at each ridge the impact of landing weakened and twisted the construction. Packed snow concealed the gaps developing in the joints, and the most joyfully entertaining failures produced a catastrophic and explosive separation of component parts, where runners, boards and boy each followed its own separate trajectory to the foot of the slope.

The lord of the slopes, and the envy of every boy who watched him, was Tommy Gomme. He arrived with a large, very solid, brass bowl. Original function unknown, these could be found many years after the war in the windows of antique shops, carrying a hefty price tag and selling as log bowls. About fifteen inches deep, it had a rounded base, raked sides with a turned rim, and was just wide enough for a boy to sit cross-legged inside.

The mockery that greeted the arrival of the bowl was silenced as they watched its first run. Tom stepped inside, where a couple of sacks were folded in the bottom, and the bowl was in motion and gathering speed before he had time to sit down. Somewhere outside the village, on some quiet and secluded nursery slope, that boy had been practising. The display they witnessed was one of assurance and authority. Grasping the rim with each hand he pulled, twisted and rocked the bowl and, rotating slowly as he accelerated, sped away to the bottom of the slope.

There was no possibility of steering or slowing, and he entered the final run towards the hawthorn at suicidal speed, but even that he had anticipated. Ducking low and clasping his legs, he pulled himself into a compact ball at the bottom of the bowl seconds before it punched its way into the hedge. He clambered out snow-covered, but triumphant and unscathed. For as long as the slopes were open the bowl was the source of much bribery and a few threats. They all wanted at least one run, and with promises of comics, sweets or other favours, most of them had one before the end of the day.

John's friendship with the Barhams was now well established, and as Phoebe had decreed that three boys in Clare's house was more than she could be expected to tolerate, he spent much of his time at the Barhams' when weather kept them from the woods or fields. Huge log fires kept even the remote corners of the kitchen comfortably warm, but in the passageway the doors and the frames were ill-matched, and despite some crudely fitted draught-proofing wind-driven streaks of snow crept under the door and across the stone-slabbed floor. Beyond the kitchen the house was unheated, and he could see as he approached that many of the windows remained frosted all day. The boys needed to be hardy, and they were, chasing up any jobs they could get to earn a few pence even in the worst of the weather.

In the weeks up to Christmas he met Mrs Barham more often, and his affection for the lady did not grow with acquaintance, rather the reverse. In the art and craft of child rearing the initial comparison he had made with his own mother had proved to be quite false. His mother's explosions were fierce and violent, but soon blew themselves out and were generally justified. On a day-to-day basis she was loving, lively and entertaining. He soon realised that for Mrs Barham being mean, spiteful and unloving was a lifetime vocation. Whenever she spoke to the boys it was either to demand, moan or nag, and he never saw her show them the slightest affection. She was also deeply envious of those whose life was, or was perceived to be, better or luckier than her own. When she had an audience, if only of boys, she kept up a relentless critical commentary about her neighbours, whose lives in truth would have been little different from or better than her own, but in particular about her employers.

She carried out housework and general duties every weekday morning in a neighbouring house that was undeniably grand. When she spoke of the owners her refrain recycled the same ill-natured phrases over and over. 'Just their luck.' 'That's not for the likes of us, but of course it depends on who you know.' 'They don't get what they put on the table each day from their ration books, I know.' 'Of course it's all her money, and she lets him know it often enough and loud enough.'

Her particular resentment was reserved for their son, who had got himself a commission in the RAF, a distinction which she resented and saw as achievable only by corruption at the highest level. Her younger brother slogging it out in the ranks was apparently twice as bright as their son, 'but then of course they think the sun shines out of his arse, and they pulled strings left, right and centre.' On and on she went remorselessly, and as soon as the weather relented enough for them to do so the boys escaped to the barn or ferret shed. A singular correspondence there, John thought – the ferrets and Mrs Barham.

Prior to Christmas he had seen Mr Barham only as a figure beavering away in the farmyard, or in the distance on the fields, to whom the boys would shout a passing greeting to which he replied with grunts or not at all. Closer acquaintance showed him to be lightly built, pale of face and hair, and with fine, long-fingered, almost delicate hands under the layers of farmyard grime. He hardly looked the man for the role of farm labourer, but John had seen him vault a farm gate at the run, frogmarch a recalcitrant heifer into a barn, and toss heavy sacks of stock feed on to his shoulder with ease.

At work he was a man who delivered much more than his appearance promised. At other times if he promised little, he delivered even less. He was taciturn almost to the point of silence and, on the few occasions when they met, spoke no more than half a dozen words. Having experienced Mrs Barham in full spate, which invariably meant in full spite, it was easy to understand why her husband had so seldom been around when John visited prior to Christmas: work put him beyond her reach. The January weather had closed down almost all farming activities, however, and he was at home for the day when John called early in the New Year. Even then Mrs Barham was building up a head of steam as she worked in the kitchen and hissed a redirection to the barn where he found father and boys splitting logs. He stood aside and watched a wordless, disciplined, family operation that went like clockwork.

The father may have had little to say, but the boys attended to him and worked with him as they never did with their mother. Peter stood behind a broad, heavy section of tree trunk used as a chopping block. From a pile of unsplit logs behind him he placed one in the centre of the block and stepped back. As he did so his father swung a heavy axe with a narrow, wedge-shaped blade. His action was loose, easy and accurate. On either side of the block the two younger boys stood back at some distance. As the blade bit into the log it exploded into halves, one towards each of the boys, who picked them up and threw them on to a growing heap to one side. By the time they had fallen another log was on the block, and the axe was again in motion. Except for the sound of the axe and the flying logs they worked in silence. No words were spoken unless the split logs were still too large when Mr Barham grunted, 'Again!' and the half-pieces were thrown back to Peter for a second splitting. Eventually he nodded at Peter, struck the axe into the cutting block and went back to the kitchen. They were free to pursue their own interests.

Although the ferret shed and barn were dry, they were dreary places to spend much time in cold, wet weather. On such days, when the woods and fields were denied them, and despite the potential threat of Mrs Barham's oratory, they tucked themselves on to a corner of the kitchen table with an old and simple board game or a well-thumbed pack of cards. In the worst of winter even Mr Barham felt the need to forsake his sanctuary in the barn and join them. In one of the easy chairs he sat by the log fire with the cat on his lap and the wireless playing softly at his side. The *Daily Mirror* occupied him for a few minutes, but he was not a great reader. A few moments on the *Jane* cartoon strip, a run through the pictures, a desultory read here and there was the measure of it. For the rest of the time he sat listening quietly with his eyes closed, gently stroking the cat, or gazing into the flames as he smoked his home-rolled cigarettes. News broadcasts he digested without any visible change of expression whatever was reported and he remained throughout as silent as the door post.

At such times with a captive audience Mrs Barham was, in Peter's words, like a dawn cock on a dung heap. It took her a few moments to select her key and main theme, but once that was done she could develop her variations and counterpoint endlessly, and moan on auto-pilot for as long as she had listeners. As they sat playing Peter kept up his own running commentary loud enough for his brothers and John to hear, but not his mother, who seemed in any case to be oblivious to the laughter his frequent near-obscenities provoked. Her tide washed over Mr Barham as the stream does over the resting trout – he remained totally unmoved by it and completely unresponsive unless she forced the issue to breaking point when he would grunt or string two or three words together. What satisfaction she could possibly derive from her performance it was difficult to imagine, and John eventually concluded that she moaned about the house much as his mother and aunts sang about the house, for the pure pleasure of the performance.

During those early months of the year the Luftwaffe offensive on Britain's cities continued unabated. In Loosley Row there were occasional alerts and bombers were heard passing overhead, but otherwise the war had no local impact. Of the war on land the news that came to them seemed encouraging. In North Africa Italians forces were sticking stubbornly to their caricature representation of lacking stomach for a fight and in one engagement surrendered 20,000 men, 200 guns and 120 tanks to a British force of 3,000. 'Never was so much surrendered by so many to so few,' said Eden, paraphrasing his prime minister, but he spoke of the Italian campaign against the Greeks in Albania, not as is supposed of North Africa.

Winter clung on tenaciously into March and April with cold winds, sleet and snow flurries sweeping down on to the village over the tops of the woods to the east. By the end of February, however, although the hills were still white, the snow cover was slowly wasting away. The surface of the slopes was soft, sledging was over, and at the weekends the woods became the boys' principal playgrounds.

Snow still lay in isolated, shrinking patches, or clung on more deeply where it had drifted against the bases of the hedgerows, but elsewhere beneath the trees the sodden leaves of autumn were showing in broader and broader sweeps, and despite the weather the earliest spring flowers of the new year were thrusting their way through the forest litter and flourishing. Drifts of snowdrops swept through the woods, sparkling above the duns and browns of the winter debris, or half-invisible against the last, thin film of winter snow. Spurge laurel gleamed dark green against the pale beech trunks, filling the air with a heavy musky perfume as they kicked their way into the woods. Banks of green dog's mercury speckled with diffident pale flowers stretched away before them and blue-bells would follow, but once that first flush of spring flowers was over little else other than fungi grew on the floor of the beech woods.

As the lengthening daylight hours and increasing warmth drew out the leaves of the beech trees, less and less of the sunshine penetrated the high canopy. By mid-summer, the heavy shade, the thick, dead carpet of old fallen leaves, and the greedy surface roots of the trees themselves had created an environment where few plants would grow, but in the trees and undergrowth of the woods John had an introduction to birds and wildlife that had not come his way in Essex. When the snow was still thick on the ground Peter had stopped him on one of their walks and pointed silently ahead. Together they crept towards a fox curled up asleep in the snow at the base of one of the beech. Only at the last moment did it start and dart away, leaving a depression hollowed out in the

299

snow and the dead leaves below still warm from its body heat. Twice at dusk badgers were glimpsed in the distance, but they slipped away before the boys could get closer. Stoat, squirrels and mice scuttled around them in the undergrowth. Treecreepers, nuthatches and woodpeckers scoured the beeches over their heads. It was a different, much richer world than the scrappy copses and hedgerows of the plotlands.

23

Summer's Lease

For the eight months following the outbreak of war the holiday arrangements of the nation had proceeded much as usual, subject only to the restraints imposed by the blackout. With the rigours of the great frost behind them, Folkestone, Hastings, Eastbourne and other coastal resorts were reported to be making plans for the usual summer-holiday influx. Hotels were popular and doing a flourishing trade on the back of an exemption which allowed those who could afford it to stay for up to four days on full board without surrendering their coupons for any of the foods on ration, and the early Easter of 1940 saw holidaymakers thronging to the coast and visiting the sights of London much as they had done in peacetime. Following the German invasion of France and the fall of Dunkirk all that was to change.

By the end of June 1940 a prohibited area had been introduced that ran from the Wash to Rye. By the end of July that had been extended from Bexhill to Portland. Holiday or casual travel into those areas was banned and anyone entering them had to satisfy the police or military that they were entitled to do so. Clacton, Cromer, Southend, Brighton and a score of other popular coastal towns were out of bounds and access to their beaches prohibited. During the Easter break of 1941 motorists were stopped when trying to enter Brighton, and by the August Bank Holiday visitors were being turned back at the barriers of Southend and Brighton railway stations.

But in Loosley Row, as the early months of 1941 slipped away, Phoebe was fretting more and more under the enforced separation from her mother and the family at large. By the time of the Whitsun school holiday, despite continuing cold and miserable weather and all the difficulties and discomforts of wartime travel, her restlessness could no longer be contained and she determined on a visit at least to Essex and perhaps further. Jack was at work but would be well cared for by Clare. Moira chose to remain in Bucks with her father, and so it was just Phoebe with her son by her side who set off down the hill to the little halt that was Saunderton station.

Prohibited areas apart, any form of casual, non-essential travel was by this time actively discouraged, both by persuasion and legislation. The coach and charabanc services that once carried Londoners on their casual day or weekend jaunts to Southend, Brighton and other coastal resorts were virtually non-existent, and on the railways movement of troops, official personnel and materials essential to the war effort were invariably given precedence at all times. In every railway booking office the prospective traveller was confronted with a large poster of a Tommy in full battle kit pointing accusingly, and asking, 'Is Your Journey *Really* Necessary?' For those who were not dissuaded, the journey itself could be a sufficient deterrent to any further inessential travel. Trains were dirty, smoke-filled, seldom on time and always crowded. It was not unusual for the longest of journeys to start and end with every seat taken and corridors and guards' vans crammed with passengers standing or sitting as best they could on suitcases, kitbags or any other luggage that would offer support.

Despite all that, Phoebe was determined on having her time away, and the last of John's wartime letters to Elsie recorded their travels.

Dear Els.

How are you geting when will I be seing you again I hope it will not be for long.

I wish I was at home becous of the blincin earwicks They get on your bread as well as your nerves when you open your bed of a night you se runing all over the place.

Is it very warm were you are, we gete no sun at all here, it is more like winter than sumer.

We went to pitsea in my holidays for five days then we went to briton but we wer not stoped When we got there I found I had lost my mack on the train and saw a lot of ships I allso went to the pictures to se the gost of saint Micals.

Me and John O'Connar went to a park.

Don't forget sixpence.

Love from John

xxxxxxxxxxxxxxxxxxxxxxxxxxxxxx

The letter was lost sight of for more than thirty years until it came to light in Elsie's collection after her death. She would certainly have forgiven the unhappy ambiguity of the opening sentence, as she would have responded generously to the peremptory final directive, but time had eroded memories and whether it was a sixpence, or possibly a shilling, that eventually arrived, carefully wrapped as it always was in a little tissue paper, it was impossible to say. Nor did John have any recollection of the earwig traumas he reported so passionately. The contemporary record he accepted, however, and found some consolation in the thought that Clare was unlikely to have been aware of his damning indictment of her domestic economy. For scholastic offences of grammar, spelling, style and syntax he might have pleaded two years of fractured, interrupted education, or none at all, but he offered no excuse. He had written then as a student in a wider world beyond the Halls of Academe. Adventure books, comics and the moving pictures were his study, the Academy of St Michael's his faculty, Will Hay his mentor, and graduation was too far off to be contemplated with anything but indifference.

The time they spent in Essex hardened Phoebe's resolve to return there as soon as it could be arranged. It also revived John's homesickness to be close once again to his gran, aunts and cousins, and while he renewed those contacts it was the possibility of a permanent return to Essex that Phoebe was endlessly pursuing with her mother. During the five days of their stay, there were frequent alerts, raiders came and went, and there was fighting high overhead, but it was all happening as the bombers passed to and from distant targets. It had little or no direct impact on their lives. The threat of invasion was no longer seen as looming large, and Lou and Charlie were asked to keep a lookout for somewhere to rent nearby. When eventually they arrived back in Bucks, it was with a fixed determination on Phoebe's part to press for a return to Essex as soon as it could possibly be arranged.

The Brighton trip was made to visit Kit, the wife of Jack's younger brother, Dan. Until the Blitz they had lived in a small house in Canning Town. Dan was a lighterman on the Thames, and as they had no children Kit also worked managing the affairs of a small riverside factory engaged in the cleaning, repairing and restoring of used sacks for return to circulation. Vast quantities of the goods passing through the docks were wrapped or packed in sacking, and during the war and for many years after the trade flourished, but as shortages came to an end and new packing materials were introduced the world turned to embrace the throw-away concept and Kit's trade joined the many other recovery and recycling operations that became defunct.

When the buildings and contents of her London works had gone to fuel the fires that raged during the first days of the Blitz, Kit moved to manage another depot that was opened at Portslade-by-Sea, three miles or so from Brighton. For most of the war she was there without Dan who served throughout in the merchant navy. To Portslade with her, refugees from the Blitz, went her mother, two sisters, a sister-in-law and an aunt and there they lived together in one large house with a communal atmosphere that reminded John of his pre-war days in the Poplar terrace.

Brighton was one of the stretches of the south coast considered to be likely landing grounds for invasion forces should they ever come, but even in restricted areas there was no absolute prohibition on non-residents entering provided the reason was a valid one. Phoebe and her son did not have the appearance of holidaymakers, and she talked her way without difficulty through such casual questioning as they met at the barriers when they left the station.

They were not on the best of terms on the final leg of their journey. The loss of John's raincoat would have annoyed Phoebe at the best of times. They didn't come cheap she informed him, and money was tight. That was invariably true as he well knew, but only a few days earlier clothes rationing had been introduced, and so the offence was compounded by the fact that his carelessness represented two months' clothing coupons down the drain as Phoebe reminded him several times on their way from the station.

From the top of the bus it was clear that prohibition apart there would be little to attract the casual holidaymaker to Brighton or Hove for some years to come. Tennis courts, bandstand, lawns and bowling greens, all were out of bounds, and as at Southend the seafront and piers were inaccessible behind a tangle of barbed wire and anti-invasion defences. The beaches were mined and strewn with anti-tank obstructions. Strong points and gun emplacements dotted the esplanade, and to deny any possible invader its use, a section of the Palace Pier had been removed.

At Portslade Kit's house and the little yard behind it were just one in a long terrace that formed the top third of a three-layered cake of buildings cut into the rising land between the wharves and factories alongside the Adur Canal and the coastal road from Brighton. At canal level there were workshops, on the first floor warehouses, and sitting on top of these the house itself with a view to the rear which, if unremittingly ugly, was one of constant activity and interest to any young boy.

Perched on a ladder against the backyard wall John looked down thirty feet or more to the canal-side road, the roofs of the factories and warehouses, and the timberyards and wharves alongside the canal. Beyond the canal, on the narrow spit of land separating it from the sea, the same scene was repeated, but with the addition of the towers, chimneys, steelwork and cranes of the power station, and the bunkering yards for the little ships that ran to and from the port. They were a far cry from the Blue Ribbon liners whose models shone out in the windows of the cruise-line offices on his trips to the West End. These were the common drudges of the shipping lanes. Weather-beaten, sea-stained, rusty and thick with the coal dust that drifted from the discharging cranes of the power station, they slipped in through the lock gates on one high tide, stayed long enough for the coal or timber to be discharged and stores to be carried aboard, and were off again running the gauntlet of U-boat and bomber attacks.

The canal, its warehouses, factories and wharves were all secure areas hidden away behind walls or fences with entry gates protected by Royal Navy guards, but Kit as factory manager had her pass, and as neither Phoebe nor John were perceived to be a threat to national security they were nodded through by the sentry for a morning visit to the factory. A few workers lounged outside waiting for Kit to arrive with the keys.

'What's Dan going to say about your new boyfriend then, Kit?' The call came from one of the girls waiting at the entrance. They were always girls if they were under fifty-five, and often if they were over.

'What the eye don't see, Edna – and you keep your eyes off. He's all mine for the weekend.'

She unlocked the door to a building that was dark, silent and heavy with a cocktail of scents given off by the residues clinging to the piles of sacks waiting to be cleaned, checked and repaired. It was a pleasant, comforting smell as of something chewy, sweet and tasty. Much the same, John thought, as the smell that had drifted from the open doors and windows of the warehouse alongside Bow Bridge.

The throw of a master-switch brought light from the rows of hanging lamps, followed almost immediately by piped music from Tannoy speakers hanging from the walls. Within minutes the machinery was humming and the workers were at their places and singing their way through the current favourites. Young or old there wasn't a man among them. That was promising for John – it usually meant he would be spoilt, and he was. Sweets weren't easy to come by, but there were a few about, and during the morning he got more than his fair share as he pestered the girls with his chatter, while Phoebe followed Kit on a round of the sorting, cleaning and machining processes that produced growing piles of sacks to be despatched for reuse.

Nothing was wasted. As the sorted sacks were beaten and shaken, grain, seeds, vegetable pieces and other residues were accumulated in separate piles that went either towards the local collection of waste for pig food or to nourish the fine collection of chickens and ducks that Kit and her sister maintained on an empty plot beside the canal. With eggs rationed at four a month, and a bird for the pot a prize well worth a little trouble, the fowl were kept doubly secure overnight behind the locked doors of an empty workshop and the watchful eyes of the Royal Navy guards.

Their visit to Brighton was soon over, and although Phoebe did not know it when they returned to Bucks, there would be little time left to them there either. Eight months had passed since they arrived. Eight months of undisturbed nights and uneventful days, when they saw and heard next to nothing of the war apart from the distant sound of aircraft passing overhead and the news brought to them by wireless, paper and cinema newsreels. It was a time when isolated minor successes on the battle front could not mask the continuing pattern of major reversals. Greece had been abandoned to the Axis forces. In North Africa German troops and armoured units under Rommel were reversing earlier successes against the Italians. Early May brought news of the heaviest night raids to date on London, with serious damage to the Houses of Parliament and Westminster Abbey, and later in the month HMS *Hood*, under-armoured and outgunned by *Bismarck*, had taken almost fifteen hundred men with her when she split in two in a catastrophic explosion that came less than ten minutes after the

306

start of the engagement. Without the revenge taken on *Bismarck* just a few days later, May would have been the darkest month in a grey, monotonous daily round in which there was little to lift the spirits.

Then after month upon month of mean, cold, fretful and uncharitable weather, virtually unbroken since their arrival, summer settled on the Chiltern Hills. They bloomed and blossomed, and subject to the restraints and restrictions of a wartime economy, the people did the same.

Those were the years of double summer time. Starting in the spring of 1941 after normal summer time had been extended throughout the winter, a further extension of an hour was made for the four months through to August. In the long, hot days around the summer solstice the sun did not set until ten-thirty, and over the fields and lanes twilight lingered for another hour or more. Even at midnight, for those who were still out of bed to enjoy it, the woods on Bledlow Ridge were fringed with the last faint glow of sunset. The evenings were warm and relaxing: a time to be out in the world on the footpaths and rough country lanes, now white with chalk dust underfoot and fringed with fool's parsley pierced by the long spikes of maturing foxgloves. 'Plough Now – Grow More at Home' had been the ministry maxim in the autumn, and throughout the country ancient pastures had been put to the plough for the first time in living memory. In soil newly opened to sun and weather, thousands of wild-flower seeds, dormant for many generations and seized by the old imperative, had leapt to life, and in the fields of corn that stretched beside the lanes the gold of the ripening crop was flushed with the brilliant red of poppies.

Double summer: a summer of excess. That was how it seemed when July arrived with a blast of heat and sun that the old hands in the village claimed was the best in years. Throughout the long days the countryside shimmered in the heat haze. During the warm, sultry nights windows were flung open, blackout blinds were ignored, and light flooded into the rooms from a moon that in the Chilterns brought no threat of bombers. Normal rules and discipline were relaxed. At school classes moved out on to the grass; nature-study trips were arranged to the woods; and events for sports day practised on the field behind the playground. When the weekend arrived, bedtimes seemed to be forgotten, and the children of the village were loosed into the long, warm summer evenings until dusk fell, when the loud halloos of mothers summoning their strays back home for the night echoed around the hills like the cries of ewes calling for their lambs.

After long winter months fretting behind blackout blinds and curtains, everyone whose working day was over was to be found outside, either for the lazy pleasure of sitting to watch the summer sunsets, or strolling the local walks through woodland or fields. The straight and open ridge-road to Parslow's Hillock, with its wide views over the valley to the western sky, led on to rides and walks in the deep shade of the beech woods beyond. The footpaths and lanes to the neighbouring village of Speen brought the added pleasure of leaning on gate or fence and watching those whose working day was not yet over, farmers and land girls, grabbing every extra hour of daylight that double summer time was intended to give them.

Evening walks were always chosen to have a pub around about the halfway point. Despite all the many restrictions and restraints of the war, drink and cigarettes were never formally rationed, although shortages imposed their own form of control, and there were many places where the few choice items were kept under the counter for locals or favoured customers only. Fortunately for Jack and his fellow walkers that did not often apply to beer, although it was quite possible to arrive at the local and find it dry until the next delivery.

On the Parslow's Hillock loop the pub was the romantically named, but otherwise quite undistinguished, Pink and Lily. Just outside Speen, snug in the hollow of Flower's Bottom, the Plow Inn was a much more attractive proposition. Remote and unassuming, it had its moment of glory in 1936 when the prime minister's daughter Ishbel MacDonald became licensee. The American ambassador paid a courtesy call. Locals lost their corner seats to a flood of London visitors, and Miss MacDonald carried off the captain of the darts team as husband. By 1941 only the memory lingered on. Surrounded by hedgerows, trees, cornfields and pastureland, and tucked away below low flint and mortar walls, it looked shabby and time-worn, but the brick and trellis porch overhung by an apple tree was welcoming, and it had some ancient seats and tables outside where walkers could relax, sup their beer and smoke their Woodbines in the gentle warmth of evening.

With a sense perhaps that neither sunny days nor his time in the hills could last for much longer, John was at home only to sleep and eat and spent every daylight hour when he was free from the tedium of the schoolday routine far away in the countryside with Peter and friends. The Carlton cinema in Risborough provided a highly spiced diet of war films for their imaginations to feed on, the Chilterns a backdrop for their games much richer than the streets of Poplar, and everywhere, in the barns, behind the trees, in the ditches, along the hedgerows and through the lanes, the staccato bark of their machine guns and the burst of their exploding mortar shells carried the sounds of their own personal war.

On a number of occasions following Phoebe's trip away the matter of a return to Essex was discussed, but Jack remained uncertain about it, and the matter was left unresolved. The first of the events that led to their departure came on a Sunday towards the end of June on one of the long, dry days in that halcyon spell of weather. John returned home in the dusk from an afternoon with the Barhams to hear the news that Germany had invaded Russia. Churchill had spoken on the wireless and told the people of the nation that the Russians were now to be their allies. Within weeks Comrade Stalin had been metamorphosed to Uncle Joe; the Don Cossack marching song was filling the airwaves; and Joe Loss and his orchestra were serenading their lovely 'Russian Rose'.

The news was vaguely interesting to John, as was anything to do with the war, but it all seemed to be happening a long way off, and unlikely to have any immediate impact on his life. He was wrong. In the Führer his mother had found an unlikely ally in her campaign to return to her home ground. Beyond John's private world the strategic significance of the German campaign in Russia was immediately seen, analysed and discussed at length. Within a few days it was agreed that there was no longer any reason to stay away from Essex. Hitler would not choose to be engaged in major conflicts on two fronts, and an invasion was no longer considered a threat while the Russian front was open.

As the weather was breaking in mid-July with a series of thunderstorms that burst violently across the Chiltern Hills, a letter came from Lou. A house to rent was to be available from the beginning of August. It was bigger than one family would want or could afford, but Doll and Charlie were willing to share to relieve the pressure on Bayhurst. If there had been any doubt about accepting, it was resolved immediately when Phoebe learned of its location at the top of the hill, no more than a hundred yards from Bayhurst.

In practical terms their departure was speedily and easily managed. They had arrived with little. They had added little, and they would leave with little. In emotional terms it was much more complicated. In Peter, John was sure he had made a lifelong friend, and Peter felt the same. They parted with an exchange of gifts: John's draughts to Peter, Peter a treasured fox skull and a couple of splendid marbles to John. They would write, they said, and see each other when the war was over. The written exchanges lasted until the following Christmas when they each sent home-made cards. After that there was nothing, and they never met again. The separation from Clare and Ted was a more intense and emotional affair. There must have been times during the ten months when they longed to have their home to themselves as much as Phoebe wanted to be back with her family, but if they did they never showed it and had been unstinting in their efforts to make their visitors feel at home.

At the parting Clare was in tears, and Ted uncharacteristically uneasy and embarrassed as Jack told them just how much their welcome, love and generosity had meant to him. Phoebe, always sparing of emotion at such times, was as close to tears as John ever saw her until his gran's death many years later. The attachment formed in those ten months was long-lasting. Letters and presents were exchanged throughout the war, and visits made in the years that followed. Ted died first, many years after Jack, and Clare just a few years before Phoebe. On John's last visit with his mother, Clare, with his reputation as a trencherman still in mind, presented him with a lunch that would have defeated a working lumberjack and a tea fit for a rugby fifteen.

24

The Anchorage

Brambles and woodland were reclaiming the site of their first Essex home when John returned to it many years after the war. Nothing remained to show that a house had once stood there but the crumbling brickwork of a derelict hothouse, where a stunted fig tree lingered on hopelessly nursing a handful of withered and mildewed fruits. There were few places in the muddy wastes of the plotlands where a hothouse would not have seemed absurdly out of place, but The Anchorage was one of them. Built for a retired sea captain, long since a widower, and given its name in what must have been a fit of nautical nostalgia, it was unusually large and quite out of keeping with its neighbours.

How or why it was that the captain no longer lived there never became clear. Strange things happened to properties in the early years of the war, especially in areas of high risk, and when the two families moved in they found the house much as its owner had left it, fully and handsomely furnished. The rooms were many and generous in size, providing plenty of space for them to live there without being thrown too closely into each other's company. Grand as the house was in size and furnishings, it suffered all the practical disadvantages of Bayhurst, and more. It was approached up a steeper section of the same mud road; lighting was by gas; the lavatory was outside, brick-built but of the same chemical, dig-and-bury type. Unlike Bayhurst it was without a mains water supply.

For those living on the upper half of Clarence Road the water main ended at a standpipe locked inside a brick-built box at the junction with the side road. Every house had a key to the box, but for those who were served by the standpipe, access to fresh mains water meant a long, hard slog back up the hill with full buckets or cans, and it was used sparingly for cooking and drinking only. The particularly fastidious may have used a little for personal ablutions,

311

but most thought that rainwater was more than good enough for that, and capacious water butts or tanks captured all that fell on roofs and sheds.

At The Anchorage there was also a well. The water from its depths was cold, sweet and reliable, but it was a daily labour to provide the house with all that was required. Every morning and evening, once the pump had been primed, fifteen minutes pushing and pulling would draw enough water into a loft tank to keep the house supplied for the next twelve hours. Of all the properties above the side road it was the only one to have a piped delivery system from a loft tank, and as John was assigned the evening stint at the pump he was particularly resentful of excessive use of the taps. After the modern domestic amenities enjoyed in the Chilterns it looked as though life at The Anchorage was going to be an uncomfortable and basic affair, but it proved to have its compensations.

In size the house was similar to the old home in Carters Terrace. On the ground floor there was a good-sized hall, a passageway and four rooms: a generous kitchen/scullery, a large living room, a smaller dining room, and a little workroom with storage cupboards. Stairs from the hall led to three large and two small bedrooms.

They took little that was their own into The Anchorage. Personal clothing and bedding stored during their absence went with them, as did some books, games and personal possessions, but those apart little else was needed. So complete and intimate were the furnishings that they seemed to have stepped in at one door as the owner stepped out of another, and for a few weeks they had the uneasy feeling that they were trespassers to be evicted when the captain returned to claim his own.

One matter of immediate concern was the safekeeping of the clutter of bric-a-brac, knick-knacks, ornaments, china and glass that lay around the house, a reflection of the captain's travels and his late wife's taste, but too much at risk where two or more young children would be on the move. Within a couple of days a sweep had been made through all the rooms, and vulnerable items brought together to be stored out of harm's way in the loft. Clustered around the foot of the stepladder, they watched as Jack stepped up, pushed open the wide loft-hatch and held up a lighted oil lamp. He stood for a few moments looking around him before standing the lamp in the loft and coming down again.

'Have a look up there, Charlie.'

Charlie looked, and so in turn did the rest of them.

The hatch opened into the centre of a fully boarded floor. Here and there a glint of sunlight flickered thinly between loose tiles on the roof, and in each quarter of the loft the glow of the oil lamp dimly illuminated what must have been the captain's collection from a lifetime of travels. Little could be clearly seen. Much was packed in boxes pushed back into the confined angle spaces between floor and roof. The larger pieces standing nearer the hatch were shrouded in sheets, and overall there lay a thin film of dust and a sprinkling of bat droppings.

For the time that John stood at the top of the ladder, balanced by his father's outstretched arms, and with his head at loft floor level it seemed to him that he was gazing into Aladdin's cave. Behind the dusty glass in three display boxes stacked one upon the other, collections of stuffed birds and animals, disturbed in their long slumbers, glared out resentfully at him. From nails driven into the timbers of the roof just a few feet above his head hung framed collections of butterfly wings: huge, multicoloured and glowing; iridescent even in the faint light of the lamp. Books spilled out across the floor from heaps packed into the roof angles. A long native shield and a pair of carved paddles rested against an elaborate hatstand tucked under the ridge of the roof with barely an inch to spare. Half a dozen fancy walking sticks were propped through the brass rails around its glovebox. And there was more, much more, just waiting to be discovered. Boxes to be opened, dust sheets to be lifted, secret corners and mysterious objects to be explored, but already his father's hands were pulling him back down.

Inevitably curiosity got the better of Jack and Charlie, and before the pieces brought together for storage went into the loft they explored the distant corners, lifted the dust sheets, and nosed their way into a few of the boxes. John sat and listened to them describing to the other just what lay hidden up there and knew that alone in the house, with enough time in hand and the ladder available, he would find the temptation to explore hard to resist. The same thought occurred to Jack, who had a few words with him on the subject and concluded with a strict prohibition on any attempt to enter the loft and meddle with its contents.

At The Anchorage, for the first time in his life apart from his brief evacuation to Cornwall, John had his own bedroom. It was the smallest of the five, at the back of the house, with a window opening on to the wood and an outlook towards the fields and the estuary. That night, alone in the room, with the curtains open, and faint moonlight illuminating the still-strange surroundings, he went to sleep dreaming of the forbidden delights resting in darkness just a few feet above his head: unexamined, untouched and unexplored.

An acre or more of land enclosed the house. To one side, in a separate paddock, ungrazed for many years and already sprouting scrub, the hothouse stood in reasonable order. Paint flaked from the framework, but most of the glazing was still unbroken. The small pear-shaped fruits hanging from the fig tree were hard, green and unappetising, but bunches of grapes from a vine trained along the roof were beginning to ripen and promised a welcome addition to a dull and restricted wartime diet. In the event they tasted few of them. The hothouse door had no lock and local opportunists carried away the best bunches just a few days before they were ready for picking. Mickey Heard's casual approach to property rights made him the principal suspect, but he admitted nothing, and if the near-ripe grapes eventually went to feed his sow they went in a good cause.

From the road the path to the house passed through trees and shrubs which screened it from sight and darkened the rooms at the front with their shade. To the east open fields bordered the long, wide strip of land. Behind the house, chicken sheds and runs stood ready to be brought into use again, and a wide expanse of vegetable garden was not yet wholly overwhelmed by weeds. Beyond the garden all was woodland to the end of the plot, where a circle of tall and ancient elm trees ringed and shaded a spring-fed pond still dark with deep water despite the previous weeks of dry and hot weather.

For several days the sounds and sights of war were distant and unobtrusive, and it seemed that their peaceful Chiltern world had followed them to Essex, but before long daytime alerts and night sirens shattered that illusion, and the business of war was resumed although not quite as before. The bombers no longer came wave upon wave in the overwhelming numbers of 1940, but in smaller groups: fifteen, twenty or twenty-five planes using hit-and-run tactics on specific targets. Smaller, yet still deadly enough for those on the receiving end. In almost two years of war, however, there had been no major bombing incidents in the immediate area, and in the homes scattered across the plotlands many preferred to accept what was seen as the remotest of risks and stay in their beds rather than spend a restless night in a dank, cold and clammy shelter.

At The Anchorage, when an alert came, they were left with no choice as it had no shelter. For two or three nights they left their beds and gathered together when the sirens sounded, but even that practice was soon abandoned as no one place in the house was safer than any other. The sights and sounds of the raids were unchanged: the throbbing drone of the bombers, ack-ack guns hammering away from the many batteries on the flight paths to London, and searchlights sweeping the skies, but the smaller numbers were soon past and they saw little of them.

It was early August when they arrived from Bucks, and most of the school holidays, week after long week of them, lay ahead. All of John's family, his gran, Clara, Elsie and Kath when they were home on leave, were once again around him. No longer just along the passage or up the stairs as in Carters Terrace, but little more than a short walk down the road. Carters Terrace had been long abandoned, and Bayhurst, now permanently occupied, seemed more homely and welcoming. Mick was there dancing on his perch to greet him and a new cat had joined the household. Terry had not been replaced. While the families settled in to their new home, John looked forward to exploring once again the paths and haunts familiar to him from earlier visits and, with old and new friends, to pushing further afield where the business of war would provide much to engage them.

The land levelled off at the top of the hill where The Anchorage was the last house on the southern side of the road. Beyond it there were four or five plots of land intended for sale, but never developed. The posts and fencing once marking them off had long since fallen and disappeared, and casual grazing by goats, geese and assorted livestock had created a broad green to the end of the road where the cornfield began.

On the northern side of the green all the plots, with one exception, had been developed in the best plotland tradition of basic, single-storeyed holiday dwellings that had gradually been altered, extended and improved for permanent living. All were surrounded by a clutter of privies, sheds and livestock houses for the mixed menagerie grazing the green. The exception was a larger, better-built, two-storeyed house standing almost opposite The Anchorage. As the family living there included Martin, a boy of his own age, John soon got to know them well.

The Arrowsmiths, unlike many on the plots, were not refugees from the Blitz, but had lived there since before the war. They would probably have seen themselves, and been described, as middle-class, but were unusual in that it was the wife and not the husband who went to work each day. Like Clara she was one of the many who rose early and in all weathers made their way down the tracks of muddy side-roads to wait in the lane for the local coach which ran an early morning and evening service to and from Pitsea station and the trains to London, where most of them worked. If they missed the coach there was no alternative but the long slog up the lane to catch a county bus on the main road, followed by another walk to the station from Pitsea Broadway. With petrol for private use rationed to thirteen gallons for three months for a 9 HP engine there were few private cars to be seen on the roads. By June of 1942 that had been cut to half, and from then on the use of cars was banned except for business or other essential purposes.

The London workers were a close-knit community drawn together even more tightly by the knowledge that the Southend to London railway lines on which they travelled continued to receive occasional attention from the Luftwaffe even after the mass raids on London had ceased. The refineries at Thames Haven and Coryton, the docks at Tilbury, shipping moving on the river, and the many industrial and commercial sites that lined the Thames into London continued to be subjected to the smaller hit-and-run raids. For German pilots, trains moving along the estuary presented a tempting target for strafing as they passed, and the line had not been free of tragedies.

The local coach service was operated by the same Campbell who had served the family so well in their earlier travels from Poplar, and later to the Chilterns. Sadly it lacked the antique, idiosyncratic charms and entertainment value of Farmer's Bus, but it made up for that in its reliability and a reputation for cramming into its limited space a seemingly unlimited number of passengers. Many an intimate relationship was formed, forced and finally blossomed in its smoky, hothouse interior. All the regulars were well known. If they failed to appear as expected at their usual place the bus would stop briefly to make sure they were not about to come into view. It was the exchange for local gossip, a debating chamber for progress on the war, and a platform for daily reviews of the previous night on the wireless.

Mrs Arrowsmith must have been a year of so younger than Phoebe, and was referred to with some respect as a 'good-looking woman' and a 'professional lady'. The latter may have meant no more than that she worked in an office, but whatever her occupation, either she was paid exceptionally well or the family had some other source of income, for as John got to know them better it became clear that their local reputation for being well-heeled was more than justified.

It was easy to understand why her looks were so frequently commended. Of more than medium height, and on the well-built side of slender, she had a figure that compared favourably with the popular favourites seen at the cinema. In appearance and stature she was a slightly homelier version of Myrna Loy, the elegant lady in *The Thin Man* films from those vintage Hollywood days.

Of the quality of her legs it is enough that even Clara grudgingly acknowledged that they matched those of the women in the family, and although none of them were by nature vain they were certainly proud of their legs and ankles. Nor was it an attribute confined solely to the distaff side of the family, and in the far-off post-war years John himself would be more than happy if he could strut his amateur dramatic stuff in doublet and hose and display to advantage a finely turned pair of calves and shapely ankles.

The clothes she wore for work never varied – a smart, snug-fitting, two-piece suit in a blue pinstripe material over a smooth cream blouse, court shoes and a jaunty little hat with a wisp of lace. Neat, tidy and formal at all times, her dress at home was an older, well-worn version of the same outfit, minus the hat. The only feature that marred her looks was a cautious and thin smile, entirely out of keeping with a pair of warm, sparkling eyes, and concealing perhaps a less than flattering set of teeth. She was a woman who knew her own worth and, without assuming any air of superiority, relished the thought that she was a cut or two above her fellow commuters and neighbours.

In the early days at The Anchorage Martin was lending a hand with John's evening stint at the pump when Charlie met him for the first time. The exchange was a brief one.

'Who's this then, John?'

'Martin.'

'That's Martin Chuzzlewit is it?' asked Charlie.

A trifling, insignificant bit of nonsense it might easily have been forgotten, but it caught John's fancy at once and was to lead on to better things. Martin was Chuzzy to him from then on. Within days he was Chuzzy to all his friends. Within weeks he was Chuzzy generally, and in time Chuzzy to his sister, and later to his wife. For the rest of his days the name Martin lived on only with his mother, who was far from pleased with the nickname. Little as she liked it, however, it would perhaps have caused no great aggravation had Charlie been able to leave well alone.

A couple of months later, in early evening, he was waiting with Harry, a distant cousin, for the local coach to Pitsea. The service ran from the station to the end of the lane and then returned picking up on the way the few passengers who might be waiting. On its outward run that day it was full with commuters returning from London. They included Mrs Arrowsmith, who smiled her thin smile at Charlie, exchanged a few words and then set off for home. Harry looked after her admiringly, as did most of the men, and asked Charlie who she was. 'Oh that's Mrs Chuzzlewit,' replied Charlie. For Harry, insensible of the delights of literature beyond the pages of the *Daily Mirror* and *News of the World*, that rang no alarm bells. If he thought the name unusual he made no comment and moved on to other matters while they waited for the coach to return.

Harry was not one of the regular group of commuters, but soon after that chance meeting he had occasion to travel up to London on the early train and arrived at the end of the road where the usual cluster of regulars were waiting for the bus. Clara was among them with Mrs Arrowsmith. Harry, a genial, inoffensive chap, had a few words of greeting with Clara and then turned to her attractive companion. Although married he had an eye for the ladies and looked forward to an enjoyable journey to London in the company of a new acquaintance. Deceived by Charlie, oblivious to the mantrap sprung wide before him, and within hearing of all her daily travelling companions he embarked on his opening gambit.

'Good morning Mrs Chuzzlewit. What a lovely . . . . . .'

She fixed him with a basilisk glare that would have chilled a warmer man than Harry and silently turned her back on him to look for the coming of the coach. Harry stood bewildered in the silence that followed. The others had heard his words or were aware that there had been some sort of confrontation, but ignorant of the Chuzzy background, were as mystified as Clara by Harry's greeting. Clara motioned him aside.

'What was all that about then, Harry?'

'All what?'

'The "Mrs Chuzzlewit" bit.'

All that there was to tell was soon told. Disabused by Clara, who took some pleasure in explaining the Dickens connection to him in detail, Harry travelled on to London wrapped in his own little world of embarrassment.

It was nobody's fault of course that the incident and its origins were soon common knowledge. It was a choice bit of entertaining gossip, and from then on Mrs A was Mrs C in all circumstances other than within her hearing. With Harry, Charlie's relations suffered a temporary chill. With Mrs A, when inevitably she learned of his part in the affair, they fell into a deep and permanent frost.

Those who remember the summer holidays of their wartime childhood as unbroken, golden, sun-kissed affairs must conveniently have forgotten such weather as blighted most of the first month in The Anchorage. After a fine June and a hot July, much of August 1941 was wet and cool as only an English August can be when summer holidays have been long anticipated. On morning after morning John peered through rain-spattered windows, across a sodden vegetable plot and chicken runs, to the wood dank and dripping under the grey skies of yet another Atlantic front. Gutters and water butts overflowed as squall after squall dumped still more rain and pressed the harvest lower and lower into the mud. Water stood deep in the ruts of the road, and at the end of the wood the pond was brimming beneath the elms.

As days of rain followed one upon another, surface water streamed from the fields above the lane. In the deep ditch that drained the hill it swelled into a flood and in between the downpours, from top to bottom of the lane, the local lads followed at a jogtrot as the torrents in the ditches swept away their ships: old tin cans, broken seed boxes or offcuts of timber. On wide and narrow channels, under bridges, and through culverts and drains they pursued and harried them with stones, sticks and clods of earth, until finally they watched them over the weir and beneath the arterial road into the stream running on through the fields to Battlebridge and the winding creeks that would carry them out to the North Sea. And when the waters eased they dammed the ditch, jumped the ditch and inevitably fell into the ditch.

If they were caught out when the next shower arrived there was often a pillbox nearby in which to shelter. None of them was manned, and it was an easy matter to slip in through the narrow entrances. Ugly, grey, concrete-box intrusions when constructed, they were already beginning to blend into their background. On some, irregular patterns of brown, green and dark-grey paint had originally been added as camouflage, but a season's growth was already providing a natural screen for those that lay deep in the clay, and from their firing slits, through wild flowers and the seed heads of tall grasses, the outlook was east to the fields across which the German panzers had been expected to advance. Inside the boxes, now used more for natural than defensive functions, the air was already acquiring the faint, acrid taint of urine, to which, with the instinct of young dogs cocking a leg, the boys added their own youthful contribution before they left.

As Charlie was briefly out of work and Jack had returned to Essex with no job waiting for him, they spent their time during the few dry spells in refurbishing the chicken runs, clearing the vegetable plot of weeds and, where the condition of the soil permitted, preparing it for the few plantings that could be made so late in the year. Accumulated droppings scraped from the bottom of the chicken houses, and the top couple of inches spaded from their runs were put to one side for use as fertiliser. Just inside the edges of the wood a rank-smelling and nettle-infested heap marked where kitchen waste and garden refuse had been dumped and left untouched for years, but beneath the top levels, which they threw to one side, the material was well-rotted compost and ideal for the garden.

As early as the second Monday after they moved in, Jack and Charlie caught the weekly bus to Wickford taking John with them. A journey of less than four miles, it seemed much further on the twisting, narrow country lanes that lay beyond the arterial road.

Once again it was the ubiquitous Campbell who provided the service to the little town where, once a week, the local cattle, stock, poultry and associated general market was held.

The journey to Wickford had much of the variety and interest that marked their travels in Bucks. In addition to his passengers Campbell would accept anything for transport as long as it didn't foul the floor of his coach; a refinement that they welcomed after their experiences on Farmer's Bus. Geese and ducks travelled with necks and heads protruding from old shopping bags or sacks. Chickens and rabbits were more closely confined in a variety of home-made containers, and young chicks cheeped their way to market inside cardboard boxes. Fruit, vegetables, eggs, honey, jars of pickles, trays of seedlings for pricking out, young plants for growing on and any other commodity that was surplus to the owner's needs but might satisfy another's: they all made the journey in season and the objective was as often barter as a sale for cash. On the outward journey the bus itself could become a mini-market where deals were struck between the regulars on the basis of supply and demand and exchange rates hammered out over the years.

As beginners to those rear-your-own, grow-your-own and bartering activities they travelled to market empty-handed on their first journey. They returned with three point-of-lay pullets, six day-old chicks, two goslings, bundles of winter brassicas for planting out and a variety of seeds. In the hothouse, as glass was not readily available, pieces of old linoleum were cut to patch the broken panes. Seed boxes were improvised out of spare timber from Bayhurst and filled with sieved soil and compost. The earth floor was thoroughly worked over, beefed up with compost and old chicken droppings, and by mid-September the first seedlings were showing. Two of their fresh egg registrations were surrendered to obtain a ration of poultry meal, and the nucleus of their modest smallholding was established and thriving.

All household waste, peelings, cores, green leaves, anything edible, together with anything from Bayhurst was saved to be chopped, boiled, mixed with the meal and fed to the birds. When eventually the fine weather returned and the local harvest had been brought in, they passed an hour or so each evening gleaning on the adjoining field and added two good-sized sacks of corn ears to the stocks for the fowl.

Despite the litter of personal possessions left behind in the house there was neither portrait nor photograph to satisfy John's curiosity about the captain and his lady, and in the course of the many wet evenings that kept him indoors, he spent his time raking through the few remaining traces of their lives not consigned to the loft. Stretched out on the floor in front of the base of a large, old-fashioned bookcase, he sifted his way through a jumbled collection of magazines and papers from the pre-war years: old copies of *Picture Post*, tattered editions of *Sea Breezes*, *Jane's Fighting Ships of 1919* and a large, thin volume of colour illustrations of famous clippers and liners with notes on their history. A selection of brochures from shipping and cruise companies trumpeted the delights on offer before the coming of the U-boats: 'White Line Winter Cruises – 17 Days from £36' or 'Cunard Atlantic Holidays to U.S.A. and Canada from £38 Return.'

On the upper shelves of the bookcase, behind glass doors, *The South Pacific Directory*, *Castaway on the Auckland Islands* and *Knots and Splices* sat alongside books on stowage and navigation, full of plans, diagrams and illustrations at once fascinating and totally incomprehensible. And for relaxation off-watch the captain had, amongst others, *Lord Jim*, *The Mirror of the Sea* and *Three Years Before the Mast*, all of which John would recall and turn to as he grew older.

There was very little there without some nautical link except a few books of reference and a six–volume pictorial history of the Great War, and as he lay leafing through the images of that old slaughter, he listened with the others to the wireless reports of the new. They dealt extensively with the Eastern Front, and almost without exception they were accounts of defeat after defeat for the Russians in an onslaught that by the end of the month saw the Germans at the gates of Leningrad. In their best, well-modulated Oxford English, unhurried and unemotional, unseen, and possibly still dinner-jacketed according to the Reithian code, the announcers presented their summary of events, and gradually he came to terms with those strange names, so often repeated: Timoshenko, Voroshilov, Zhukov, Popov, Kuznetzov. In time they were as familiar to him as Monty, Ike, Bradley and Patton would become as the war progressed.

In *Jane's Fighting Ships* among representations of the crude and clumsy-looking battleships of earlier years he found the plans and

322

photographs of the *Hood*. Slim, sleek and bristling with aggression, she was not commissioned until after the Great War had ended and looked a Dobermann beside the other ancient and ponderous bulldogs keeping her company, and yet he knew that just three months earlier she and her crew had been lost in that brief encounter with the *Bismarck*.

Dry and warm weather from the end of the month released him into the country at large with a week or more to spare before the autumn term started at his new school, and in company with Chuzzy he joined the other boys of the lane as they set about making their own special contribution to the war effort – the German one.

From the upper windows of the house the long lines of anti-glider defences could be clearly seen, their ropes dipping from mast to mast across the fields. There was little talk now of invasion, and to young boys it seemed a pity that such useful assets should be left just wasting away and blowing in the wind. They looked for fields well screened from observation so that they could examine the problem more closely.

Sagging from top to top of the tall scaffold poles the ropes hung well out of reach to allow any farm equipment to work the field unhindered. It should have been the lightest and most agile among them who made the ascent, but it was of course the most gullible, and they watched with interest as Billy grasped the pole, wrapped his legs around it and dragged himself to the top.

Billy Abrey was a new acquaintance from one of the cottages on the wide stretch of green at the top of Clarence Road. Always eager to please and win approval from the group, his failure to make even the most superficial appraisal of the risk and probable outcome of his actions drew him frequently into conflict with an unforgiving and brutish father. This was to be such an occasion. From the top of the pole he reported to them. The rope was thicker than it appeared to be from the ground (it subsequently proved to be about an inch and a half in diameter) and was clamped to the top of the pole in such a way that tools would be needed to release it. It would be impossible to do this and cling to the pole at the same time. They accepted his assessment with disappointment and watched as he slid slowly to the ground.

In wind and weather the unpainted pole had been slowly rusting for more than a year. Much of that rust had now transferred itself to Billy or his clothing. His legs, hands and one cheek glowed a rich and handsome burnt sienna, and from one shoulder down his chest, through his crotch and along his thighs a broad band of rust fouled his shirt and trousers. They were reminded often enough by their parents that clothing was rationed and knew that even the old clothing they were sent out in was replaced only with difficulty. It was typical of Billy that despite the thrashing that he must have known awaited him when he finally summoned the nerve to go home, he remained unremittingly cheerful until he parted from them.

It was obvious from Billy's report that the only way to get their hands on the ropes was to cut them. The span between the posts was such that the lengths they obtained would still be more than adequate for their purposes. The dilemma that faced them was created by the rust on the poles. None of them was ready to repeat Billy's mistake. It was Mickey, inventive as ever, who had found a solution when they met with their knife the following day. He arrived with a long sack snaffled from a nearby farm. At the bottom of the sack holes had been cut in the centre and at the sides, so that when inverted it could be pulled over his head and allow his arms to slip through. Despite this protection he took no chances and stripped off before dropping the sack over his head.

Stripping for Mickey was not a time consuming affair. Even before the war poverty would have restricted his clothing as effectively as ration coupons, and it was more than likely that underwear had never formed a part of his limited wardrobe. Slender and agile he shinned to the top of the pole like a monkey and, clinging comfortably with one hand, soon had the rope on both sides of the pole cut and dropping to the ground. Four more ascents and they had as much as they wanted, but the thick, coarse ropes were heavier than they expected and it took two journeys and some time to carry them to the pond at the end of The Anchorage wood by a circuitous route well out of sight of the windows of the house.

In a broad, saucer-shaped depression, the waters lay dark and still beneath the overhanging trees. If the pond had a natural origin, it had also been remoulded and deepened at some time in the past by an artificial dyke of earth and clay thrown up around its margins. Within the dyke, now broken and eroded, the surface of the water lay some two feet or more below the level of the surrounding banks. Of the elms that fringed the pond, those that leaned inwards over the surface of the water were the focus of their interest, and on one of the trees they found what they were seeking, a stout, thick bough reaching out over the water at the right height.

Tree climbing came as naturally and easily to country boys as walking and running, especially on the rambling, coarse-barked Essex elms, and in a matter of moments two of them were up in the canopy astride the branch. They inched out over the water, well aware of the elm's treacherous reputation for shedding branches without warning, but careless of the risk. A thin, weighted line was lowered, swung to the edge of the pond, and then with more effort than they supposed, the thicker, heavier rope was hauled up, turned several times around the branch and secured. Below, at pond level, it was knotted and cut to length.

There are swings and there are swings, but what the boys had before them in return for their labours was the very nonpareil of swings. From thirty-five, perhaps forty feet above them the rope snaked down towards the pond. Reaching up Mickey grasped it tightly, pushed back and launched himself. Sweeping from the highest point of the bank he swung in a long, leisurely arc, dropping down towards the water of the pond until the frayed end strands of the rope rippled the surface, before rising again to drop gently on the bank at the far side.

A length of broomstick thrust through the strands above the knot made a seat under their rumps, and with the straining rope gripped tightly in one hand they lay back and like swallows skimmed low across the pond, flicking the surface of the water with the tips of their fingers as they passed. Other risky, exhibitionist manoeuvres followed, each one inviting disaster and a soaking, and yet throughout they remained dry. There were no spills, no mishaps. The waters and the trees were in benign mood it seemed and welcomed the company after their long years of isolation.

In the pleasures they took then, and in the long years of war still to come, they might well have said that 'to be young was very heaven'. Not yet old enough for the distant realities of war to have any profound meaning for them, they moulded to their own purposes the ancillary instruments and artefacts of warfare and played their games with innocent enthusiasm and enjoyment in an environment that war seemed to have created just for their interest and occupation.

In Europe, while they were playing, the enormities of the extermination camps built toward their climax, and in the world at large men, women and children no different from them died in their millions.

'Why them and not me?'

It would be years before they matured to puzzle themselves with that question, and to conclude, the more they looked at the matter, that like Waterloo it had been a damned close-run thing that chance might well have swung the other way.

25

An Old Salt's Tale

Gilmore's luck ran out when he signed off for the last time and, after more than forty years at sea, came ashore to the East End where his life had started. Following a series of miserable jobs in the kitchens of West End hotels, he finally retired to meet a violent and lonely death in a two-roomed flat in East Ham.

Old and in indifferent health, he had a standing arrangement that he would telephone Dan each weekend to confirm that he had no problems. Eventually a weekend came with no call, but past experience had shown Gilmore to be unreliable, and it was not until the Wednesday that Dan made the journey from Basildon to the flat in East Ham. It was summer, and it was hot. His duplicate key opened the door to a stink of corruption that told its own story, but Dan gulped some fresh air and stepped in to confirm what he already knew with complete certainty. Gilmore, his head badly injured, was lying dead on the floor in a mess of dried blood. His death brought to an end more than seventy years as a close friend of the family.

Christened Reuben Samuel Gilmore, he was born within a few days of Jack in the closing months of 1899. The fifth child of Ruth, who was American-born, he was black like his mother to whom he came late in life, when she was forty-three. Of his father he knew nothing. He had the distinctive facial characteristics of the Abyssinian people, and photographs showed that when young he had a fine head of hair, but by his mid-thirties not a thread remained and Gilmore was inseparable from the soft Trilby hat that covered his baldness wherever he travelled.

To Birchfield Street in Limehouse, Jack's father brought home a secure, above-average wage each week, and the family lived a working-class life that was comfortable and a little above average. Just a few streets, but a gulf in living standards, separated them from the worst of the slums where Ruth struggled hopelessly and alone to lift her family from a life of crushing poverty. The two boys met on their first day at school: Jack well shod and clothed; Gilmore in bare feet and wearing little more than rags.

It is uncertain just what created the initial bond between them, but from that childhood meeting was born a friendship that was firm and lasting. It had its turbulent moments but ran on for almost sixty years until Jack's death, when John became a junior partner until Gilmore himself died. Whatever it was that attracted Jack also caught the eye of his father, and if Gilmore was not adopted by the family, he was certainly helped along the way as a boy. It would have been little enough: outgrown clothes, some well-used footwear, and a good meal now and then.

At the earliest opportunity he swapped school for work and the chance to earn a few shillings to call his own. Few they certainly were as a latter-day galley slave peeling, chopping, scouring, washing and dobying in whatever rust bucket or superannuated relic of the sailing era was prepared to take him on for the pittance he was paid. His mother died shortly after he started at sea, and from then on Gilmore's base when he was back in port was one of the many seamen's homes, refuges, rests or cheap dosshouses that could be found on the streets around the docks.

As he worked he watched and learned what little he could of basic cookery from the tired old hacks who passed as sea-cooks in the galleys in which he slaved. Shortly after the Great War ended, with enough money stowed away to go ashore for a few weeks, he completed a cookery course with an appropriate nautical slant. Armed with his certificate, a set of chef's knives bought second-hand from one of the pawnshops and a couple of cookery books he was ready to look for something a little better than he had known until then.

His early years at sea had been spent almost entirely on coasting work, dossing down in cramped, dirty, vermin-ridden quarters with little to relieve the monotony of his menial chores. But with his newly acquired qualification to back his practical experience he sought out deep-sea work, with its long absences away from home, nights on distant seas under tropical skies, strange customs in foreign lands and perhaps, if the opportunity arose, a little loving in foreign ports. In short all the romantic experiences in the spiced-up stories that the old hands would have spun him.

He was in his late thirties, a seasoned hand with many years' experience of the sea, seamen and foreign ports of call, before he began to feature in John's life. At intervals of three, four or five months he was an occasional visitor to Carters Terrace where Jack, by then a married man, was living with his young family. Despite his long friendship with Jack, Gilmore was seldom received with anything more than sufferance by Phoebe and the rest of her family. They were never overtly hostile to him, and it might be doing them an injustice to suggest that there was a whiff of racism in their attitude, but with Lou and the aunts he was always 'Darkie' when they talked of him in Jack's absence and their use of the word was not affectionate.

When he was in port he passed his nights for the three, four or five days that he was onshore at the nearby Seamen's Rest, but for all the hours that Jack was available, he and Gilmore were together. Sometimes they met with other old friends, sometimes walked by the river and docks, but mostly they just settled down together talking, sometimes arguing, interminably. Politics, working conditions at home and at sea, the books they were reading, the political situation in Europe and Russia: it was all grist to their mill, and it simply washed over John as he sat vaguely aware of their talk but busying himself with his own activities, comfortable as he always was with the background murmur of familiar voices.

But when they turned to Gilmore's accounts of his voyages and ports of call, he left his games and moved closer as he caught at names that whispered of those magical, faraway places to which only Gilmore had the key: Pernambuco, Buenos Aires, Port-au-Prince, Haiti, Panama, Maracaibo and Valparaiso. Throughout John's childhood and youth Gilmore was the romantic bird of passage with tales to tell that kept John from his play and imbued those workaday ports with a mystery and romance they never had in reality.

One of his earlier trips, after he became a sea-cook in his own right, had been on a small tramp steamer running between ports along the Norwegian coast: remote spots with no communications inland and only infrequently in touch with the outside world by sea.

In one port they had tied up for a couple of nights and Gilmore, off duty for a spell, tidied himself up and stepped ashore for the hour or so it would take to wander around the main streets of the little harbour town. Before he was off the quay he was stopped by the harbour master who spoke a little English. A few words were exchanged, and Gilmore set off on a tour of the town with the master as guide and escort. Their brief exchange had made the situation clear to Gilmore: no coloured man had been seen there before and he was being taken on a round of introductions to the local worthies.

In the years after the Second World War, as racial prejudice in London became more of a problem, Gilmore was increasingly sensitive about his colour, but in his youth and between the wars, despite the coolness of Phoebe's family, his colour had never been an issue. Within the world and society in which he moved there was no overt discrimination. He was accepted on the same terms and in the same way as other men, and so he offered no objection to the harbour master's proposal. If anything he was flattered and a little amused. When at the end of his tour he returned to the ship he had become an instant celebrity, with competition keen for the right to entertain him on the two evenings the ship was in port.

In each of the houses that he visited the rooms were crowded with neighbours pressing for the opportunity to see and, if they had any English, speak with him. He detected some disappointment when his hosts realised that he was a Londoner born and bred and could give them no authentic account of his ancestral homeland, but he was a distinguished and good-looking young man with stories to tell and they were happy enough with his company for the evening.

He never failed to contrast that friendly encounter in Norway with his early experiences in the United States, where the coolness of his reception, the calculated insults and the frequent rebuffs made it very clear to him that he was not to be accepted there as he was in London. Lost, and trying to find his way to the local Seamen's Rest, he stopped to ask a policeman, but in some way, either by word or gesture, he gave offence. Perhaps he was standing too close, perhaps the English accent grated. He received no reply, but the officer's baton stick was lifted to prod Gilmore a little further from him and then pointed in the direction of the rest house. That was in New York, not one of the southern states.

John looked on at only one of Gilmore's departures from London. It was quite impossible to gain access to any of the

330

London docks without proper authority, but on one occasion Gilmore's ship was berthed not in the docks, but in the Pool of London, and when he left the terrace to rejoin her he knew what tide she would be sailing on. Later that day, when the waters of the estuary were still flooding up the Thames towards the Pool, John stood with his father on Limehouse Pier looking towards Shadwell for the first sign of movement. Three ships came out of the pool on that tide, well separated and moving slowly down the channel bows-on to them until they swung broadside to sweep round the bend and make the run down Limehouse Reach.

They saw Gilmore waiting at the stern rails of the second ship and waved him on his way until she swung again into Greenwich Reach and was lost to view. It was only then that Jack looked down and saw John standing there silently with tears washing down his face and dripping off his chin. Something in that seaward parting had caught him as never before, perhaps some imagined connection with the melancholy songs of exile his father sometimes sang, and for a while he was inconsolable.

Lucky in surviving the Great War at sea, encountering neither danger nor adventure, Gilmore was not to be so fortunate when the second war came some twenty years later, and throughout the war years his contact with the family was erratic and uncertain. It was with him as it was with millions of others – it was never known where he was, how he was, when he would next be seen, or indeed if he was still alive. Losses in the merchant fleet were desperately high, particularly in the early years when the U-boat packs were in the ascendant. He had been at sea at the outbreak of war, and from then on the only contact with him for some months had been a brief scrawl on a postcard from Liverpool, Bristol, Glasgow or wherever in the UK he happened briefly to be in port.

It was late spring in 1940 before he was seen again. By then the first alarms of war had faded; many of the children swept away to countryside and coast in the great September evacuation had returned; and the parks and play streets of London were no longer silent. Dunkirk may have been just around the corner, but at home the talk was still of a phoney war and, shortages apart, life in many ways seemed to go on much as usual. But in the docklands of London and the ports around the country the seamen from the ships that kept the nation's life-blood flowing had experience of a very different reality, and Gilmore brought a first-hand account of a war that, far from being phoney, was endured day in day out by all merchant seamen as a matter of life and death.

He had travelled down on a short spell of leave from Liverpool, where his ship had docked after their convoy dispersed, and for once it was not just Jack, but everyone in the house, who gathered to hear what he had to say. They listened in silence as he described the strange conjunction of boredom, anxiety and tension that marked life lived minute by minute in the knowledge that an attack could come at any time, unheralded and from an enemy unseen and unheard.

On deck by day the regular routine of his working schedule in the galley might push that nagging thought away. At night, off watch below deck, in a narrow bunk uncomfortably distant from a companionway, and pressed against a hull that would prove all too fragile in an attack, it was impossible to drive it from the mind. During those hours, awake or asleep, he lay oblivious to the unceasing rumble of the engines, but at all times immediately alert and on the move at the first alien sound. For the crew of every ship in the convoy but one, that sound when it came, would be the dull, dead thud of a distant torpedo strike carried to them through the water.

It came all too often. Sometimes, even before he could reach the deck, it would all be over. The ship would be gone; the crew struggling unseen in the waves, or carried down with the ship. More often there would be flames or explosions far distant across the water, glowing, flickering, fading and falling slowly astern; to be quenched at last as a ship went under. They all knew well enough that if it came to their turn and the ship was lost, they too would almost certainly go with it. The convoy did not pause or deviate, but continued on its way, their prayers and hopes with the victims, but powerless to help. A chance pickup by one of the escort ships was the only faint hope of rescue.

During the eight or nine months since Gilmore had last been seen, he had been on both the North and South American runs. In December his ship had been loading in Montevideo harbour when the *Graf Spee* sought refuge there after its fierce and destructive encounter with *Exeter, Ajax* and *Achilles*. Gilmore had stood with the rest of the incredulous crowds that lined the waterfront when the German battleship, its few days of neutral refuge at an end, steamed away slowly into the fading evening light, blew its scuttling charges and settled into the mud of the bay.

Almost immediately local entrepreneurs were on the water, circling the corpse with their cameras, and Gilmore returned home with a fine selection of photographs showing the ship still belching smoke from the fires following the explosions that opened up her hull. But there was nothing in this that was new to the family. In the preceding January all the local cinemas had been trailing their forthcoming newsreel attraction *The Scuttling of the Graf Spee*, and items of such good news were rare enough for most of the population to pay their entrance fee just for the satisfaction and reassurance of watching the film of that one substantial and visible success. If Gilmore's images were familiar, his vivid account of the damaged battleship's arrival, the funerals of the dead sailors, and the sensation caused by Captain Langsdorff's suicide three days later added a new and intimate touch to what they had seen and read.

In complete contrast to those images of war, he brought with him from Rio a stereoscopic viewer and a collection of coloured transparencies of the city. They had seen nothing like it before, and one after another they sat in grey, deprived, war-embattled London, and gawked at the gaudy three-dimensional scenes from a world away: Rio, lush and glittering at carnival time, each woman an image of Carmen Miranda, and the men handsome, well-fed and bronzed; sun-lit, tree-lined boulevards; cafés awash with food and drink; and night scenes of a city ablaze with a kaleidoscope of light. Lou flicked her way through and turned to Gilmore.

'Worth the journey then, Gil?'

He would have experience and reasons enough to give a considered and negative reply to that question by the end of the war. If there had been an award for survival against all the odds, admittedly by luck rather than good judgement or personal initiative, Gilmore would surely have qualified for it.

They saw and heard nothing from him again before they left Poplar after the first great raid of the Blitz, and it was not until late in the year that a letter arrived in Bucks after a few weeks tracking Jack from the Poplar address. He had heard and read reports of the raids, and their impact on the East End, and his immediate thoughts were for his friends and their families. He was writing purely in hope of course, for he had no way of knowing

333

whether they were alive or dead, nor had they any way of reassuring him until much later when a letter sent to him via the shipping office finally came into his hands telling him how and where everyone was.

Next in his letter came the news that his ship had been lost in a U-boat attack. Everything he possessed had gone down with the ship, but he himself was safe and unharmed and had not even been in the water. The attack had come in daylight; lifeboats had got away with all the crew except those killed by the initial blast; and within hours they had been picked up by one of the escort vessels.

In the two years or more that remained before the Atlantic was finally swept clear of U-boats, Gilmore saw two more ships go to the bottom, and in each case he survived. The second occasion was pretty much a re-run of the first, apart from a wetting and the uncertainty of a much longer wait in the boats before they were spotted and picked up. After the torpedo struck he had started to make his way to the cabin for his jacket and money but felt the ship going, and considered himself lucky to have got off just in time.

He might well have supposed that by then he had paid his dues to the Kriegsmarine, but there came a third time on the South American run when things did not go so well. The ship went down quickly at night. In the confusion and darkness Gilmore went over the side into oily waters, but was able to make his way to one of the boats. When dawn came they were alone on the South Atlantic with nothing but a modestly swelling sea between them and an empty horizon. There were seven of them, filthy with oil, with only a few scraps of clothing each, and nothing more than the emergency supplies stored away on the boat. They were all ordinary crew members, cooks, fitters or ABs. They had a vague idea of their position, but none had any knowledge or experience of navigation, seamanship, prevailing currents or winds, or indeed any asset other than common sense to help them. There was nothing they could do but wait and hope. They were on a well-frequented route, and there seemed every prospect that they would be sighted and picked up before too long.

All that was sensible they did at the outset, apportioning from the emergency rations on board the minimum possible allocation of water and food for distribution each day. The weather was set fair, meaning that the sun was their main threat, and they had no prospect of rainwater to collect. No flying fishes dropped into the boat as sacrificial offerings to supplement their food rations, and for sixteen days they endured with what they had without sighting a ship.

During those sixteen days they were burned and scorched by sun and salt spray. Those with lighter skin more than the others, but even Gilmore suffered. They were hungry, they were thirsty, and as the days passed their weight fell away and dehydration set in. Days of constipation were succeeded by days of diarrhoea, but despite the grimness of the story he had to tell, Gilmore still found humour in the detail with a colourful and graphic account of the practical difficulties of staying on board while sitting with his arse hanging over the gunwales to avoid fouling the boat.

Eventually, at the end of sixteen days, sympathetic currents brought them within sight of the South American coastline. Assisting the currents with the oars, for which they found more strength than they could have imagined, they finally grounded on a fine sandy beach, dragged the boat clear of the surf, allowed themselves an extra helping of rations and dropped down to sleep in the shade of the trees lining the shore. Their luck had finally turned for the better, and by the end of the day fishermen from a local village had spotted the boat on the beach. Taken to the village they cautiously took their first, modest hot meal, slept, ate a little more, and rested until the news of their arrival brought transport to take them inland to the nearest town with hospital facilities. There they spent more than a week enjoying the same sort of celebrity status and hospitality that Gilmore had received in Norway many years earlier. Eventually their idyll had to come to an end. They received news that they had been assigned a ship, and were moved on to be flown out and sign on for the voyage home.

When next they saw him, some months after the events, it was a colourful and gripping account that he gave them. It was a good story, and he told it well, with humour and a grim enjoyment. John listened to it open mouthed and heard it often. For many years, until long after the war, if Gilmore was with them when family or friends called in, they knew that he would not be long in steering his way to an account of his sixteen days in an open boat. 'Have I told you . . .?' he would start, and even if they had heard it all before none of them was hard-hearted enough to tell him so.

Gilmore was lucky in surviving to tell his tale, many had not, and little enough was known generally of the sacrifices they made and the ordeals they endured. There was nothing that was glamorous about the merchant marine: little or no chance to fight back, no glorious victories to be won, just survival with their ship and its cargo until the end of one more crossing. They were non-combatants all of them, and yet by the end of the war 35,000 were dead. At one in four the death rate was much higher than in any of the armed services, and with the men went almost two and a half thousand ships.

Of the terms of engagement under which they were required to serve none spoke with anything but bitterness and contempt. Despite the constant rigours and dangers of their life at sea, no provision existed for paid leave when a ship returned to port. A man wanting to visit family or friends, or simply recover breath and balance after months of danger, had no alternative but to sign off and go off-pay. Even more despicable was the law which enabled shipowners to stop payment of wages once a ship went down. For the families of those who went with it, and for those who survived their time in the waters of the North Atlantic, the result was the same – pay stopped on the day of sinking. There were some shipping lines that adopted a more enlightened approach when a ship was lost, but there were plenty that did not.

During the early years of war they saw little of Gilmore, but in 1942 he burst upon the grey austerity of their wartime world like showers upon the desert, and for a few days and weeks they flourished and waxed fat. It is only in the context of the severity of wartime deprivation that the impact of his arrival can be fully appreciated. Its details have been documented to excess, but it was in brief a world where nothing was available but what was essential for survival, where what was essential was itself limited by rationing or shortages, and where choice was almost non-existent. If 'they' had it, you were glad to get it. Excluded from the austerity were such of the wealthy as chose to be, and those who lived on the fringes and through the flourishing black markets.

While the ship was loading in the USA Gilmore had learned that the intended port of arrival was to be London. Although rationing of sorts had been introduced in the States following Pearl Harbor, it was not extensive nor remotely as severe as at home. Gilmore and his cabin mate found no difficulty in buying what they wanted, and they must have sat on it, slept on it, and stepped over it for the duration of a voyage home that was blessedly uneventful. Gilmore as cook also had use of the ship's cold room.

The war in the Atlantic was in Churchill's words 'the Battle *for* Britain', and for the work they did and the sacrifices they made, the men who made the crossings were held in the highest regard by all who understood that work: by the men of the escort vessels; by those who received and cared for survivors on shore; and, most importantly, on their homecomings, by the men of the customs service whose blind eyes were in the best tradition of the Nelson touch.

It was midsummer 1942. Jack and his family were out of The Anchorage and had been living in the bungalow on Pound Lane for just a month or so when Gilmore walked in, unexpected and empty-handed. After their greetings, which were always warm when he arrived out of nowhere after months of silence, he asked them to give him a hand to bring in his gear. That was most unusual: usually he arrived with one suitcase, perhaps two.

They followed him to the gate where his taxi was still standing. The driver grinned as they approached.

'You lucky people!'

Gilmore opened the taxi door and pulled away a piece of canvas covering an assorted collection of tins, boxes, parcels, bottles and shiny packets, all cunningly stowed away to occupy every inch of space. Yet more goods were packed into the boot and alongside the driver, who helped to carry them into the house and left well satisfied with the packet handed to him as a tip.

In a society of plenty, awash with consumables, spoilt for choice, overindulged beyond measure and with a sense only of wants not needs, what came into the house that day would seem unexceptional and commonplace. In the circumstances of the time it was as though the horn of plenty had discharged itself into the living room. From the ship's cold room, still well frozen, came steaks and a pack of bacon. There were round tins of ham, long slab-sided tins of corned beef, packs of coffee and tea, tins of salmon, a sack-like container of sugar, tins of butter, cardboard boxes holding bars of chocolate – milk, nut, fruit and nut – long glossily wrapped packs of Chesterfield, Lucky Strike and Camel, 200 cigarettes in each, and for those who hadn't a taste for American cigarettes, tins of 50 Wild Woodbines, export grade, packs of dried fruit, packs of nuts, packets of silk stockings, tins of jam and guava jelly and half a dozen or more bottles of spirits. Last of the treasures from Gilmore's argosy came a small hand of bananas, waxy green just ripening to yellow and with the scent of the tropics still upon them.

Spread around the room it was Scrooge's vision of Christmas Present – 1940s style – and Gilmore was the presiding spirit. With a twist of the lid he sliced through the thin silver foil on a tin of Woodbines and the sweet, aromatic scent of the tobacco teased John's nose with its fragrance. One or two brief encounters with cigarettes had left him with a taste for more, and he had his own plans for one of the American packs. A bottle was opened, the chocolate broken, and while Gilmore began to tell his story Phoebe began a preliminary division and sorting of the spoils.

'Here, take those up to your gran.'

She handed a bag of tins and packets to John and some chocolate and bananas to Moira. When they returned from their errand the rest of the chocolate was missing apart from one unopened bar on the table.

'You can look at me like that as long as you please. I know what you're like, and it's all been put away till Christmas.'

As events were to show her determination to hide the chocolate succeeded far beyond her intention or expectation. He searched, of course, whenever he was alone in the house. He searched cupboards, drawers, and suitcases stuffed under the bed; he looked on top of the wardrobe; he balanced on a chair and poked his head through the little hatch into the loft; he even explored the inner recesses of the piano: it was a fruitless, a fruit and nut-less, search. It was a long run to Christmas, and as the months passed he searched again and again, but without success. On the first day of December he reminded his mother of the chocolate and the proximity of Christmas, but got short shrift.

'Now don't you start or you won't get any at all.'

He knew her well enough to know that she would never stick to that, but years of experience had taught him that she was proof against all his wheedling, and appeals to his father produced only a smile and shake of the head.

On the last day of term he returned home from school to find the secret hoard once again on display, and his own reputation under a cloud. His mother was convinced, and his sister and father agreed, that there had been more bars of chocolate than were now before them on the table. Suspicions were, of course, focused entirely on John.

'What have you done with them? Have you found them and been stuffing yourself quietly somewhere?'

Phoebe always favoured the direct, boots-first approach, but his father looked up at him and must have been satisfied by the expression of utter bewilderment on his face. There were more dark looks from his mother, but then the matter was dropped and a division of the spoils made: a bar, perhaps two, wrapped up as extra presents for each of the family households within visiting distance, and the remaining half dozen or so kept for Christmas. The chocolate lasted until the end of the year, and the few remaining tinned goods were eked out into the following summer, but by the next Christmas they were back to a depressing austerity which seemed even worse by contrast with their brief period of plenty.

Two more Christmases passed, and as another new year moved towards autumn Phoebe burst into a short period of domestic activity. She hadn't got many possessions of consequence, but what she had she liked to move around the house in a search for a little variety. After a few false starts sideboard, display cabinet, table and chairs had all at last ceased their wanderings, and John was lounging in a low armchair that had come to rest alongside bookshelves fitted into a recess by the chimney breast in the front room.

It was raining. He had nothing to do and out of boredom pulled one of the large books from the bottom shelf. He would never put his hand to a more interesting volume: H.G. Wells' *A Short History of the World*, magazine editions with colour pictures, all bound together inside a home-made hard cover. As he sank back into the chair he saw a faint glint of silver at the back of the empty space left by the book, and within seconds held in his hand an untouched bar of fruit-and-nut chocolate. More books removed disclosed six more bars. This was the missing part of the hoard, originally stowed away in haste by his mother while he was out of the house and its location forgotten.

He was over-young to be faced with such a moral dilemma and had to give the matter thought. Slipping one bar into his pocket he replaced the books and grabbed his coat.

'Just going up to gran's, Mum.'

That was not unusual and he went out into the rain. Passing

behind Bayhurst he slipped into the shed unseen and unwrapped his loot. The chocolate was bleached by age and heat to a chalky, milky-brown colour, but happily the taste was quite unaffected. Out of the rain, sitting comfortably in one of the deckchairs, he worked his way slowly and methodically through an eight-ounce bar. One square at a time, disciplined and unhurried, he sucked off the chocolate, crunched and swallowed the fruit and nuts, and turned to the next. By the time he had finished the rain had stopped and he was stuffed to capacity.

He completed his cover story by calling in to see his gran, but by the time he returned home he knew that he could never keep the matter to himself and that somehow he had to disclose the existence of the hoard. Back in the front room he sat for a few minutes before calling out in surprise at his remarkable discovery. His story was, he thought, convincingly told, and he managed to conceal his lack of enthusiasm when one of the bars of chocolate was broken and handed round. The rainy weather passed, summer returned and several days of the school holidays slipped away uneventfully following the disclosure of his find.

Monday-morning breakfasts were using-up meals, and he could smell bubble-and-squeak frying in the kitchen when he went to the table. His morning greetings from the others were unusually solicitous, but otherwise all seemed normal. Two plates of bubble-and-squeak came in: one for his father and one for Moira. Beautifully browned, even a touch burned – just the way he liked it. Neither started to eat, but sat watching as his plate and its contents were placed before him.

There, carefully opened up and smoothed out, the torn and wrinkled silver wrapping and outer cover from his clandestine fruit-and-nut bar lay accusingly before him. Searching for dirty handkerchiefs for her washday, his mother had found the screwed-up paper in his jacket pocket. Faced with such overwhelming evidence there was nothing for it but a full disclosure. It was an embarrassing breakfast time for him even when, at last, his own bubble-and-squeak appeared, but the immensity of the temptation chance had thrust upon him seemed to be understood, and even his mother was not inclined to pursue the matter. Only Moira had a comment to offer: 'Trust you to be that stupid.'

From the time they moved to Harcourt, Gilmore usually stayed with them for two or three days, kipping down for the night on a bed-chair in the front room, and while he was with them John listened to his stories over and over again quite happily. They saw him many more times before the war was at an end, but no subsequent visit was as sensational or well-provisioned as that one golden homecoming.

If he arrived from one of the northern ports it would be with no more than a night to spare and carrying just a couple of pieces of hand luggage. On those brief visits he could bring little except his own personal items, but there were always some cigarettes for Jack, a few little luxury items of food for Phoebe, chocolate for John and, later in the war, nylons, lipsticks and make-up for Moira, who was by then of an age to be interested in such things.

When Jack died, many years after the war, Gilmore was as usual far away and was sent the news by cable. As he grew older he lost the taste for deep-sea work and turned again to coasting where he had begun. When eventually he came ashore for good he moved through a string of hotel kitchens until eventually he retired to the little flat where Dan eventually found him dead.

The police were called, and Dan for his pains was grilled and pestered for many hours. When Gilmore's body had been removed and their inspection completed, the flat was sealed by the police until their enquiries were completed. The conclusion they reached, endorsed by the subsequent inquest, was death by misadventure. Gilmore, they decided, had been standing on a chair to reach up to a light fitting, had fallen and caught his head on the corner of the table. No further investigation or enquiries were considered necessary.

Dan was the principal beneficiary of Gilmore's small estate. In processing this it was found that his bank account had been closed just a week or so before his death when the balance, over £3000, representing the bulk of the estate, had been withdrawn in cash. No cash had been found in the flat, nor any evidence that it had been invested or used elsewhere. When access to the flat was finally obtained, it became clear that an expensive chess set and two or three other items of value he was known to have possessed were also missing. Advised of these facts, all of which were new to them, the police were less than indifferent. Another possible addition to the crime statistics – no thank you. The matter had been investigated, a conclusion properly reached and the case closed – end of story.

26

Call Me Madam

September saw John and his sister return to regular, uninterrupted schooling again for the first time in two years. The command economy of wartime Britain permitted nothing but the essential use of cars, and as few of the children had bikes the school run of 1941 was made by most of them as it had been for a century or more: in shoes, boots or wellies, come fair weather or foul. From The Anchorage it was a mile and a quarter to St Margaret's Church of England School in the little hamlet of Bowers Gifford, and except in the worst of weather it was a pleasant enough way to start the day: a gentle, uphill walk past fields, bungalows, side roads and the few shops, with the numbers of children swelling all the way. A leisurely, rambling affair it all too easily declined to a dawdle or standstill at any of the diversions along the way.

At the top of the lane they turned right for the last half-mile on the main road through open farmland and a scattering of houses. To their left Church Lane ran away towards the hazy skies above the estuary. It started as a long, level stretch of road running between hedgerows, but then dropped steeply down the hill to the isolated parish church of St Margaret's and beyond, under the railway bridge, the lonely marshes and creeks that were a regular playground for the local youth. Further along the main road came the little cluster of houses, in one of which the school's formidable headmistress lived with one, or sometimes two, of the teachers who had the nerve and strength of character to lodge with her from time to time. Next, and most destructive of early-morning time-keeping, they passed, or stopped at, the old forge and workshop of Alfred Markham, Blacksmith. A little further on Reddington's, the village grocer, hardware, general shop and post office, also had its attractions, but by then they could be clearly seen from the school and it was folly to linger.

By 1936 the old National School at the foot of the hill had served the parish for more than ninety years and reached the end of its days. When it was replaced by the church, the new school was built at the top of the hill immediately alongside the old rectory, where it was much more conveniently placed for the rector to exercise the supervisory brief that was customary.

The building was modern in style: inoffensive but utterly undistinguished, and perceptively described by one of the teachers as 'classic cowshed in design'. Built in brick, it was a single-storey, long, low building with a utility block at each end: girls to the east, boys to the west. Behind the covered veranda that linked the two blocks there were just three classrooms, one self-contained, the other two separated by a sliding partition. At one end of the double room there was a little stage used for assemblies, plays, prize-giving and other formal occasions, when the partition was drawn back to create one large space. Light, airy and south-facing, the rooms had been thoughtfully provided with generous expanses of glass windows by an architect who had no reason to anticipate the hazard they would present in the event of bomb blasts, and so day after day through a latticework of anti-blast tape the sun traced the same intricate pattern of light and shade across children, desks and floor.

The buildings stood well back from the road, at the end of a drive through a large plot of land carved from one of the fields alongside the rectory. In one corner of the plot, closer to the road than the school, an older L-shaped, insubstantial-looking building contained the basic school canteen and St John's chapel, a simple affair that during the week served as a chapel-of-ease to save parishioners the long haul to the church. Behind the school building there was a hard surfaced playground, a wide expanse of grass, and then the boundary hedge, elm trees and the corn fields rolling away into the distance.

At the head, and firmly in charge of her little kingdom, was the headmistress, Miss Gladys Ashton. An imposing figure of a woman she exuded an air of authority that she did not expect to be challenged. Her success could be judged by the fact that not only the pupils, but the staff and parents all called her Madam, a title she assumed as of right. Only to the rector, the Revd John Bryers, during his regular school visitations was she Miss Ashton. It is inconceivable that anyone, anywhere, ever called her Gladys.

Prior to September 1939, life for the school staff would have been a sleepy, unruffled affair with manageable classes of placid country children, and a pattern of working days that followed the rural, national and liturgical rounds of Easter, Harvest Home, Empire Day and Saints' Days from one year into the next, and despite the changes, stresses and difficulties that war brought, many of those old traditions continued on into the war years.

Country areas remote from cities and factories were not considered to be likely targets for the terror bombing that was feared, and so there had been no evacuation from Bowers Gifford. On the contrary, despite the location of the parish at the centre of what might have been the main thrust of the anticipated invasion, evacuees had been moved into the area in the early months of the war. It was one of the ironies of the contingency planning of wartime that even as this was happening, schoolchildren from Southend, just eight miles down the road and considered as at high risk in the event of invasion, were being sent to places of safety in Nottinghamshire and Derbyshire. Had the Germans come, Bowers Gifford would have been directly in the line of their advance towards London.

The evacuees came again in much greater numbers after the first major raid on London, transforming the size and nature of Madam's little empire, and it was a school with classes bulging at the seams and comprising as many Londoners as local children when John joined it in the autumn of 1941.

At St Margaret's children started at the age of five and left when they were eleven. With good fortune and ability (competition was intense and both were needed), a few passed the scholarship examination and went on to higher education in Brentwood either at the girls' high school or at Sir Anthony Browne's, a minor public school for boys. The few who failed the examination and the many not even selected to sit it, moved on to Craylands Secondary School from where, despite all that was said to the contrary, opportunities and career prospects were much less promising.

Pressure of numbers meant that classes were held not only in the three original classrooms, but on the stage and just off it in a small room where scholarship classes took place for the few that had been marked out by teachers and Madam as fit to be brought on to sit the examination. Inequitable and unsatisfactory as that

344

process of preselection was, it was accepted by parents without demur.

Guided, directed and at times overawed by Madam were her staff of young, or relatively young, women. Miss Balaam, the oldest, had responsibility for the babies in the reception class in the one self-contained room. Petite, with kind, earnest eyes, her wavy hair, centre-parted, was already greying and the soft downy outline of a moustache forming on her upper lip when John first met her. More than twenty years later her appearance was virtually unchanged. Miss Powell had the bloom of youth still fresh on cheeks fringed by dark, wavy hair, a smile to dazzle, and a figure that brought her a weekend following of young men from the nearby service units.

And Miss Faulke, adorable Miss Faulke, was John's first romantic entanglement. Her voice was ever soft and sweet, and her looks bewitched him. One apple for such a teacher was as nothing. He would have cast bushels of apples at her feet for just one smile that was all his own, and he was torn between his love for Miss Faulke and incipient desire for the girl from the local dairy with the pouting lips, long dark ringlets and mocking eyes.

To Miss Faulke he never told his love, but worshipped and suffered in silence. The girl from the dairy was alas in the senior class, his superior both in years and style. Her indifference fanned the flames of a naive passion, and he persisted, but without much reward. Following the golden visit from Gilmore in 1942, and just before she was to leave the school, he made a last bid for her favour. Secretly cut and wrapped at home, carried to school with care, and offered with great delicacy, as he thought, he placed before her his final tribute, a substantial slice of ripe banana. The girl from the dairy was not impressed; she didn't like bananas and, as she made clear, didn't like him very much either. The incident still rankled enough a few years later for him to feel some satisfaction on hearing that she had married, 'had to marry' was inevitably the local gossip, Charlie Wright, a great lump of a boy, always excluded from John's group at school because of his impenetrable thickness.

They must have seemed porous, uncertain and leaky pitchers for Madam and her acolytes to fill with such wisdom and knowledge as they were able to carry to them, and the times and

345

conditions in which they worked did little to assist. What they did do was taken for granted, of course, and not always welcomed. Only in retrospect could it be seen just how inventive, tenacious and single-minded they were in protecting and pursuing the welfare and education of their children in the face of the distractions and difficulties that war imposed on them.

The original funding of the school buildings by the local diocese not only created and perpetuated a curious division of financial responsibility between the Church and the County Education Authority, but also areas of uncertainty that both were only too eager to exploit. Into this limbo fell the provision of air-raid protection for the children and staff. When the County had finally and irrevocably denied any responsibility for the work, Madam took her fight, as only she knew how, to the Church, yea even unto the bishop himself. She carried the day, as she usually did, and by the time John started at the school substantial walls of sandbags made the cloakrooms in each utility area as safe as they could be, and they were their shelters in time of danger.

In the secure, unrationed days prior to the war, children had either walked home or brought sandwiches for their lunch, but as rationing was extended and shortages increased, malnutrition among children was recognised as an increasing danger. Although local authorities were authorised to provide school meals and substantially reimbursed when they did, many took little or no interest in doing so and fewer than ten percent of schoolchildren benefited.

With the risk of air attacks on the way to and from home for lunch, and the pathetic, limited potential for sandwich fillings that rationing imposed, neither option looked attractive any longer and Madam opened her campaign for a school canteen with the County. This she prosecuted with her customary vigour, and while she did so Misses Powell and Faulke started their days with an unusual pre-school session of cleaning and preparing vegetables, and in the little hall off St John's chapel, on an ancient and uncooperative gas cooker, with some parents assisting and an assigned ration of cheap cuts of meat, they conjured up a lunchtime stew for their multitude.

By the time John arrived at the school however Madam's campaign had been successfully concluded. The hall had been properly converted for dining; a modest but modern kitchen had been installed; permanent kitchen staff had relieved the two mistresses and their helpers of their menial duties; and the pupils sat down to lunch each day bathed in that special aura from overcooked cabbage, watery custard and dirty dishwater that pervaded all wartime canteens.

In exchange for their funding the Church imposed a syllabus that in addition to dealing perfectly adequately with the basics, lent generously towards matters of the divine. Pictures with religious themes featured heavily in the classroom decorations: St Francis surrounded by his birds on the door of the babies' class; St Christopher midstream with the Christ Child on his shoulders at the end of the large room, and on the walls assorted scenes of an improving nature culled from the Old Testament. All assemblies and formal gatherings began with prayers, and on Friday mornings the Revd Bryers presided over a Low Mass for a selected few in St John's Chapel. On saints' days and other special occasions from the liturgical calendar, the school processed to the mother church of St Margaret's. The children welcomed these interruptions to their normal routine, and there was a theatricality about the event which always drew a few onlookers from the local houses and provided some light relief for everyone in days which could otherwise be unvaryingly drab.

The Revd Bryers in his vestments led the procession, followed by a cluster of white-gowned choir boys and other robed church officiants with brass-topped staffs held high. Madam followed, and then the classes one by one. Each shepherded by a teacher, they proceeded in crocodile file along the main road, past the shop and forge, where Markham paused in his work and hung over the half-door to watch them, and on to Church Road. There the footpath ended, and they walked the long, level stretch between hedgerows and cornfields as far as Bowers Court farm where the ground fell away sharply, opening up the view to the marshes and the river beyond.

If there had ever been a settlement close by to justify the building of a church in such a remote spot all trace of it had long since disappeared. With the open hill rising at its back, and the marsh creeks stretching away beyond the churchyard walls it stood shaded by elms, isolated, little used, and hushed, unless the sounds of the Sunday service or a passing train rumbling over the bridge broke the silence.

As the door swung open the church eased itself of a long-held breath, heavy with the scent of damp, decay and long departed de Giffords to whom the headless, one-legged brass of fourteenth-century Sir John was the only surviving testament. For the children the service itself was a tedious interlude between the walk out and the walk back, and while the rector droned on relentlessly through his sermon, eyes glazed and heads drooped, although the young congregation stood and sang lustily enough when the time came. Mostly they fidgeted uncomfortably on hard oak pews, looking restlessly around and impatient for release. There was little there to interest them. They'd gazed unseeing at it all before: ancient cobwebs hanging like drapes high in the roof, or drifting down from the beams; the scene in the stained glass window high above the altar; sunlight streaming through a haze of incense; names or initials carved into the pew backs before them; and on the brass memorial plate long lists of the names of those who had died in the Great War. Familiar local names many of them, unknown uncles or grandfathers perhaps of the boys who sat and gazed vacantly at them.

When at long last the service concluded, they burst with relief through the porch, back into the sunlight and fresh air, and from then on the return to school was an informal, relaxed, less disci-plined affair. The steep climb up the hill presented no problems for their legs and those of the young teachers. For Madam and the rector, now walking together and chatting as they led the way, the hill was more demanding and their progress was leisurely. She walked close to him, almost brushing against him, and attending closely to his every word. It was her behaviour on such occasions, and the occasional unguarded comment to her confidants, that fostered the widely held conviction that she had a preoccupation with the clergy, nobody put it any stronger than that, and secretly cherished the idea that one or the other of them was deeply interested in her; a belief that proved to be entirely without foundation.

Behind them the children had time to scout off into the verges to pull the flat, broad leaves of grass they needed to blow the ripest raspberries, to seek out the burrs and goosegrasses that clung to the hair and clothing when thrown, and jockey for position to shoulder one another into ditches or nettles. Almost anything was tolerated until the main road was reached, where they once again came under general observation. Then they re-formed and class by class made a disciplined return to their lunch.

Later in the war, although the tide had turned decisively against the Germans, hit-and-run raiders still passed to and fro along the estuary, and from one of those homeward bound a bomb dumped at random fell close to the school. Although there was damage to the buildings it was out of school hours and there were no injuries.

That one incident apart, the effects of the war on the children's schooling were indirect. School materials were at a premium. Paper from all conceivable sources was recycled for them to write on. Pencils were reduced to fragmentary stubs. Books broke their backs, shed their covers, lost their bindings but, dog-eared and tattered, remained in use indefinitely. Painting materials, pen nibs, rulers, blotting paper, all the consumables of day-to-day school life were in short supply. In the winter months the supply of coke for the school boilers was irregular and uncertain. The classrooms were seldom comfortably warm, and on a number of momentous occasions they were sent home when the boilers could no longer be properly fired.

Normal lessons were suspended throughout any alert, when the classrooms, far too vulnerable to blast with their expanses of glass, were abandoned. They each took a small cushion, gathered their books or papers and filed along the veranda to the cloakrooms protected by their walls of sandbags. There, with a cushion between their backsides and the hot-water pipes, they sat it out until the all-clear sounded. Often nothing was heard of the action, and then there was either some attempt at normal lessons, or the time was passed with spelling bees, reading, times-table chanting, or simple word games.

But there were also times when the distant sound of the ack-ack, the rattle of cannon and machine-gun fire above them, and the occasional crack of shrapnel falling on to the roof, meant that any attempt at lessons was abandoned, and orchestrated by Madam they howled back a sing-song of defiance, assured by her that their voices would certainly be heard by those far, far above them. In country areas there were no public shelters, and if the sirens sounded as they were on the way to or from school they either turned back to home if that was nearer or pressed on as fast as they could to the school shelters.

Wherever possible all the traditional celebrations, festivities and activities of the pre-war years were continued. Towards the end of May they celebrated Empire Day. As it approached senior boys were dispatched on foraging expeditions into the bowels of the storage space under the stage, and competition for this exciting task was keen. It was controlled by Madam, who knelt before the low stage door on a folded towel, directing her foragers into the dusty recesses with the light of a torch, while those behind her whispered smutty jokes about the size of her rump. They returned with the bunting, rolled posters and prints, flags, old tableau backdrops and other assorted props that would be used in dressing the school for the occasion.

When Empire day arrived veranda and classrooms were draped in multicoloured bunting and flags of the Commonwealth, and the Union flag decorated the stage. Coloured pictures and prints of lively, imaginative scenes from the far-flung Empire hung from the walls, all glowing testimony to the many achievements of benevolent Imperial rule and the evident satisfaction and gratitude of its citizens. Young as he was John sensed something wrong about all that. Years of living and listening in a family that took a more jaundiced view of the British Imperial adventure were already colouring his views, which, if naive and childish, were earnestly held.

The first hour or so on the morning of the great day was given up to informal activities for the school alone. The partition between the two rooms was pushed back, the whole school crammed into the one large room created, and an ad-hoc choir trained and accompanied by Miss Powell sang a few songs – of Commonwealth origin they were told. Next, against a worn, tattered and vaguely African backdrop making its once-a-year appearance from storage under the stage, the senior class gave the school a preview of their Empire tableau in which spears, sheets, brightly coloured cloth, feathers and other assorted items from the teachers' wardrobes played a part. With a little time still to spare Miss Faulke read stories about the lives of their Empire cousins until the arrival of the Revd Bryers with a few local worthies and guests, when the short formalities of the day began.

He conducted prayers, spoke a little about the great part the Empire was playing in the war, and then Mrs Hayward from the village choir led the school into 'Rule, Britannia!', her ripe solo

350

contralto booming out the verses, and the children howling out the chorus with mounting enthusiasm and vigour. The Empire tableau was repeated for the benefit of the visitors, and then Madam introduced the Revd Bryers' special guest, a Canadian pilot from a nearby RAF station. He was a man who remembered well what it was to be a child and grabbed their attention at once. He said little or nothing about the war, but spoke instead of his life as a boy and young man in a remote little town on an inlet of the sea on the Pacific coast of Canada. By the time he had finished his tales of logging, rafting, grizzlies, black bears, whales and porcupines there wasn't a boy in the school who could see any future before him but emigration to British Columbia and the life of a backwoodsman. Their time indoors finished with the National Anthem, and then they assembled in the playground where the girls danced around the maypole. Why Empire Day was chosen for this was never explained. The school then closed and the rest of the day was holiday.

Speech days were held a day or two before the summer holidays started. The rector spoke of all that Miss Ashton (not Madam everyone noted) and her staff had done for the children in the most difficult of circumstances, a sentiment enthusiastically echoed in a round of applause from the parents. Those leaving the school for the last time were sent on their way with every wish for the greatest success in their future endeavours, and the presentation of a few modest trophies for achievement in attendance, behaviour or academic work brought the function to a close.

They held their sports day on the field behind the school, celebrated Harvest Festival with a grand parade to the church, and at the end of the year they had their Christmas celebrations. The Christmas play presented no problem. It made no unusual demands on scarce resources, and most of the props required had been in storage under the stage since the production of the previous year.

The Christmas party was a different matter altogether. It was meant to be special; an event for the children that would stand out against the bleak round of rationing and shortages that otherwise formed their daily lives. Traditionally it had been provided in large part by the staff, but the many constraints of wartime meant that parents had to be called on for a contribution. Despite their joint efforts, each passing wartime Christmas taxed their ingenuity, resourcefulness and determination to the limit.

Their greatest triumph came with the year of banana sandwiches and gingerbread men. At the beginning of December Madam convened her commissariat of teachers, cook and cook's assistant. The meeting was not productive. Times were hard, and parents were going to find it difficult enough to devise something special for their own Christmases let alone have anything to spare for the school party. It began to look as though the teachers' best intentions were going to be frustrated. There were no other resources to turn to, and there seemed to be no hope that anything would turn up. The meeting adjourned for a week for each member to give the matter thought and explore any contacts they had.

For national news the little parish had the newspapers, the wireless and the cinema newsreels, but for local news and gossip it was the milkman and the postman who provided a fast and efficient distribution system for the choicest titbits. On the Friday after the meeting cook called to see Madam. She had been informed that day by the milkman, always reliable and discreet in choosing who should hear his news, that Mrs Reddington in the shop opposite the school had received a delivery of golden syrup. It was unrationed and was to be sold next day on a first-come, first-served basis. If Madam would see that cook received two tins of syrup, cook would guarantee gingerbread men and banana sandwiches for the Christmas party.

Madam could see the route to the gingerbread men clearly enough and undertook to make delivery of the syrup to cook on the Monday. But banana sandwiches? Bananas were no longer imported and had not been seen in the shops since mid-1940. How was it to be done? Cook would say no more than she did before. Give her the syrup and she would finish the job.

Madam was well aware that demand for such a resource as syrup would be keen at any time. With Christmas just a few weeks away it would be overwhelming, and sales would almost certainly be limited to one tin per customer, so to make quite certain of the second tin Miss Faulke, who was then lodging with Madam, was pressed into keeping her company. In the chill of the Saturday morning, keen that their children should not be disappointed, they were first on the shop doorstep and stood chatting together as the inevitable queue formed behind them. At nine Mrs Reddington opened her door and looked down the queue.

'The news got around all right then? I thought I wouldn't need to advertise.'

The queue shuffled forward into the shop.

'Two tins of golden syrup please, Mrs Reddington.'

'No tins I'm afraid. It came in a barrel and I'm selling it loose: a pint a person.'

The milkman's news had been accurate, but incomplete. In the queue behind them the ladies smiled smugly as they looked on. They had been better informed and came well provided with jugs, basins or saucepans. It would have been pointless for Madam to leave and come back later with a container. There would have been no syrup left.

She looked around her. At the back of the shop, looped through string and hanging from one of the beams she saw some white containers.

'What are those?'

'Children's chamber pots.'

'Could I see them please?'

Mrs Reddington unhooked the pots and brought them forward to the counter. The queue looked on with interest.

Madam tapped one and considered it at arm's length.

'These look about the right size. Don't you think so, Miss Faulke?'

Miss Faulke offered no opinion.

'How much are they?'

'Three and three.'

'I'll take one. Dust it out please and put two pints of syrup in it.'

There was some laughter, a murmur of approval and, more softly, a few comments not intended for Madam's ears. Syrup and container were paid for, and holding the near-brimming chamber pot Madam left the shop with as much dignity as the circumstances permitted. At the road she turned to her companion.

'I've just remembered that I need to pop into the school for a few moments. Would you take that back to the house for me, please?'

Miss Faulke, brimming pot in hand, was left standing on the pavement as Madam disappeared up the drive towards the school. She looked down the road towards the house just a few yards

353

beyond the smithy. On most Saturday mornings the road would have been deserted, but Miss Faulke's cup was full in more senses than one. At the blacksmith's they were fitting a rim on to a new cartwheel. This was a popular spectator event with the local boys, and five or six of them could be seen clustered around the fire just beyond the forge.

At one hundred yards she had been spotted. At fifty the container she carried so carefully had been identified. With less than twenty yards to go not only the boys, but Markham and his assistant had turned aside from their work to line the path and watch her pass. Unflinching, and looking Markham squarely in the eyes, she carried it off with commendable style.

'Good morning, boys. Good morning, Mr Markham.'

She passed them with an insouciant air, as though it was the most natural thing in the world to be strolling the Southend Road on a Saturday morning while nursing a brimming chamber pot. Whatever ideas they may have had concerning the true contents of the pot, the sheer simplicity and directness of her performance stunned them into a purely conventional reply.

'Good morning, Miss.'

'Good morning, Miss Faulke. Chilly old morning.'

'Yes, isn't it?'

Moments later she was past them and safely in the drive to the house. By mid-morning, instigated by Markham, the boys had carried the rumour far and wide into the countryside. A Jerry had been sighted sneaking along the Southend Road. The Home Guard had been alerted and were investigating.

The syrup made its final journey to the school kitchen in a covered container, and long before the day of the Christmas party rumours were circulating that there was going to be something special. Amongst the children ham sandwiches followed by fruit trifle and cream was the wildest speculation, sausage rolls and fairy cakes the most realistic. Eventually there was an authorised leak, and expectation focused on banana sandwiches. This caused some confusion for a few, and not only in the infant ranks. What were bananas? No attempt at descriptive explanation appeared to work until the rector, always in touch with developments at the school, produced a book on tropical fruit from his library complete with colour plate.

On party day the children processed to the canteen and assembled in ranks in front of the decorated tables. There were the gingerbread men, glazed and gleaming golden-bronze. There were the cups and bottles of lemonade and cream soda. And yes, there were the banana sandwiches they had been promised. Plate upon plate of them, generous slices of standard loaf, and between each slice thick, lush, creamy-yellow fillings of banana purée.

There were few jaded or fastidious appetites in wartime, so the popularity of the sandwiches could not be judged by the fact that it took precious little time for the tables to be cleared, but most seemed to like them and would have welcomed more. One sandwich each had been set aside for the teachers who tasted, tested and savoured without getting any closer to a solution to the puzzle.

Finally Madam looked at cook. 'Well?'

'Puréed parsnip, banana essence, colouring and a touch of syrup blended in.'

27

Short Trousers and Arctic Blasts

In between the alarums and excursions of war there were many days when daily life proceeded undisturbed and the children made their journeys to and from school much as they had for a century or so. In the fields, banks, ditches, hedgerows, trees and ponds passed on the mile long journey the boys found all they needed for frequent distractions, and they made a rowdy, tumultuous progress until they reached the point where they could see the school and the teachers could see them.

Excluded from the daily riot were the youngest children, heading for Miss Balaam's class, who were delivered and collected by their mothers, or perhaps an older brother or sister. Most of the girls too, apart from a few hard cases who gave as good as they got and sometimes better, waited for the boys to pass, or made good time ahead of them; and there were a few privileged lads with bicycles who swept past the common herd with a jangle of the bell, and the flashiest displays they could conjure up. Riding no-hands was the favourite performance: certainly impressive, but fraught with a potential for disaster which an envious audience was always ready to exploit with a well-aimed missile.

There was little mixing or mingling on the journeys to and from school. Boys living close to each other formed their own groups or gangs. Rivalries arose and hostilities were common. Alliances once made were not readily broken, and it was the friends John had made during his early visits to the area who eased his way into the new school.

By and large the majority of children at the school were from a working-class background. Within that category there were some families who enjoyed a standard of living comfortably above the poverty line, but there were more than enough like the Heards who lived their lives on or below it. The appearance and dress of the boys when they turned out for school reflected this diversity. Hair was worn short, often near-shaven, serving the dual purpose of economy and nit protection. Boots were standard wear for most of the country boys: thick-soled, metal-tipped at toe and heel and often clumsily repaired at home. Clothes, frequently hand-me-downs from older brothers, were altered, patched and oversized. Most of the mothers turned their hands to home knitting, but there were few who possessed Phoebe's skill with the needles, and at morning assembly it was a motley collection of lumpy, misshapen, sagging and ill-sized knitwear that Madam saw ranged before her. 'Don't be ashamed to wear shabby garments, they are as honourable as a soldier's battle-stained uniform.' That had been the message from the minister when clothes were rationed. He would have been proud of the patriotic enthusiasm with which the concept was embraced by the youth of the plotlands.

The diversity of clothing was matched by equally eccentric standards of personal hygiene. An antipathy to baths was near universal. Even modest supplies of hot water were not easily come by, and wartime economies imposed yet further restraints on its use when available. There was little that was inviting about the regulation five inches of tepid water at the bottom of a galvanised bath in a chilly scullery or outhouse, and a cat's lick and a promise was considered by many as more than adequate, not just from weekend to weekend, but month to month. Some were more clean, some less so, and the wartime emphasis on self-sufficiency meant that more than one or two brought with them to school not only their own individual fragrance but also the faint yet distinctive odour of pig. When, after a physically active playtime, an air-raid warning brought them crammed together in their cloakroom shelters, slowly simmering above the hot-water pipes, their natural reticence about soap and water, combined with a rustic readiness to void the bowels of excess gasses when the need arose, could make an extended winter alert a very special and demanding experience.

For the first part of the walk to school there was no footpath, and field hedges or bungalow gardens edged the lane. Along the eastern edge, where the drainage ditch ran deep and wide, the gardens were entered over narrow bridges of concrete or wood. Alongside the ditch a bank made of spoil from the original excavation had at one time been wide enough to serve as a footpath.

357

For as long as the lane was a country byway it would have remained so, just high enough to keep the feet of an occasional passer-by out of wagon ruts in foul weather, but with the plotlands and later developments came a more destructive form of traffic than wagons. In wet weather, when the streams were in spate, dam-building fever seized the boys, and clustered around the narrower sections of the ditch they beavered away at their construction projects. Their building materials came from broken branches, and sections of the bank hacked and chopped out with the heels of their boots. Even their best efforts were soon overwhelmed and swept away by the water, and year after year, as the bank was eroded and lowered, the ditch grew wider and shallower.

Things changed along the lane in the decades after the war. The elms were lost, first to disease and then to the saw, and the groundwaters were consigned to culverts deep beneath paved footpaths. On the back of succeeding property booms plotland shacks were transmuted to twin-garaged executive establishments, and nesh young Essex lads, cosseted inside the second car, and whisked past by Mum on an altogether different school run, had no conception of the fascination, pleasure and sheer delight of mucking about in ditches.

At the top of the lane, beyond Mann's the butchers, the buildings ceased and an ash and cinder path had been cut into the field beside the road. In making the path the old hedge had been grubbed up and replaced by a metal post-and-rail fence. There, perched like sparrows along the top rail, on the way to school and on the way home, the children paused in their journey, and season by season throughout the year watched over the last hurrah of old-style agriculture on the fields.

In Bowers Gifford, as in many parts of the country, the transition to motor power had not been completed, and when ploughing began in autumn it was with horses not tractors. With their ploughman or land girl in attendance the team of two, or perhaps three, would have been in the field since early morning and seemed to make light of the effort required to draw the plough through the stiff, clinging clay. Like the draught horses drawing the brewers' drays in Poplar they were great, powerful, beautiful beasts towering above the men or women who cared for them.

As they passed on their way to school, many of the children paused and waited to watch the horses more closely as they turned on the headland. By then, despite the cooler mornings, they had warmed to their work, and the scent of the sweat gleaming on their flanks was heavy in the misty cloud of breath that drifted and enveloped the little group standing to watch them as they turned at the end of the latest furrow. Within a week of the new term the children had got to know two of the horses well. One grey, the other the colour of ripe chestnuts, they saw them regularly on the fields and during their visits to the blacksmith.

When harvest time arrived in the year following their return to Essex, Mickey encouraged John to go with him to watch the start of work on the big fields at the top of the lane. When they arrived the horse-drawn reaper and binder had already been at work for some time clattering its way along each side of a rectangle of standing corn that diminished with every swathe cut. On the stubble between the hedges and the uncut corn a few men with shotguns and dogs, whippets or similar, watched the last stand of corn keenly until the first of the rabbits, hemmed increasingly tightly within the diminishing perimeter, made a wild dash for the hedge and a refuge. Such lone runners were invariably rabbit pie by the end of the day, and it was only with the last mad rush that sheer weight of numbers carried a few of them through to safety. Unable to resist the temptation to stay there and watch, John stuffed his ears to drown out the screams of the rabbits caught by the dogs, and was haunted by memories of the sounds as he lay in bed at night. The guns were quicker and cleaner, as Ted had already shown him.

After the binder and harvester had passed on, the bound sheaves of corn were propped together in stooks and left waiting on the stubble for the cart that would carry them off for threshing. There was no agricultural imperative demanding symmetry and pattern in this, but the Land Army women who did the stacking had a military eye for what was right, and before they left the field the stooks stood neatly dressed rank upon rank in parade-ground order. So they should have remained, but the field lay on the children's route to school, and from Mann's the butchers the long diagonal across the stubble to the smithy was too inviting a shortcut to be ignored. A race led to a chase, and the chase to pursuits and fights in and around the long lines of stooks. The dry, sharp stubble was an unforgiving surface to knees and elbows, and it took only a few falls on to its short, needle-like tips for their enthusiasm for the sport to fade, but by the time they had passed on to school stook after stook lay in disorder, its sheaves trampled into the stubble.

Some half an hour after lessons had started, while a few of them were still teasing out thin splinters of stubble from their skin, the two top classes were called together below the stage and Madam appeared with the butcher's wife. The rampage through the harvest corn had been observed from start to finish. Half a dozen culprits were fingered, Mickey was one of them, and called up to the stage where they waited while Mrs Mann was thanked and left.

There was nothing oppressive about Madam's discipline, but it remained firmly rooted in the hands-on approach of the old school, and the cane was used when the occasion demanded it, but with restraint and fairly. This she considered was one such occasion, and while Mickey and friends stepped up in front of the school to receive three sharp strokes on each hand those who had not been spotted congratulated themselves on their luck. As the villains stood wringing their hands, Madam reminded her audience that men were dying on the Atlantic to keep food on their tables, that every grain of corn was of vital importance, and that if any other children were so much as seen in the fields while the harvest stooks were still standing there would be the same treatment for them, and a little more.

About the dark recesses of Markham's forge there still hung something of the magic and mystery once associated with the ancient and secret craft of the smith who drew flashes of fire from the metal under his hammer, beat sullen steel into serviceable tools and had his own secret way with the horses he shod. From the time of the National School and earlier the smithy had stood as a distraction and temptation to boys who should have been about other matters or on their way to school, and still it drew them to its doors.

The size of a small barn, the forge was built in traditional shiplap style. The long boards of the walls, curved and twisted from exposure to a century's weather and blackened with coat after coat of tarry preservative, were pierced with a few windows and two entrances. One, a divided stable door, led into the forge itself. The other wider entry, a double-door, opened on to the travus, the separate working space where the horses were shod.

Alongside the smithy, on a patch of wasteland, a thick, circular iron plate, perhaps five feet in diameter with a large hole cut in its centre, was bedded into the ground on a wide patch of earth scorched and blackened from fires that had burned there since the smithy first opened its doors. This was Markham's open-air workshop where iron tyres were wedded to wagon wheels fresh from the wheelwrights. It was an occasional event, but a lively and fascinating one that drew spectators at any time, and if it was in hand when the boys passed by on their way to school then all of Madam's sanctions for latecomers could go hang.

A haze of smoke and a burst of flame seen as they turned into the main road was enough to set them running to the forge, where one new wheel, all clean, bright oak and elm was propped against the wall waiting to be shod. The other was already in position, its fat nave sunk into the central hole of the plate and the spokes running flat and true to the wheel rim lying snug and level against the outer edge. Beyond the wheel, on the scorched earth, a ring of fire flared where the iron tyre began to glow cherry red on a bed of burning timber. Clustered around the fire they watched and waited.

Markham stood apart, his eyes fixed on the tyre, until judging the moment to be right he ushered the boys away, nodded to his assistant, and with long-handled tongs they plucked it from the fire and dropped it over the wheel rim. The fit was a close one with the glowing metal of the tyre lying snug against the felloes, and for a moment they flickered into flame before being doused with the buckets of cold water kept ready to hand. The tyre cooled and tightened, the wheel rim and spokes contracted and cracked, and in clouds of steam the performance came to an end. Red-eyed and reeking of woodsmoke they hurried on to Madam's retribution. She would have been well aware of Markham's activities and excuses would be pointless.

Markham's other work as smith and farrier went on day in day out, a constant attraction and diversion for the boys as they passed, for the top of the stable door was always open. Inside in the centre of the floor stood the anvil, firmly clenched to the top of an ancient section of elm trunk scorched and blackened from years of exposure to heat, hammer and red-hot slag. On a signboard nailed to a beam above was Markham's maxim: 'Measure Twice: Cut Once.' On metal racks against the wall, strips of brass, tins and bottles of minerals, oils and fluxes lay alongside the lengths of iron that would be hammered into horseshoes, beaten into billhooks, forged and welded into farm axles, or worked to just about any agricultural requirement. Beyond the anvil, at the foot of a curved brick wall containing the hearth, a couple of buckets stood filled with plunging water, and on top of the wall ready to hand, the hammers, pliers, cutting pieces and other common tools of his trade. From the top of the bellows at the side of the hearth a long arm, curved and shaped like a single shaft from a light farm cart, reached out into the workshop, its handgrip blackened and polished by skin, sweat, iron scales and many years of pumping.

Covering the walls to the remotest, shadowy recesses of the workshop, hung a collection of curious and ancient tools, implements and devices made perhaps by grandfather or great-grandfather for that one special job, then put aside, but never thrown away. Already layered decades deep in dust, they had a few years left to gather a little more before they were finally swept away as the ancient craft of the smith went into decline.

During the war when Greenwich Mean Time was abandoned, summer time ran throughout the year, and on the short days around mid-winter sunrise was after nine. A distraction at the best of times, the forge was at its most mysterious and enticing on those drear, dark mornings when it was barely light as they passed the smithy on their way to school.

Little of the faint morning light filtered in through windows and door, and if the smith was not at work the forge looked dull and dead, but competition was still keen for the prime viewing position hanging over the bottom half of the stable door, where dark and lifeless as it seemed, they could feel faintly on their faces the presence of heat and power at the heart of the forge. It wanted only the smith's hand, and a steady pull on the shaft of the bellows, to breathe life and action back into the smithy.

Eventually Markham appeared from the shadows at the back of the forge, slipped on his leather apron and reached up to the shaft above his head. At the first long sigh from the bellows a film of dust rose as the hearth stirred. With a few more strong, steady pulls a soft glow showed at the centre and soon burst into the white and red furnace heat that the work demanded.

On a winter morning, with their collars turned up and the wind at their back, there was nothing more comforting than to thrust forward over the door so that their half-frozen faces could soak up a little of the heat radiating from the forge. There they hung drowsily in the warmth, lulled for a few moments by the steady breathing of the bellows, until it died away and the work in hand was drawn glowing from the hearth to be shaped and moulded between hammer and anvil.

In the half-light within the forge it was a dramatic, electrifying performance that Markham gave to his young audience. Flames and flakes of hot ash rose from the hearth as he thrust and raked to find just the right spot to heat the piece as he wanted. Sparks and red-hot iron scale flew, and the anvil rang out as he hammered, cut and teased the metal into shape. Clouds of steam rose from the buckets of quenching water as the piece was repeatedly plunged, reheated, hammered and plunged again. It was a demanding, time-consuming, laborious process, and much as they enjoyed the spectacle there were few of them who thought of smithing when he dreamed of his future.

Summer was the season to catch Markham the farrier at work, and by the time they arrived on the way to school the forge would have been open for an hour or more. With the sun already high and warming their backs they crowded together in the open doorway of the travus, as impatient for the performance to begin as the horse shuffling and stamping inside.

If it was true that the old farm horsemen had mystical secrets giving them power over their charges, then Markham had inherited some of their magic, and in his hands the great, heavy horses were as docile and gentle as lambs. Brought by their usual horseman, and tied loosely in the travus they were left for a few moments before Markham came in from the forge for his introductory ritual. He stroked and patted the muzzle of the horse, breathed gently into its nostrils and whispered softly into its ears. His audience was impressed, and so apparently were the horses which invariably behaved as though they had read the farrier's manual. When Markham bent to remove the old shoes he did no more than tap the fetlock and gently tug at the tuft of hair for the horse to lift its leg, and rest the hoof conveniently on his thigh.

His tools and equipment he carried in a battered wooden box: nails in one section; knives, hammers, pliers, pincers, rasps and cutters in another. Carefully lifting and cutting the clenches of the old nails, he then withdrew them easily throwing them towards, and often into, a box in one corner. The old shoes he tossed into a heap in another.

The horses arriving at the smithy were all local and well known, and shoes prepared in advance needed few modifications before they were ready for use. With the old shoes off, any rough or damaged sole was pared or rasped away from the underside of the hoof, leaving the surface smooth and clean, and as soon as the horse was steady the new shoes came in still hot from the forge, were tried against each hoof, then shaped, hammered and custom-ised as necessary before being burned into a final snug fitting.

It was difficult for his audience to understand that the horse felt no distress from his treatment. From Westerns they were familiar with the angry reaction of cattle to the branding iron, and to them the swirling smoke and hiss of the burning shoe on the sole of the hoof looked just as painful, but unlike the cattle the horses remained impassive and aloof throughout. Finally as the iron cooled the nails were driven and clenched. The horse carried away a new set of shoes for the next few months. The audience carried with them for the rest of their lives the memory of that distinctive, evocative smell of forge, sweat, hot metal and burning hoof that embodied those fleeting moments of childhood on their daily passage to and from school.

For most of them, on most days of most months of the year, that walk to and from school could fairly be described as a pleasure. The intermediate business of education was an unfortunate necessity that they could take or leave alone. There came a few days in winter, however, when they paid in full measure for the pleasure they enjoyed on so many others.

After the delights of that first golden, autumn term with mild and generous weather right up to Christmas, the New Year of 1942 came in with two mean and cruel months that made any movement out of doors a misery. Each day opened and closed under leaden skies. It was bitterly cold without remission and there were frequent heavy snowstorms. Easterly winds, direct and unimpeded from Siberia the local legend had it, scoured the snow from the fields and dumped it in drifts across the lane. What looked like fun when it started soon became a torment in the fight to and from school. 'Never mind,' said Markham as they passed, 'Just remember what it's doing to the Krauts on the Russian front.'

364

There were many days when the lane was impassable for the station bus, and long before school time the snow would already have been well tramped in the darkness of early morning by the London workers who had plodded their way through it to try for a bus on the main road. For those of the children who were single-minded enough to follow in their footsteps, it was difficult enough to arrive at school dry shod. For the many who were not, it was impossible. In a school that was seldom warm enough, wet socks quickly led to cold feet, cold feet to chilblains, and chilblains to day after day of torment desperately scraping one foot against the other in pursuit of some relief from the itching.

Feet were not the only problem. In the 1940s few schoolboys wore long trousers until they had left junior school, and their battle with the elements was conducted with twelve or more inches of soft and tender flesh between mid-thigh and mid-calf exposed to all the rigours of frost, snow and sleet, and a wind that chased and chivvied them relentlessly to school, but opposed and battered them on their journey home. For those who had them, and there were all too many without, even top coats offered only partial protection. Young and delicate skin, on thighs alternately wetted by snow or sleet, dried by freezing winds and chaffed by the damp bottom seams of trousers, soon chapped and bled despite liberal applications of Vaseline.

In addition to chapped legs, short trousers and freezing winds combined to create yet another discomfort to add to the general gloom of wartime winters, but one which provided them, at least in retrospect, with some lavatory humour. On the fair-weather days of summer as they arrived at school with breakfast drinks and a long walk behind them, it was customary, if not strictly essential, to visit the boys' urinal before classes began. It was a basic, primitive facility in a separate space behind the cloakrooms that were their air-raid shelters. Above a shallow drainage channel at the foot of one wall the brickwork had been rendered and painted black to a height of about three feet where a line of flushing water pipes was fixed. Against the wall in better and warmer times they conducted their usual competitive sports with the unrealistic expectation that one day they would make their mark on the pipes themselves.

In the iron tyres glowing in the circle of fire outside the smithy they had witnessed a practical demonstration of expansion under heat. Now, after the long morning trudge to school exposed to Siberian blasts round, up and about their pathetically short trousers, they had personal experience of the converse. When their numbed fingers had finally fumbled their way past the buttons on their trousers' flies and into winter underpants, they found all too often that they had nothing to declare, or so little that any normal performance of the function presented difficulties – competition was out of the question. Nature, perhaps wisely, had shrivelled and retreated in the face of the Arctic challenge, and what they had left to handle was fit only for the coarse jokes that each faced from the others.

That natural reticence and self-effacement of their private parts would have been no more than a laughing matter had it not been for the attendant problem of post-urinatory drip. The condition, a function of age in older men and carelessness in young boys, was particularly difficult to control in an environment hostile in the extreme to a relaxed and leisurely performance of the natural functions. It was embarrassing enough in the best of circumstances to feel the stealthy creep of urine along the thigh on the walk to the classroom. When, as they warmed at their desks, a minor seepage became an uncontrolled trickle over flesh already chapped and cracked, it was a stirring, stinging and memorable experience which put the minor itching of chilblains into perspective. An urgent request to be excused and prompt personal attention in the privacy of a lavatory was the only solution to the discomfort. Gentle sponging with a wet handkerchief went some way to abating the agony, but only a smear of Vaseline provided true comfort.

On the worst of the winter days their one-third pints of milk on the veranda had frozen and popped their cardboard tops long before the caretaker arrived to take them in. Placed to defrost over the hot-water pipes, they were still cold comfort at morning playtime.

There were a few occasions when it was impossible to heat the school adequately, and they were sent home as soon as they arrived. In general, however, despite the foul weather and the stress and disturbance of continuing air-raid alerts during the long winter nights, schooling continued methodically and uninterrupted for those of them not caught up in an epidemic of chicken pox and German measles that almost halved class sizes for many weeks. It seemed natural enough to the children that something as nasty as measles should be German, but the Revd Bryers' home-grown psychology had persuaded him that it was bad for morale to call it that, and from then on at his request Madam and the teachers all spoke of rubella.

Schooldays at St Margaret's fell into a regular, comfortable pattern that invariably began with a service of simple prayers, children's hymns and a talk from Madam, or less frequently from Revd Bryers. If, as occasionally happened, there were successes in the war to be celebrated they were mentioned and thanks given to God. Continuing reverses were ignored, apparently God had no hand in those.

The educational hardware available to the children was typical of the primitive paraphernalia of a 1940s junior educational establishment constrained even further by wartime restrictions. They fidgeted through lessons on double bench seats fixed behind desks with lids that could be closed with a satisfying crash. Wooden pen holders, their ends shredded with chewing during moments of reflection, boredom or desperate concentration, held steel nibs with points cunningly designed to cross and spatter ink as soon as they were applied to a clean page, but fitted with old nibs they did at least double effectively as darts during school playtimes.

It was with those few tools, plus books, globe, world map (Mercator Projection with lots of Empire red), blackboard and chalk that Madam and her staff with their own special skills somehow managed to make something of the assorted raw materials before them, most of them quite indifferent to their own enlightenment.

Morning lessons over, they marched in file down the ash-and-cinder path to the dining hall in the old St John's building. Winter or summer the kitchen door stood open, and the smell of cooking drifted over them as they passed. Whatever the menu the smell was the same. Nothing but the general privations of wartime could have sharpened the appetite for those lunches, but there were few too fastidious or finicky to leave their meal unfinished. Protein came in a variety of guises: liver, blackened and knife-defying; greasy mince of uncertain provenance; occasionally a genuinely tasty stew; and all too frequently Spam, a composite meat product relished in a thousand music-hall jokes as it never was on the plate. Cold, fried, baked, grilled or battered it made no difference. The cook had not been born who could impose any variation in flavour.

367

Vegetables in season were boiled without mercy to a uniform, bland tastelessness, and the flavour of the meal, if it could be said to have any, derived from the gravy. In that respect they were lucky, for someone in the kitchen had a way with stock and flavouring which transformed many an unpromising plateful into an acceptable meal. The puddings were by far the best part of the lunch. Rice puddings, steamed pudding with jam, semolina and a special concoction called sweet potato pudding were standard fare, and they soon emptied their dishes. In the wartime diet it was above all sweetness that they craved, and that at least the puddings provided.

Some fifteen minutes before closing time formal classes were wound up and the day ended with a story. When they finally left for home it was with the adventures of Mr Toad, Alice, the Swiss Family Robinson or any one of a score of others occupying their thoughts as they passed in reverse the diversions of their walk to school: Markham, relaxing and rolling a cigarette as he rested across the half-door before putting in his last stint of the afternoon; the farm workers or land girls in the fields, already tired, and looking forward to the end of a hard day; and finally the lane with the ditch waiting to be dammed or leapt. Their time was their own now. On the homeward journey there was no hurry, and opportunities were unlimited for a shoe full of water, or worse, before their day was done.

28

No Bells for Christmas

Despite the austerity of wartime life and its day-to-day dangers, real enough though remote, no time in the young boy's childhood would be happier than the ten months at the old captain's Anchorage. The house was solid, comfortable and large enough to escape from supervision into its more remote corners, and for the first time he had a room of his own free from oversight by his sister. The outdoor life with the garden and livestock was an extension of the new interests made in Bucks, and beyond the garden he had his own wild wood, pond, unmatched swing and the wider countryside which he was now old enough to explore without restraint beyond a few sensible precautions. Within a few weeks Jack and Charlie had found work in small factories on the edge of the marshes near to Pitsea station. Their hours were long, but the pay was good, and while it lasted life was better for the family than it would be at any time in the future.

The ten months they spent at The Anchorage coping with their little local difficulties saw the scope and character of the war at large utterly transformed. Russian reverses continued, but neither Moscow nor Leningrad, although besieged, had fallen to the swift, initial onslaught. Early December of 1941 brought the first reports of major German defeats in the face of fierce Russian counter-attacks that removed the threat to Moscow and forced the first German retreats. Both armies by then were held fast in the grip of deep frosts and savage winter conditions. The Russians were prepared and trained for it, the Germans were not, and in cinemas across the country the newsreels screened those chilling, grainy, grey images of frozen bodies locked in the grotesque contortions of a violent death, and audiences watched with grim satisfaction the lightning displays from the pipes of 'Stalin's Organ', a disarming euphemism for the Katyusha, a multiple rocket-launcher that

369

must have put the fear of God into any enemy who lay under its fire.

In the same month, concurrent with the attack on Pearl Harbor opening their war with the United States, came the Japanese declaration of war against Great Britain. Within days the British battleships *Prince of Wales* and *Repulse*, caught without air cover, had been lost to Japanese air attacks, and Germany had followed Japan with a declaration of war against the United States. The conflict was now global.

Despite the disasters in the Far East and the Pacific, the news of Pearl Harbor, so shattering for America itself, was almost without exception heard with relief. A second powerful ally had been enlisted against the enemy, and the opinion of many was that with the powerhouse of America came the promise of ultimate Allied victory. Within a couple of months British Movietone newsreels would be showing pictures of the arrival of the first of the thousands of GIs who were to flood into the country in the following years.

When the family met at Bayhurst that Christmas there was for the first time a faint note of optimism in their voices when they talked of the probable outcome of the war, although there was still more than enough bad news for those pessimists who wished to dwell on it. Hong Kong fell to the Japanese on Christmas Day, Singapore just a few weeks later, but at the end of May, just as their time at The Anchorage was coming to an end, came the RAF's first thousand-bomber raid on Cologne. Two more of the same were soon to follow on Essen and Bremen. This was the whirlwind Bomber Harris had promised, and it was just starters according to General Arnold whose US Army Air Force would soon be joining the RAF in the skies over Germany. In September 1940 Louisa and her family had stood and watched helplessly as hundreds of German bombers made day trips up the estuary to burn and destroy the docks and their East End homes, and news of the raids was heard with a feeling that the balance had at last been redressed. It was a deeply satisfying response to Hitler's boasts before the Blitz.

As the days shortened, the darkening winter evenings in the countryside provided few opportunities for entertainment. There were cinemas just a few miles away at Pitsea and Hadleigh, but by late evening there were no buses down the lane, and few on the main road. After a long day at work not even the promise of the company of Hollywood's beautiful and best and a couple of hours of escapism was enough to overcome the distaste for the cold, dark walk before and after the film. Cinema apart there was nothing but home-grown entertainment and the wireless.

For a few months at the beginning of the war the offerings of the BBC did precious little to lighten the hearts of the nation. The fledgling television service from Alexandra Palace and all regional radio broadcasting ceased. Only the Home Service continued with schedules that by and large still followed the old Reithian directive 'inform, educate and entertain', but with precious little emphasis on entertainment. In January 1940, however, in response to demand for something a little lighter, a limited Forces Programme began transmissions and was soon on air full time. With it came dance and popular music, requests and serial thrillers, and slowly one by one all those little nuggets of entertainment gold that are looked back on with such affection and nostalgia embedded themselves in BBC schedules that in most other respects remained as conservative as before.

Bandwagon appeared briefly with Murdoch and Askey; *Garrison Theatre* with Jack Warner; *Happidrome* with Lovejoy, Ramsbottom and Enoch; and *ITMA* with Handley and a cast of eccentrics that over the decades evolved into Goons and Pythons. Into the lives of the nation came Funf, Mrs Mopp, Frisby Dyke and that jovial old military soak, the immortal Colonel Chinstrap, whose capacity for drink was matched only by his ability to construe any remark addressed to him as the offer of a quick one. Such programmes and their like were the backbone of evening entertainment. Their characters lived in an enchanted parallel universe. It brushed against the everyday world, mirrored its events, touched on its concerns, but always with humour and humanity. It never, ever, brought anyone to harm – Nazis excepted of course.

> *We're three country comics, three north country comics,*
> *With a job to do.*
> *We bring you a tonic, for laughter's a tonic,*
> *And just let me tell you . . .*

sang the *Happidrome* trio, and they were right. Those radio comedy shows were great morale boosters, and if much of their humour now seems simple and naive, it worked and delighted then because it was played out against the dark backdrop of danger, shortages, deprivation and a life that was already grim and depressing and promised only more of the same.

Starting with *Bandwagon*, perhaps earlier, catchphrases were their lifeblood, and they spawned them by the hundreds. Young and old, the people took them to their bosoms and patched them into the fabric of their lives. They became a wartime vernacular, heard in the playground, on the train, in the factory, the office and on the phone: *The day war broke out – I don't mind if I do – This is Funf speaking – What would you do chums? – Can I do you now sir? – Just let me tell you – I go, I come back – After you Claude, No after you Cecil – I'll 'ave to ask me dad –* and *It's That Man Again:* (originally Hitler of course). On and on they went, easy to recall, and a lazy way to add a little flavour to the bus-stop chat.

Even Max Miller, the favourite of the halls, master of innuendo and the not-so-ambiguous, was eventually allowed an airing by the BBC, if only on a very short leash. His material was a little too rich for John to understand, but the flavour of what was going on was obvious enough to him from the response of the adult audience around him. It was very clearly something naughty. He was one of Lou's favourites and she took him to her heart, coming out particularly strong against the BBC when they banned him for stepping beyond his approved script in a live broadcast.

Comedy apart, there were a few other programmes that in time became old favourites and obligatory listening: *Monday Night at Seven –* later *Eight – O'Clock, In Town Tonight, The Brains Trust*, and news and war reports at all times. Generally speaking, however, the diet offered by the BBC remained stodgy and unadventurous. Radios Luxembourg and Normandie, its only competitors for the pre-war audience, disappeared with the fall of France, and in between the howls and whistles that came as standard with the old valve wireless sets, a twist of the dial now brought only the sounds of occupied Europe. Foreign voices from distant places were transmuted into orchestras, singers or deep, mysterious basso hums that throbbed threateningly and incessantly without any apparent purpose. Hamburg, of Lord Haw-Haw notoriety, Budapest, Paris and Cologne surged and faded. But they offered no

372

entertainment value, and not until the arrival of the American Forces Network (AFN) was there any alternative to the BBC. It didn't take the public long to find the wavelength. Jack Benny, The Ink Spots, King Oliver and his Creole Jazz Band, Glen Miller and the other big bands all made their appearance and from then on the delights of jazz and swing slowly seeped through to the home wavelengths.

But in winter 1941 the AFN was still almost two years away and at The Anchorage the choice was between the BBC or silence. The Forces Programme started the morning on a light note with record selections or a variety orchestra, and followed up for the rest of the day with programmes designed for those in the services at home or abroad: – *The Blue Peter*, a magazine for the Merchant Navy; *News from India*, for the Indian forces; *Greetings from Canada*, for the Canadian troops – all interspersed with variety shows, dance bands and sports reports. The Home Service opened up in sober mood with a selection of solid, educational programmes – *The Kitchen Front*, *The Radio Doctor*, *Morning Exercises for Men and Women* – but then relaxed for the rest of the day, and by late afternoon when John had completed a slow and diversionary return from school there was just time to snatch a slice of bread and jam (a thin scrape of butter under the jam if he was lucky), before settling down with Uncle Mac to a *Children's Hour* – Toytown, Bunter, plays, talks or readings – they all came as grist to his mill, and the day was incomplete if he missed it.

With the end of the news at six-thirty their winter evenings slipped into a regular pattern. The wireless was on for Phoebe and Doll whose hands were seldom idle. The wartime *Make Do and Mend* programme publicised with such vigour by middle-class men from the ministries as a novel wartime expedient was nothing new to the working classes. Financial constraints had made it a necessity for generations, and as the two of them listened to the radio they were busy at the old skills. Thinning sheets were cut and turned middle to side, worn knitted items were unwound and the wool salvaged for reuse, collars were turned, socks darned, coats altered and women's clothing cut and revamped. They were both more than adept with their hands and were usually happy with the results.

The early patch-free years of Poplar that John had so deplored were long in the past, but now his patches meant little to him.

Patching was universal, and neatly patched garments were actively promoted as a patriotic contribution to the war effort. 'Wear Your Patch with Pride' – now that would have been a slogan worth airing, but the best the ministry men could come up with was 'Patriotic Patches'.

And of course they knitted. Phoebe, with fingers still young, slender and mobile, nimbly twisted her wool and slipped her stitches on and off the speeding needles. Doll, although younger, moved more slowly and with difficulty, her fingers already showing the thickening and knotting of the joints from the arthritis that was eventually to cripple her.

Nor was making-do confined to the women. For the men there was snobbing to be done to keep boots and shoes up to scratch, the few fowl to be attended to as much in winter as summer, an ailing pump on the well to be jollied along, and with four adults and three youngsters the outside privy needed regular servicing. With the ground hard frozen a proper interment was often impossible and the contents had to be tipped in an out of the way spot to be disposed of with the thaw, and such was the cold following Christmas that a small oil lamp had to be left burning inside the privy box to prevent the contents of the bucket from freezing solid. At night its light provided a soft, welcoming glow when the lid was lifted, and the warmth of its gentle convection currents eased just a little the torment of a winter visit in the harshest of the weather.

Both Jack and Charlie continued their old interest in amateur wireless and brought with them from Poplar a collection of valves, coils, rheostats, meters and assorted bits and pieces that occupied a table and some cupboards in the workroom. If the household was lucky, when the wireless fever grabbed them they would be content with pottering there. If unlucky, they turned their hands to 'improving' the reception on the one working set the house possessed. One or two silent evenings ensued. Then irons were heated on top of the gas stove, and the scent of solder and flux drifted through the house before the wireless sprang to life again: greatly improved they were told, but it always sounded much as it did before. They both read, and Jack wrote a lot. He still kept in touch with a few old friends from his political days and wrote regularly to Gilmore, who often ended up receiving a bundle of four or five letters together when the mail eventually caught up with his ship.

Moira was the quiet one, with her head buried either in her

Picturegoer magazines or books about the theatre, but with the family settled at last the time available for that was limited. She too had returned to regular schooling, and that meant homework after a day that had already been long and tiring. Attendance at the girls' high school in Brentwood meant an early start and a time-consuming and tedious journey. First the long walk up the lane for a bus to Pitsea, followed by an unsheltered wait in all weathers for the school bus. The distance was little more than ten miles as the crow flew, but on its daily round the bus rambled to little hamlets, along minor byways, and waited for latecomers at the end of farm tracks far from the main roads, and the journey seemed interminable. Moira already had a particularly effective and colourful vocabulary, a sharp tongue when she chose to use it, and a voice that in later years could swell from the stage to the most distant seat in the gods. She was vociferous in her denunciation of the journey, the school, the teachers and homework, and she expressed her views frequently. Phoebe murmured conciliatory noises. Jack explained the benefits to be derived from seeing her education through to the end, even if she did eventually intend to make a career on the stage, and for the moment the confrontation passed.

His evenings untroubled by homework, John watched and listened to all that went on, while busying himself with his own interests. When the air war intensified the newspapers published plane-spotting charts with pictures and details of German aircraft. Intended primarily for local defence volunteers they were taken up by the youth of the nation with enthusiasm and dedication, and were soon supplemented by other publications sold for a few pence: *Spot Them in the Air* and *The ABC of Plane Spotting*. Had the country but known, it had at its command a potential army of dedicated plane spotters with sharp eyes, 20/20 vision and a power of recall for aircraft that they never had for their lessons, and yet they were never called to the colours. At school there were regular competitions between the boys, and the quiet evenings were a chance for John to hone his spotting skills.

'Dad! Dad!' It usually took two or three calls to prise him from his book. 'Will you hear me go through my spotting?'

With resignation, and the sooner to get it over with, Jack took the charts, called out the names and checked off the details.

'Junkers Ju 90.'

375

'Four engines, two rudders, square cut wing tips etc.'

'Junkers Ju 52.'

'Three engines, fixed undercarriage, single rudder etc.'

So they went on: Dorniers, Messerschmidts, Heinkels and Stukas until eventually Jack wearied and called a halt.

John's own books, the captain's illustrated books and magazines, and the Meccano which had arrived from Poplar occupied the rest of his time until just before nine when tea was made and they settled down to listen to the news. There might perhaps have been an occasional murmur of sympathy from Phoebe or Doll at some particularly sad report, or a few comments and a shake of the head from Jack or Charlie as the bad news continued to roll in, but otherwise little was said as they listened to the war reports. Some of the air raids they knew about already. They had heard the bombers and the noise of their reception as they moved in from the sea, and in the night sky the glow of fires towards the estuary or Shell Haven marked where they had passed. To The Anchorage itself and the houses round about there was little threat. It would have been an unlucky chance that drew a stray bomb to those outlying areas so far away from the targets on the estuary. They did not keep late hours in winter. Coal supplies had to be carefully conserved, and often before John was asleep he would hear the last footsteps coming up the stairs, and the house fell silent until morning.

John's friendship with Chuzzy continued, and during the worst days of winter, when bad weather kept them indoors, he gradually got to know a little more of the mother and of Doreen the sister, who seemed quite grown up but was probably about eighteen or nineteen. She was dark-haired, good looking and lively, and not above a little knockabout fun with two younger boys.

Mr Arrowsmith was altogether a more remote figure. Chuzzy seldom spoke of him, nor did he seem to have much to do with Chuzzy, certainly not when John was there. In the fine weather up to Christmas he was often seen working in the garden when they passed through, but he never approached them, nor did Chuzzy ever speak to him. On a couple of occasions when John was in the house he opened the door to a room unaware that John was there, saw him, turned and went out again.

Jack was always more than willing to engage with the young boys who came calling, often to their confusion when they knocked on the door for the first time to be met with a promise that he would be out to play with them as soon as he got his coat on. Chuzzy soon learned how to deal with that sort of thing, but John was at a loss to understand Mr Arrowsmith who puzzled him a great deal. Details of his background, as far as local hearsay could be accepted as fact, were brief. He had served as an army officer throughout the Great War and been invalided out shortly after it ended, although he showed no obvious sign of injury or disability. From the time the Arrowsmiths arrived in the house he had never been seen to go beyond the garden. No more was known.

John's initial encounter with him was accidental and a surprise to them both. Chuzzy was disappearing into the outside privy as John entered the garden, and called out to him to go in and wait for him. He walked into the room to find Mr Arrowsmith sitting by the window with a book in his hand. He was silent, and for a moment it seemed that he might get up and leave the room without a word.

'So you're Johnny from The Anchorage, are you?'

It was John who was silent now. Chuzzy must have been talking about him.

'And I'm Mr Chuzzlewit. Is that right?'

Surprisingly that made things easier. John smiled and shook his head. At that point Chuzzy came in. Nothing more was said. They left for the garden and Mr Arrowsmith returned to his book.

John never really got to know him much better, but from then on at least he didn't bolt if they met, and John was increasingly in his company. Even so he spoke little; just a few words to his family or to John, and that was all, apart from one exceptional occasion. It was teatime at Chuzzy's. Despite rationing it was not unusual for John to have a meal with Chuzzy's family, or he with John's. They used each others homes indiscriminately throughout their friendship.

They were at the table listening to the news when Mr Arrowsmith began to speak. John's attention had been focused on the food, not the news item that seemed to have provoked him. It may perhaps have been some passing reference to the coal or oil reserves that were Hitler's targets in Russia. He spoke excitedly and at length, but to himself rather than to anyone at the table.

377

They listened quietly until eventually Mrs Arrowsmith leaned across and touched him on the arm. He started, was once again his silent self, and they returned to their tea. It was the only time John heard him string more than a couple of sentences together, and it would have been memorable for that alone, but the unusual circumstances and the strangeness of what he had to say were such that the substance, if not the detail, of his outburst was not forgotten.

For many years if John recalled the incident at all it was by virtue of that odd trick the memory has of dredging up unprompted the seemingly trivial and unimportant. Then decades later, in early reports on global warming, he caught an echo of words and ideas that seemed familiar. They threw a new light on the events of that teatime thirty or more years earlier, when to his uncomprehending audience of four, Chuzzy's father had delivered a passionate tirade against the plundering of the world's resources, the reckless burning of fossil fuels and a warning of the bill that Nature would ultimately present. He hadn't put it in those words, but that had certainly been his theme.

It was 1942, in the darkest days of the Second World War, and at the dead end of a muddy road, in a remote corner of the Essex plotlands, an ex-army officer invalided out following the first great war, spent his days concerning himself with the long-term future of the planet. Perhaps that explained his remoteness. John had little opportunity to know him any better. A couple of years later Chuzzy called for him after school and as they set off together up the lane turned and casually said, 'My Dad died last night.' He showed no emotion and made no further reference to the matter, or to the funeral.

From The Anchorage most of the shops necessary for day-to-day living were within easy walking distance. Furthest away at the top of the lane the butcher also undertook the slaughter and dressing of home-reared livestock that the owners were too squeamish or incompetent to tackle themselves. Nearer to hand, at the junction where crumbling concrete roads led off into the small estate of bungalows, there was a cluster of three shops: the post office and newsagent's, with a clutter of free-standing advertising boards around it; Hawkes the dairy; and a general/hardware store reeking of soap and paraffin oil. In the opposite direction towards the arterial road were two small general grocers and one greengrocer. Somehow despite a modest local population and the constraints of rationing they all made a living and were still there when the war ended.

Pitsea, the local metropolis, was almost two miles away, but apart from the early and late service for commuters the only buses through the lane were those to the market on a Saturday morning. On other days there were only the buses on the main road from the top of the lane, and even those were considered an unnecessary indulgence by a few hard, and hard-up, cases like Mrs Heard. For her economy took precedence over ease, and from the comfort of the market-day bus she could be seen in all weathers trudging the two miles home, with a sulky Denny or Mickey in tow, weighed down by shopping bags.

At the Saturday market, on a number of outdoor stalls and under the rusting corrugated-iron roofs of what may at one time have been barns for a livestock market it was still business, if not quite as usual, for Alf the Market Man and his like. Despite the war and rationing, the open markets still had enough on offer to draw a steady flow of customers, but after the fascination and variety of pre-war Chrisp Street it was a colourless and dull affair.

Phoebe and Doll muttered darkly about the black-market dealings that kept the traders going, but given the money and inclination to try for a little something under the counter they might have been hard pressed to find one ready to oblige. Comfortable-looking ladies just like them with a convincing air of domesticity, and perhaps a child in tow for extra conviction, were just as likely to be undercover inspectors for the local Food Control Officer as needy housewives looking for a little extra. Desperate times bred desperate remedies: informers were encouraged, and the Ministry of Food was not alone in having a network of operatives that would not have shamed the Stasi.

Just around the corner from the market the Broadway Cinema substituted for The Gaiety, but the kiddies' Saturday-morning film show no longer held any attractions for John. Now he was looking for stronger meat in his entertainment sandwich, and in between the 'Road' films of Hope and Crosby, the madness of the Marx brothers, and the Garland and Rooney pops, he and his friends worked their way through *The Maltese Falcon*, *The Wolf Man*, an

379

extensive diet of mystery, suspense and mayhem from home and abroad, and yet another showing of *Scarface*. Left open-mouthed by Paul Muni's violent simulation of Al Capone as his tommy-gun ripped its way across the Broadway screen in the St Valentine's Day Massacre it would be many weeks before their playgrounds ceased to echo with his cry, 'Get out of my way, I'm gonna spit.'

Life could be tough for a young cinema buff in the 1940s. The British Board of Film Censors imposed a rigid code of censorship, and many of the films which suited John's maturing taste came with a Category A classification as more suitable for adults, with children admitted only if accompanied by a 'parent or bona fide guardian'. Not in his wildest dreams did he see his mother, father or sister keeping him company on his regular film-going excursions, and the Board might have been surprised at the number and variety of 'bona fide guardians' found to accompany him through the doors of the Broadway until he looked old enough to pass muster by himself at the cash desk.

Every Saturday afternoon during term time, and on any day of the week during the holidays, he joined the group of 'orphans', mainly boys, waiting outside the foyer to be adopted for the afternoon. They operated in an orderly and self-regulating way on a first-come, first-served basis, with no queue jumping. One or two of them at most would be positioned on each side of the entrance doors, with the others keeping a discreet distance until their turn came. To anyone who looked remotely like a soft touch, male or female, young or old, singles or doubles, they held out their few pence and pleaded, 'Will you take me in please?' Once inside they went their own way. As an arrangement it seemed to have all the ingredients of an abusers' charter, yet the practice was knowingly accepted by all the parents, and in those years there were no incidents to suggest that they were mistaken.

Programmes of main feature, supporting film and newsreel were continuous from one-thirty or two on Saturday afternoons, and from mid-afternoon during the week. There were a few short intervals for refreshments, but once it was open the cinema only emptied when it finally closed for the day in the late evening. Working hours were irregular, free time was limited and people grabbed their viewing when they could. It was not at all unusual to arrive in the middle of a feature and stay until a whispered 'This is where we came in' had them nudging their way past their

neighbours to the exit, while the usherettes roamed the gangways flashing their torches to identify the vacant seats for those
still waiting. To keep the ticket office clicking there was always
an entirely separate programme on Sunday evening, and by
early evening on any day of the week there were likely to be
queues.

As an opportunity for a brief escape from a grey and drab
reality it was unrivalled, and for cinemas across the nation it was a
golden age. An old newspaper for the Midlands for 20th June 1940,
less than one month after Dunkirk, when the threat of invasion
was believed to be imminent, shows how Britain forgot its troubles.
There were 83 cinemas in the Birmingham area alone, showing in
the same week a choice of 58 different main features from *Band
Wagon* to *Destry Rides Again*, and from *Mutiny in the Big House*
to *Naughty Marietta*. Given the time and the money, picture-going
was one of the few things in life where choice was virtually
unlimited and the product unrationed, and in the Broadway in
Pitsea, in the Kingsway in Hadleigh, in any cheap fleapit that he
could reach and his funds stretch to, John flung himself into that
great escape.

Christmas Day 1941 saw most of the family coming together again
for the first time in many months. Only Kath was missing, having
once again drawn the short straw for Christmas working. At The
Anchorage they breakfasted like kings. Iris the Wonder Hen, one
of the three point-of-lay pullets brought back from Wickford
market, carried wartime productivity to excess. Her near-daily
deliveries of large, brown eggs returned tenfold the care and
attention they showered on her, and seven of them sat down to an
egg, a slice of bacon and, thanks to Phoebe's tenacious pursuit of
the butcher, fried chitterlings. No butter on the bread with their
bacon of course – Phoebe's principles of domestic economy were
enforced even more rigorously in wartime. Toast, marmalade and
tea completed the best meal of the day. It seemed almost like old
times.

The same would not be said of the rest of the day. Their day-
old chicks had produced four cockerels, but to everyone's relief
they were judged to be too immature for the table. Naming the
birds and making them family pets was proving to be a great

mistake, and when, much later, the goslings Lottie and Freddie went to the slaughter it was a black day of tension and family mourning. So instead of fowl they had pot-roast; a stringy hunk of meat which successfully resisted all tenderising processes and its never-ending time in the pot. In Pitsea market there had been queues for cuts from the horse-meat stall, but none of them had the stomach for that. The pudding and cake were strong on carrot, but short on fruit, and devoid of spirits. There was a wartime trifle best passed over in silence, and by and large that was the measure of the Christmas fare.

By Christmas 1941 the common knowledge that when it came to rationing there was one law for the rich and another for the poor did little to foster a spirit of goodwill and sense of common purpose between the classes. Apart from the black market, which could supply most things to those with the money, the belt-tightening that the majority of people endured could readily be avoided by those who could afford to eat out regularly. Meals taken in restaurants were not rationed, and in expensive West End establishments those who were monied and unprincipled indulged themselves with little restraint. When watching waiters and workers spread the news it unsurprisingly bred resentment. The government responded by imposing a ceiling of five shillings a meal, which the unscrupulous with time and money on their hands easily evaded by taking their smoked salmon in the cocktail bar before moving into the restaurant, or having one course here, another there, and moving on as the fancy took them. Knowing that made their pot-roast a particularly tough dish to swallow, and it seemed to them then that rationing could not possibly get worse. They were wrong. It could and it did, but Christmas 1941 suffered from comparison with 1940 when Lou's hoarded purchases from 1939 had carried them through. Those provisions had long been exhausted and Gilmore's transatlantic largesse was yet to come.

Despite requests for a special exception to be made for Christmas morning the ban on bell ringing continued. In Carters Terrace just two years earlier they would have thrown open the windows to the music of four or five churches ringing out the changes in parochial competition. Now for the second year the bells of All Saints' hung still and silent as they walked the short distance for a morning visit to Bayhurst. They arrived to find it already busy with Christmas callers.

382

'Happy Christmas, Ma.' A kiss on the cheek and half a dozen of Iris's eggs from Jack.

'Thanks Jack. The same to you. Here Phoebe, did you get those chitterlings you wanted from the butcher?'

'Where did you put those bits and pieces I brought back from town, Elsie?'

'Happy Christmas, Charlie. Do the honours for me with the bucket while you're here, would you?'

'God bless you too, Ma. What a lovely present.'

'Come on, get the glasses out, Clara, and I'll open that bottle.'

'Fancy poor old Kath getting lumbered over Christmas, but at least she's off for the New Year.'

While the family news and greetings were exchanged, Valerie and John moved around the gathering, handed over their home-made Christmas cards, received a kiss and had some little present pressed into their hands in return.

There were other Christmas visitors to see Louisa that morning. Distant cousins from Aunt Tot's side of the family, seen once or twice a year on special occasions, came and went. Harry arrived, exchanged greetings and enjoyed his drink to solicitous enquiries concerning the progress of his romance with Mrs C. Bill called with a bottle of Scotch (he was never short of contacts for that sort of thing), a dish of jellied eels and the latest East End news. The old house was still standing and, as far as he knew, those few friends and neighbours who had decided to sit tight were alive and well.

'Frumkin's copped it you know, in one of the November raids.'

There was a stunned silence. It was almost as though an old family friend had died. L. Frumkin & Co, wine and spirit dealers, and by appointment suppliers of fine liquors to the Lagsdings through many happy pre-war years, were no more. One of Bill's customers had brought him the report: no one hurt but the shop and stock lying a smoking ruin after the last raid.

'They gave us some good old times, Frumkin's. Remember their tasters, Bill? Poor old Pappy and his little cupboard of specials. Blimey, what a contrast.'

Elsie gave a meaningful nod towards the sideboard: Hall's Wine, Whiteway's British Sherry and a bottle of Sanatogen Tonic Wine plus Bill's bottle.

'Could be worse, Else, could be worse.' They needed no reminding of that.

It would be some months before they celebrated the news that rumour and report had got it wrong. Frumkins still stood and flourished and would do so for another fifty years or more before commercial pressures finally closed its doors.

They returned to The Anchorage for dinner and tea, but were back again at Bayhurst in the evening. A week or so before Christmas John had helped his gran and Clara as they clambered on and off chairs pinning and tacking the decorations that had been brought away from Carters Terrace. To these Elsie added her own decorative touches when she came home for her few days off duty. Regardless of coal shortages, fires had been burning in both rooms all day, and the house was warm, comfortable and festive.

In one way at least Bayhurst had responded well to constant occupation. The charnel-house smell of damp and decay that welcomed them on those short stays before the war had been permanently banished, but in other respects things were not so good. In the dark, unventilated spaces beneath the floorboards, old timbers, perhaps already half-rotten, were starting to show their resentment at the additional loading of furniture crammed in from Poplar. In the front room, where the piano had been tucked into a corner by the bay window, one or more joists now sagged under its weight and the floor bounced underfoot. Much too risky for a knees-up even if there had been space enough. On the piano itself even more of the keys replied to the touch with a leaden 'plonk', but there were still enough operating to give them an approximate guide to Elsie's intentions when she sat down to play.

The tiny room, much less than half the size of the London front room, was cluttered with spare furniture and already crowded when Bill and family returned for the evening. The three cousins were tucked away into the back room with a few sweets, slices of ersatz Christmas cake, lemonade and some games, and with the doors into the corridor open, they could hear all that went on: talk, songs and laughter, the piano and Charlie on the squeeze box. The content was much the same as it had always been, but subdued as it never was in the old days, and the magic of those hours of eavesdropping on the half-lit stairway high above the party room was gone.

'Who'd like a little taste of Sanatogen then?'

Sanatogen was something new, but Clara had never before disappointed with her little tasters.

'Yes please,' from John. 'No thank you,' from the other two.

In the past he had been given no more than an opportunity to dip his finger into Clara's glass. Now she returned with a glass that was all his own, even if it was less than half full.

It was never clear whether the aunts' innocence concerning Sanatogen was real or assumed. Endorsed by celebrities and the physician to the Royal Family no less, it was advertised in convincing medical terms as a nerve tonic, guaranteed to renew health, vigour and strength in those most difficult of times. Certainly the aunts always seemed the livelier for the glass or two they took on a Sunday, and John had noticed that they sipped their drinks with an evident appreciation and relish unusual for a dose of physic. As for the feeling of well-being it was advertised to promote, he had his own experience of that after he emptied his glass. Throughout the war there was usually a bottle of Sanatogen to be found in their cupboard, and it was no doubt coincidental that in addition to its therapeutic properties it had the alcohol content of Vermouth. At the end of the evening as they walked back to a dark, cold house, they may have thought again of those Christmases in the better times before the war and felt a little sorry for themselves.

In Leningrad, on the Eastern Front, people just like them were into the fourth month of a siege that would not be lifted for more than a year. Their Christmas fare was a ration of bread increased fractionally to ten ounces for the occasion. It was made of rye, chaff, flax, anything that might contain a gram of nourishment, and before their Christmas Day had ended over three thousand would have died of starvation, cold and injuries received.

It was a muted welcome they gave to 1942. Kath's few days leave had been cancelled, and, apart from Lou and Clara, the rest of the family were back on their various duties. The little gathering that met on New Year's Eve did so in reflective mood and dispersed soon after Jack had gone through the first footing. There would be work as usual the following day, and early starts to be made in the morning.

They got no welcome from the New Year. Winter was once again collaborating with the Nazis, and the first two months of the year brought in the longest cold spell of the century, with weeks of continuous frosts and winds consistently in the north or east. Workers and schoolchildren battled their way daily through the snowstorms and bitingly low temperatures of a dispiriting winter that clung on relentlessly until the end of February. Coal supplies were limited, and although they supplemented them with dead branches cut out from the wood and hedges, the warmest place was bed and early nights were the rule. Even the swing and the hard-frozen pond had little appeal in the face of the bitter weather, and although a sledge of sorts was cobbled together, the gentle undulations of Essex were small beer after the thrills and exhilaration of the Chiltern slopes. In short, that wartime winter had few attractions even for children, and they did not mourn its passing.

The Easter holidays brought with them the first warm, relaxing days of the year. They seemed to John to promise much for the coming summer at The Anchorage, but with the spring came disappointment. The joint occupation of The Anchorage had never been seen as anything more than a temporary measure, and when Doll and Charlie found themselves a little bungalow towards the top of the lane the arrangement had to come to an end. It was impossible for Phoebe and Jack by themselves to pay the rent at The Anchorage and so they too had to look elsewhere.

Within a few weeks Phoebe had found what she was after, a bungalow on the lane just as close to Bayhurst and enjoying the modern conveniences of mains water, foul drainage and electricity. They would find in due course that there was little else to enjoy about the place, and Jack was unenthusiastic, but the move was a matter of necessity, and with no other accommodation available that concluded the matter.

Phoebe and Lou embarked on a few days' scrubbing and cleaning before the move, when Moira and John had an opportunity to make their own personal tour and inspection of Harcourt. The name had a romantic, aristocratic ring to it, but they were not deceived, having walked past often enough to have no great expectations. It was a single-storey, four-roomed box with a scullery and lavatory tagged on at the back. Most homes stripped of furniture, dressings and personal possessions look bleak enough, but despite their mother's best efforts their hearts sank as they looked around them at the bare boards and mean, empty rooms and thought of what they were leaving.

Things improved, however. From under the tarpaulins in the Heards' barn and the garden shed at Bayhurst came pieces of their own furniture that had not seen the light for more than eighteen months. Old curtains from the Poplar windows were shaken out

386

and hung; old carpets unrolled and thoroughly beaten before being laid. From drawers and boxes Phoebe's cherished ornaments were unpacked and unwrapped, and gradually strange rooms assumed an air of familiarity and homeliness.

By the end of May John had put his hand to The Anchorage pump for the last time. The wood, the pond and swing, the room of his own, the captain's treasures heaped up in the loft all unexplored, and the wide-ranging space of the house itself were all things of the past. Iris and her friends went to temporary holding cages in Mrs Heard's barn until pens could be organised in the new garden. The few items that they had taken in with them were trundled down the hill on a handcart, and they turned the key in the door of The Anchorage for the last time.

PART FOUR

29

Complete Power of Control

With the move to Harcourt two and a half years of relative rootlessness came to an end. It would be Jack's home for the remaining nineteen years of his life, and John's until he left for his stint of National Service. The move also brought with it a complete and permanent change in family circumstances. Jack had been well enough to work throughout the winter without any sign of the chest infection or bronchitis of the previous year, but in March, while they were still at The Anchorage, and with the worst of the weather behind him, the problems returned and needed attention.

The reputation of the local doctor was not encouraging. A visit to his surgery in a run-down bungalow on the High Road in Pitsea was reported to be a dismal experience. He was said to smell of whisky by late afternoon and to be unenthusiastic about home visits. As far as Jack was concerned it was a reputation that totally belied him. A morning telephone call to the surgery from the post office brought him to the house by early afternoon. Pneumonia was diagnosed, but in its early stages, and Phoebe was told that the medicine prescribed should take care of the problem. By the end of the day Jack had taken his first dose of 'M & B', a generic term for a number of different prescriptions used to treat his lung condition over many years. Whatever their specific nature, their effect was such that the family came to regard them as wonder drugs. They brought about an immediate improvement, and Jack was soon recovering without any repetition of the restless delirium of the previous year.

If the drug was new to them its manufacturers were not. For returning commuters on the Fenchurch to Southend line, when the interminable stops and starts of wartime travel had blurred any perception of progress on the evening journey home, the May & Baker factory at Dagenham was the one sure and certain marker along the way. In the darkest of nights and the deepest of blackouts, with the world a featureless void beyond the drawn blinds, they could sniff it out as they passed. The regulars on the run might stir from a restless doze or lift their heads briefly from their papers in recognition. Newcomers to the line would flare their nostrils to catch and try to identify the pungent, medicinal smell of chemicals and antiseptic that seeped into the crowded train and cut its way through the heaviest fug of tobacco smoke and body odours.

Despite his recovery Jack was unable to return to work. After a further detailed examination he was told that the deterioration in his lungs was such that he would never be fit to work again, and from self-reliance they passed to such support as the National Assistance Board had to offer. In common with so many similar institutions the name of the Board was artfully framed to belie its true function. It would have been natural, but mistaken, to assume from its title that the Board was there to offer assistance whenever and wherever possible to those in genuine need. In practice the general experience of those desperate enough to turn to it as a last resort was of functionaries whose purpose was to find and interpret arcane and skilfully crafted regulations in such a way as to deny any assistance beyond a bare and irreducible minimum. Nor were their paperwork skills the end of the matter. They were efficient and thorough too, in the house calls they made from time to time to satisfy themselves that personal and domestic circumstances were properly and satisfactorily demeaning before sitting with Jack to complete the formalities and determine the pittance to be paid for the next few months.

If John was too young to understand the detailed economics of the household, he could not be unaware of the dramatic change in their situation. He was once again reliant on aunts and uncles for his pocket money. Domestic austerity was piled on wartime austerity. Everything had to be eked out a little further and last a little longer. Jack's cigarettes were reduced to a few home-rolled, wispy straws each day from a half-ounce of tobacco that occasionally came in with the shopping but was more often a present from one of the aunts.

He witnessed only one or two real 'barnies' about money between his mother and father, but tempers were often frayed when unexpected demands were piled on inadequate resources. As an observer at some of the little flare-ups he was at times uneasy, but never in any fear that matters would not resolve themselves as they had on other occasions. Overall it remained a stable background with a good working relationship between them most of the time and never productive of any sense of insecurity.

When there were words between them it was always an unequal contest. Jack was quiet and composed. Phoebe was invariably excited and lost control. His quietness fed her anger. All too often she was simply looking for a way to let off steam which his response did not provide. It wasn't deliberate provocation on his part; it was just the way he was. It is also fair to say that apart from a little cigarette deprivation for Jack, it was Phoebe who was at the sharp end. He had his books, his garden and other interests. She was the one in the market or shops who faced the problem of getting to the end of the week with a near-empty purse.

Nor was Jack beyond his own form of goading. Frustrated at the end of a session sharper and longer than usual, but unproductive as ever, Phoebe lost all sense of proportion and the ridiculous and threatened to go back to her mother. 'Sod off back to Mum' was the phrase that John remembered. Later, when the matter had blown over, even he could see the humour of the situation. There was his mother nudging forty, with a growing son and a near-adult daughter, threatening to leave home for Bayhurst, all of a hundred yards away, where Lou would undoubtedly have received her with advice to go back home and not be so bloody silly: Jack simply offered to help pack her bag.

The sixth of July 1942 came and went with nothing to distinguish it from the days before and those that would follow. Only in retrospect can it be identified as the midpoint of the European war. One thousand and thirty-seven days gone; the same number remained to endure. As it seemed at times that there would never be an end to it all, that knowledge, if they had possessed it, may have encouraged rather than disheartened them. Defeat apart, another three years could scarcely make any difference to the way in which life on the home front had been transformed by regulation and rationing. The weekly allowance of fresh meat stood at 1s 2d worth, bacon 4oz, fats 8oz (but only 2oz of butter), cheese 3oz, sugar 8oz, tea 2oz, sweets and chocolate 2oz, preserves were allocated at 16oz a month. In addition to coupon-rationed goods, there was a monthly allocation of 24 'points' which governed almost everything else that was edible: tinned fish, tinned meats, rice, breakfast cereals, dried vegetables and lentils, tinned vegetables, tinned fruit, condensed milk, soap and soap powders. Buy a 16oz tin of grade III salmon or Australian Minced Meat Loaf, or two tins of fruit, and that was the month's allocation blown away. Other goods not rationed were 'allocated': eggs at three a month, milk three pints a week for most adults, schoolchildren two-thirds of a pint a day. Dried milk, cod liver oil and fruit juices supplemented the rations of very young children. Bread and fresh fish escaped the net, but the latter was always in short supply. Wildlife was available to those who could catch or poach it, domestic livestock to those who could keep it. 'We will do our best to keep you alive until the war is over, but you may get a bit thin,' said the Minister of Food with masterly political understatement: wartime obesity was never going to be a problem. Price control was all embracing not only for food, but for the whole range of consumer products.

The annual clothing coupon allowance was minimal: 'shop till you drop' inconceivable. Should a woman have been reckless enough to indulge in a one-off purchase of winter coat, dress, jumper, blouse, petticoat, knickers, pair of shoes and gloves she would have been left with no more coupons for the next twelve months than would buy her four handkerchiefs and a pair of stockings, but not silk which had long been banned.

By the end of the year the production of domestic furniture would be prohibited except for utility furniture constructed to specified designs and materials by firms under licence from the Board of Trade. Prices would be controlled, and it would of course be rationed and available only to newly married couples or those who had lost a home by bombing.

Bombed, cold, hungry and shabby, they also bore a taxation burden that brought tears to the eyes. In 1939 the lower rate of income tax stood at 29 per cent, the upper rate (inclusive of surtax) at 70 per cent. By 1942 the comparative figures were 50 per cent and 97.5 per cent. Never was there more inducement for the unprincipled and criminally inclined to exercise their talents for fraud and evasion.

Over and above those domestic issues the population was regulated, constrained and spied upon in a way that could not have been conceived before the war. Under the Emergency Powers Act of May 1940 the state assumed 'complete power of control over persons and property for the prosecution of the war'. It was a time when every private interest was required to give way to the urgent needs of the community. There would be direction and control of labour, along with regulation of wages and, where required, business, commercial and banking operations would come under direct government control.

As in any conflict capital crimes and serious offences received condign punishment. By the midpoint of the war ten enemy agents had been executed, and convicted looters could expect up to ten years' penal servitude. But with the flood of regulations that followed the outbreak of war came a raft of entirely new criminal offences that seemed to take even the honest citizen by surprise. Neither grave nor of a capital nature they nevertheless carried penalties that ranged from fines to imprisonment, and a time when £1 had the equivalent purchasing power of £30 today the fines were seldom negligible and could be swingeing. In the jittery early days of the war a pensioner of Fareham was fined £5 for 'sounding a whistle late at night contrary to the control of noise order'. Women ran through his village in panic fearing a raid and nearby troops were ordered to shelter. A Home Guard officer was fined 10s 6d for permitting the glow of his cigarette to be visible in the street while an air-raid warning was in operation. Another breach of the blackout regulations by a second offender was punished with a £25 fine and three months' imprisonment.

Billeting was compulsory not optional. A vicar refusing evacuees was fined £5, but another more obstructive offender found himself £25 the poorer. Farmers were required to cultivate land in accordance with instructions from their local War Agricultural Committee. One who did not was fined £100. It was made an offence to sing, smoke or play a musical instrument in a shelter. Happily this was one regulation that no one sought to enforce. Under the Defence Finance Regulations every individual was required to make a return of any overseas financial holdings and, if appropriate, offer them for sale to the Treasury where dollars in particular were required. Penalties for offenders were draconian. One was fined £12,000 for concealing a holding of $28,000, equivalent to less than £7000, and there were others who were dealt with just as severely. Actors and performers in particular seemed to fall foul in this respect with George Arliss dunned for £4,500 and Noel Coward for £1,600 in respect of undisclosed foreign earnings.

Food rationing brought a rich crop of offences and anomalies: a fine of £1 for feeding the Brighton seagulls with a slice of bread, a baker fined £2.12s for sugaring a mince pie after it had come out of the oven, another £31 for baking white bread (prohibited since April 1942), a woman fined £2 for obtaining meat from her sister in Ireland – her letter had been read by the censor. More serious offences by dealers brought prison sentences of up to a year. Only the sterling work of the censor brought one particularly hardened criminal to book. In a letter to her friend in Ireland a 75-year-old diabetic widow had written:

I was glad to see you liked the sweets ... You remember I have diabetes ... I get 6s of meat every week instead of 2s and I often don't need so much, so now and again I take four or five chops to a very nice girl who owns a sweet shop. When she has sweets she always gives me first chance at them, and I get plenty ... Another friend makes me a lovely cake because I take her meat, and another new laid eggs off her farm every week. So you see everyone is good to me.

Everyone, that is, except the local magistrate. For the two offences of giving away part of her meat ration he fined her £2.

When it was finally confirmed beyond doubt that it was illegal to exchange or give away rationed goods it raised a flurry of anxious enquiries. 'Do I become a criminal if I give sweets to a child or a slice of bread and butter to a tramp?' 'No,' was the answer to the first from a ministry anxious not to stifle the flow of bars of chocolate to prisoners of war. As for the tramp, the advice was to invite him in and seat him at the dining table to enjoy his bread and butter, although it should strictly be as part of a shared meal.

Regulations concerning motoring and the petrol allocation brought many to grief. Failure to paint his car's bumpers and running boards white cost one early offender 10s. Another was fined £50 for leaving his car unlocked or otherwise immobilised, and Ivor Novello's weekend jaunts in his Rolls Royce, licensed only for work of national importance, earned him four weeks inside.

Fines or imprisonment were imposed for breaches of the retail price and sales regulations: £50 for overcharging on a tin of plums, £50 for selling soap at 3½d instead of 3d, three months' imprisonment for a Covent Garden merchant who exceeded the maximum wholesale price, and a trader fined £4 for refusing to sell onions unless the customer also bought carrots. Civilian Clothing Orders regulated the style and cut of clothes: a tailor was fined £300 for making double-breasted jackets, trousers with turnups and waist-coats with back straps, all contrary to regulations; MP Lady Astor's attempt to obtain clothes worth £10 from America cost her £50.

A council official who ignored a Home Guard's order not to enter a bomb-damaged area to return to his home and family was arrested on charges which included 'forcing a safeguard', an offence which carried a sentence of death or penal servitude for life, and must have been relieved to pay his £20 fine when that particular charge was dropped.

There were £2 fines for refusing to work, £5 for being late to work, £5 for despondent talk and six weeks in prison for a gospel missioner who spread false rumours. It was an offence to photograph aircraft in flight or on the ground (fine £3) or bomb-damaged buildings without written permission (fine £10); to throw away or destroy milk bottles, rubber or paper (a fine of £5 was imposed for burning paper on a bonfire); to waste electricity by using light on a sunny day (fine £25). Souvenir collecting was banned and one over-enthusiastic collector who kept a 25lb bomb under his bed for six months and lived to tell the tale was told that he was very silly and fined £5.

From Harcourt, untroubled by all those constraints, John moved into his first full summer in an Essex countryside where the now-deserted works, trappings and by-products of war had transformed the bucolic scenes of earlier visits into one vast adventure play-ground. To the north tank traps, pillboxes, concrete and steel anti-tank barriers and other defences straddling and protecting the arterial road were embraced by the boys in all their games. Across the open fields to the east the lines of anti-glider defences con-tinued for a while to provide a supply of rope for their operations in the Arrowsmiths' garden. But it was below the hill to the south, where the land fell away to the marshes of the estuary, that the wartime defences had left them an adventure playground without equal.

At the foot of Church Road, just beyond St Margaret's Church, an arch under the railway led to a short rough track and a patch of hard standing. From there, for more than three miles, the marshes stretched to the river, unbroken and featureless except for a couple of derelict wind pumps. Far away, marking the distant shoreline, the vague outlines of oil installations at Shell Haven might some-times be seen through a heat haze or mist, thickened all too often by drifting smoke from fires along the estuary, marking the track of bombers that had passed in the night.

One small part of the marshes has since been tamed by the creation of a country park, but in 1942 it was a wild, exposed and desolate area. A few cattle grazed on a narrow strip of pastureland beside the railway line; figures were occasionally seen moving in the distance, perhaps fowlers or fishermen, but apart from those and passengers gazing curiously from the passing trains the boys had the whole wide expanse to themselves.

Had there been nothing more than the creeks, saltmarsh, reed beds and minor waterways the area would have drawn them, but even on the marshes the business of war had left its mark in ways that added to their attraction. Alongside the railway line the land was flat, relatively firm and unbroken by the many narrow creeks that threaded their way across the outer reaches. In the belief that this might be a potential site for glider landings in the event of invasion, counter measures had been taken. From the corners of surrounding farmyards, from the remote recesses of barns, and from patches of waste land where they had been long forgotten and quietly decaying, every available piece of obsolete, abandoned or broken farm equipment was hauled out, dragged to the verges of the marshes, and scattered at random as obstacles.

For two years they had stood there enduring the continuing, slow process of decay, colonised by drifting seeds, and gradually subsiding under their own weight into the marshy earth beneath them. Antique farm wagons, still splashed with patches of bright colour despite the years of weathering, now stood immovable, their broad iron-shod wheels rooted deep to the axle. On the sloping ramps of ancient hay elevators row after row of ugly, rusting spikes were softened by a feathery growth of grasses rooted in the rotting timbers, but remained threatening enough to deter any but the most sure-footed of climbers. Muck carts still thickly encrusted with the fertile remains of their last loads blossomed with wild flowers and grasses, and rusting tractors flanked by great, iron-toothed driving wheels looked less like peaceful farm equipment than medieval war wagons straining for the call to arms. Anything that could possibly be salvaged or reused by the farmer had been stripped away long before those historical relics made their journey to the marshes. What was left the boys could do with as they wished. If they were seen, it appeared that nobody cared. Nobody interfered or came near: invasion was no longer on the agenda.

Around, underneath and on top of the carts, tractors and antiquated threshing and winnowing machines the boys acted out the dramas of the cinema newsreels: the battles on the beaches of the Pacific, the bloody engagements on the sands of North Africa, or the slaughter being fought out through the cities and across the steppes of Russia.

At weekends and on evenings when the light seemed to linger for ever they played their way through early summer and into the holidays, while marsh harriers hung in the sky above them and the mournful call of the curlew echoed their own cries of battle. Behind them trains passed by with a regularity that in time became their clock, and beyond, where the sea lavender turned the saltings blue, a new generation of marsh birds tried out their wings. It was remote and most of the time it was peaceful. What little they saw and heard of the war took place high in the skies above them. They stopped and watched its passing, occasionally crawling beneath one of the carts as much for protection from falling shrapnel as anything else, but they were only infrequently disturbed.

It was a long walk from their homes to the marshes and when they went it was often for the best part of a day. To keep them going while they were away they took with them some bread, a few potatoes, a twist of salt and anything else they could scrounge. A tap by the church provided water to drink and timber broken from carts the fuel for the fires in which they cooked their potatoes. Huddling together around the flames they raked open the centre, plastered the potatoes in thick jackets of mud, and buried them deep in the ashes. Cooking times were guesswork, but after their walk and a couple of hours in the sun and wind even half-baked potatoes with a little salt and bread disappeared faster than fancy cakes. Residual mud and ashes all went down the same way, and they flourished on it. If it rained they burrowed under a thresher or baler until it passed.

The marshes around them could be a confusing and hazardous environment for the unwary. Their main fleets and creeks were too wide and deep to cross, but the marshes were also intersected by a bewildering network of minor waterways and drainage ditches. These could be negotiated with care, often on no more than a narrow plank, by those who had the local knowledge and an eye for the stakes rough-cut from hedges and driven into the ground to mark the crossing points. Alongside the widest and deepest of the nearby channels they embarked on their one major construction project – a raft.

From toolboxes here and workshops there they carried away to the marshes the wood saws, wrecking bars, hacksaws, chisels and hammers needed for their undertaking. If any were missed they were furtively smuggled back at the end of the following day. Floorboards cut and prised from wagon bottoms formed the base tied together with stouter timbers from the sides of the wagon and secured with stolen nails and screws or nuts and bolts prised from the equipment lying around them.

After a week or more their work was done, and with a little levering the raft was launched and afloat, but enthusiasm and effort alone were not enough: their skills were inadequate and their more extravagant expectations unfulfilled. With a crew of one it floated with an inch or two of freeboard, with two the water lapped over the edges, and with three it subsided slowly into the depths beneath them. Unstable, unsupportive and tediously cumbersome and slow, it brought to an end their dreams of explorations to the far reaches of the creeks. But it wasn't all wasted effort. On the long, hot summer afternoons, while others were skinny-dipping in the cooling waters of the creek, just one or perhaps two could stretch out on the boards and dabbling toes and fingers, drift slowly in the sun under a blue sky streaked from horizon to horizon with the curling vapour trails of Allied aircraft outward bound for Germany.

And when the raft or play-acting palled they turned to the bewildering combination of parts and components crying out for exploration and deconstruction. On ancient elevators and threshing machines hatches, panels and doors opened on to fascinating and inviting interiors where shafts, gears, teeth, chains and belts linked rollers, blades, drums and spindles in confusing conjunctions. If they could be unbolted, unscrewed, levered loose or otherwise detached, and would yield to their tools and strength, they attacked them. By the end of summer deconstruction had been taken to its limits, and on the grass before them they had an extensive assortment of gears, shafts, chains, pulleys, belts and other assorted parts, but having got them, they were at a loss to know what to do with them. The failure with the raft had dampened their enthusiasm for another construction project, and so they returned to their games, fires and watersports.

As the days shortened and the weather worsened, the waterways and the open, unprotected expanses became less attractive as a playground and they turned their attentions elsewhere, leaving the marshes slowly but remorselessly to absorb and enfold their collection of parts in its soggy embrace, as it did everything else before many years of peace had passed.

During his time at The Anchorage John had more than enough to occupy him, and although he saw Mickey regularly he made no visits to the house. But with the move to Harcourt he renewed his acquaintance with the sow and her inevitable litter of piglets at the bottom of the Heards' garden. They were an eager, inquisitive brood, plump and maturing rapidly. Rationing had made them an enviable resource, however, and Mickey couldn't wait to dazzle him with his intimate role in the lawless arrangements of the pastoral mafiosi of whom he and his mother were now a part. As Mickey presented the matter, the villain of the piece for the back-garden pig breeder was the minister of food, whose regulations required not only that all pigs be registered, but that either the owner's bacon ration or half the pig on slaughter should be surrendered for the good of the public at large.

'Sod that. I do all the grafting for some other buggers to get the benefit.'

He was eloquent in his denunciation of ministerial tyranny. John was by then quite familiar with street obscenities picked up during his days in Poplar and with the Barhams, but had to admire Mickey's casual and assured employment of the words.

The Heards had made sure that their sow and her progeny lived and thrived in carefully organised obscurity. When suitably weaned the piglets moved by night along back roads, footpaths or green lanes to their fattening pens, and there was a well-established network whereby those who were to receive them passed on to the Heards everything that could be chopped and boiled to swell their swill. When the time finally came for them to fulfil that destiny to which all pigs are dedicated, they did so in uncharacteristic silence, a remarkable tribute to the skill and versatility of the local slaughterman.

It was all quite illegal, but the unwritten code of the countryman in competition with the ministry kept it all well under wraps. The clandestine nature of their pig keeping activities meant that the Heards retained their bacon ration, but of that or his pigs Mickey apparently enjoyed as little as he did before the war. His mother sold on her modest entitlement of rashers at a small profit and quite illegally, and thus they eked their way through the war. Of Mickey's home production only a pig's head, blood or intestines were occasionally returned to him, from which his mother provided them with brawn and chitterlings. The barn was now strengthened, and the sow and litter locked inside at night. Rustlers of livestock large or small roamed the lanes, and Mickey and Denny were taking no chances.

By the start of the school summer holidays Jack and his family were well established in Harcourt. It was convenient to be along-side the lane and more closely in touch with local activities. John missed neither his twice-daily turns at the pump, nor the primitive privy, and even the romantic affection for gaslight was fading. Inevitably as the weeks passed with the old, familiar furniture around him and new domestic routines established, his initial reservations and dislike of change were overcome. Harcourt became home, familiar and secure as ever.

It took the experience and perspective of a few more years for him to see it for what it was – a jerry-built, primitive and unhealthy rural dump. Although on the lane and not tucked away up one of the unadopted, unsurfaced side roads, it was typical shoddy plot-land construction throughout. Timber-framed on little or no foundation, it was lined inside with wallboard and outside with shiplapped timbers. Unlike Bayhurst it had never been pebble-dashed. Between the two skins the wall cavity was empty. Old paint flaked and peeled from outer boards shrunken and twisted by exposure just enough to allow a free flow of household heat out and winter chill in through the uninsulated void. Bricks were used only on the chimney stacks. Above the ceiling boards the loft space contained nothing but a few lengths of old gas pipe left behind when electricity had been installed. The accumulated droppings of generations of starlings provided the only roof insulation. For several weeks after the move they continued to jack-boot their way across the ceilings at daybreak until the last bird-sized hole had been found and plugged. Even then gaps between the tiles continued to provide generous ventilation and a low level of illumination in the loft. Overall the insulation rating would have been a modest grade or two above that for Heards' barn.

Behind the front door there was just enough depth for it to swing back into a shallow, open-sided cubbyhole closed off from the front room by a curtain. But space was tight, and within days of moving in it had become a glory hole for all the bits and pieces for which there was no other storage. The front door was never opened. There was no corridor. Where the internal walls crossed three doors provided access between the four rooms. The casement windows were generously sized, but so ill-fitting and poorly secured that they were almost as easy to open from without as within. The two bedrooms had been provided with mean, pinched fireplace openings, but as there was no coal to fire them the flues were closed off, and they stood unused throughout the war.

As a final blow the two youngsters found that once again they had to share a bedroom. It was less than a year since they had been doing so quite happily in Bucks, but at The Anchorage for the first time they had enjoyed their own rooms. Moira was maturing, and the six-year age gap meant that she no longer had the same enthusiasm for rooming with her younger brother. Phoebe was determined that the front room would not be dedicated to sleeping and the problem was only resolved to Moira's satisfaction when Jack fitted a curtain that could be pulled across the bedroom to provide some privacy when it was needed.

At the back of the bungalow the narrow scullery was basic. It had the only solid floor in the house, but so roughly finished that protruding pebbles in the concrete cut through the covering linoleum. Above a stone sink in one corner, lead piping brought mains water into the one tap in the house, and alongside the sink a gas cooker provided the only means of heating the water apart from the top of the living room stove. The back door, roughly constructed of tongued and grooved boards and plastered with dark-brown paint, was as ill-fitting and insecure as the windows. Of the lavatory it was sufficient for them all that it flushed. They were quite happy to accept that it was outside in a cramped, unlit, over-ventilated box tagged on to the end of the scullery.

For those to whom it mattered (John was not one), keeping clean could be tediously difficult. In summer a few moments under the tap could be invigorating and pleasant enough, but in winter teeth and flesh shrank from the ice-cold supply, and even a couple of kettles and a saucepan heating on the cooker and stove seemed unable to meet the demand for hot water during the morning rush. It was remarkable how frequently Moira's need for a complete, uninterrupted and extended period of privacy in the scullery coincided with the demands of John's bowels. When the call was urgent and would admit of no denying the casement window provided his emergency route to the privy. Old habits, born of the use of chemical toilets, lived on. After dark the unlit lavatory created targeting problems for the men that most resolved by wandering off a little into a corner of the garden where they could contemplate the wonders of the wartime sky at night as they satisfied their other more intimate needs.

As each day of the week passed the galvanised bath hanging from the outside wall of the scullery assumed a more threatening aspect. Friday night was bath night. Phoebe was traditional and immovable on that point, and John pleaded the national call for economy in vain. It was apparently depth of water, not frequency of bathing, that mattered. Even he could argue with the inconsistency of that logic, but his mother was unimpressed. Five inches of hot water at the bottom of the bath was the patriotic maximum, but in Harcourt even that was not easily obtained. A lingering, relaxing soak was out of the question.

The bolt was slipped on the back door, the curtains drawn and a gas ring or two left alight if it was cold, and that concluded the preliminaries that transformed the scullery into the bathroom. At any time it was a ritual to be concluded with despatch. In the depth of winter it was a penance. Increasingly self-conscious, John was as keen as his sister for privacy when he was in the bath, but he was not as meticulous as she with the bolt on the back door. His gran's entry was unexpected and unannounced. A rattle of the back doorknob, and there she was smiling at him appreciatively. Surprised and exposed with only five inches of water to cover his embarrassment, he grabbed for the towel. 'Don't you worry about that, darling. You've nothing there to be ashamed of, and I've seen it all before.' She passed on into the living room with a laugh.

As with personal cleanliness so with the household washing – routine was all. Rain or shine, summer or winter, Monday was washday. On the best of days Phoebe battled away against inadequate facilities with restraint and patience. The scullery back door and window were thrown open, and on every ring of the cooker kettles and pans slowly steamed their way to the boil. In a small galvanised bath, sheets, towels and other coarser items were pummelled and wrung, tormented on the rubbing board and finally wrung again before being dropped into a large enamel bucket to await rinsing. Delicate items received gentler treatment. Jack or John put a hand to the small wringer clamped to the scullery table to drive out the worst of the moisture, and for the rest of the day the washing flapped on the garden line at no inconvenience to the rest of the house.

On the worst of days Phoebe's patience and restraint all too soon went by the board and life was less comfortable. With door and window closed against rain and wind, the walls and glazing of the scullery ran with condensation. Steamy, soapy vapours percolated through the house. Mirrors misted over and the smell and taste of a particularly virulent household soap was all pervasive. If fate had finally turned its face against them, the gas ran out and change for the meter was not immediately to hand. From then on nothing could go right, and operations were conducted with dramatic thumps and bangs and a litany of abuse against the household equipment and life in general. Despite the perfectly adequate vocabulary with which she conducted her day-to-day affairs Phoebe's normally robust response to adversity was buttressed on such occasions with a liberal sprinkling of 'bloodies', 'sods' and 'buggers'. The objective was twofold – to relieve her feelings, and to make quite sure they were all well aware of her problems. They were, but there was nothing they could do to help. For the rest of the day, and if it continued to rain for the day or two following, they moved through a scullery shrouded by hanging laundry, and surrendered the heat of the one fire to the gateleg clothes horse propped open in front of it.

Two flatirons were used for ironing and pressing, one always on the gas stove heating while the other was in use. In later years

John pressed them into service as doorstops: a nostalgic reminder of the 'good old days' for his mother and all like her. In most homes on the plotlands and beyond, wet washdays would have been no better. In many they would have been worse, but the fact that it was the common lot was little consolation to those up to their elbows in suds and water.

The February of the year in which they moved from The Anchorage brought to an end the sequence of three exceptionally severe and extended wartime winters that had piled additional privation and wretchedness on to lives that in many cases were already tested almost beyond endurance. It was as well for them that they were over. In the living room the fireplace was a deep recess fitted with an old-fashioned, black-iron stove with side oven. Fortunately it was economical and efficient, and in that one room they were able to keep reasonably warm and comfortable throughout the worst of the winters to come.

In the rest of the house it was quite another matter. Beyond the living room Harcourt set a new standard for bedtime hostility. None of the heat from the living room reached into the bedrooms, and at all times except the dog days of summer they were damp. In winter the cold struck up through the floorboards, seeped in through the walls and fell like an Arctic benediction from the thin ceiling boards above their heads. Even blankets were brought out on rotation to be aired in front of the fire. For the young and the fit it was an experience that was challenging, but endurable. For the elderly or the infirm it could be a battle for survival, and it carried Jack to the brink on two occasions.

The plot of land behind the house was long and narrow. A desultory attempt at cultivation had been made for twenty yards or so, but beyond that hawthorn, bramble and general scrub flourished, and it was impossible to tell where the garden ended and the next undeveloped plot began. A track through the bushes led to the back of the Heards' and provided a rough alternative route to Bayhurst. In the hedges between the gardens, trees of shepherd's bullace were hung with a dark-green fruit. It remained hard, sharp and acid for so long that they thought it would be useless, but by November, long after the last leaves had fallen, it softened and yellowed to make passable eating and a rich, delicious jam once the rations had been eked out to create the necessary sugar surplus.

From Lou came the money to buy a couple of second-hand hen

houses light enough to be pulled around the garden, and as the pens were shifted from patch to patch, the fowl scratched and pecked away the top growth. When they had moved on Jack followed with fork and spade, but it was demanding work for his lungs. After a dozen or so spits of earth had been lifted and turned there was a long pause before he moved on, and every half an hour or so he stopped and sat for a while with his newspaper on an old wooden chair left in the garden for that purpose. It was slow, tedious work but before the end of the year a good-sized vegetable plot had been roughly dug and lay waiting for the winter frosts to do their work.

Not long before they left The Anchorage, Gilmore and Jack met again for the first time in almost two years. During that period Gilmore's homecomings had been to distant ports in the north or west and gave him no opportunity to visit them. An assignment from Liverpool to join a ship in the London docks had however provided an opportunity to call in at Stepney, where Bill's shop was so conveniently situated that for family and friends passing through London it acted as a clearing house for news throughout the war. The report he received of Jack's illness brought him down on a flying visit, but he had been and gone before John returned home from school. A pack of cigarettes for Jack and a couple of bars of chocolate were all that marked his passing.

His next arrival followed in no more time than it took for an Atlantic crossing. It was that golden, glorious moment when he deluged them with luxury, abundance and fruitfulness, and for just a while peacetime plenty returned to their wartime world. With one of the old bed-chairs to sleep in, the front room was given up to Gilmore as a bedroom for the duration of his stay. If the thought even crossed their minds, none of them attached any significance to the fact that Gilmore had never before spent a night with them.

His first night was a late night for all, and John was in bed well before the others. A bottle had been opened and Jack and Gilmore were deep in talk. Sound passed easily through the walls, and for a while he lay listening to them, but he must have been asleep for a couple of hours before they turned in. When he woke he was for a moment unsure what it was that had disturbed him. It seemed that he had heard a noise, but there had been no alert, and as he held his breath and listened in the darkness, all was momentarily quiet and still before the sound was repeated. The war was productive of many strange night-time noises, but this was quite beyond his experience. It ceased and then came again: strong, resonant, regular and undoubtedly in the house. When he sat up to listen better, Moira realised he was awake.

'My God. Can you hear that?'

'What is it?'

'Gilmore.'

'What do you mean?'

'He's snoring.'

John was not entirely without experience of snoring. The ad hoc sleeping arrangements encountered during the early years of the war had introduced him to some modest performers. Even Moira herself indulged in an occasional tremulous whiffling. The sound they heard now was stentorian and importunate. Wave after wave surged through the house, washed over their beds and was dying on the summer night as a new one was born. They covered their heads and eventually slept again, but fitfully, and whenever they woke there it was, growling and relentless.

As soon as Jack was up the following morning he looked in through the door. 'I know. We heard it too and he's closer to us. You'll just have to grin and bear it for a couple more days. Just think of his shipmates.' Gilmore's visits were never again quite so keenly anticipated.

After Jack's death the family friendship continued across the generations until Gilmore himself died, and during those years he stayed with John and his wife from time to time. They were blessed with a long, narrow house and Gilmore was always given a billet in the furthest extremity, but still, like the distant sound of surf breaking on a pebble shore, they heard him surging his way through the night.

30

A Weekend Retreat

At Harcourt John's weekends settled into a pattern that was to continue until the end of the war and beyond. In Stepney, morning and lunchtime sales would have disposed of Bill's fish allocation for the Saturday. By late afternoon the shop and counters were cleaned, the shutters dropped and the door locked behind the family until early on the Monday. As the air raids on London eased during the beginning of 1942 they had resumed living there during the week and returned to Essex only for the weekends. Each Saturday, shortly after their arrival, John joined his cousin and, apart from returning home to sleep and have his breakfast, spent most of the weekend with his aunt and uncle.

In plotland circles La Retraite was considered a pretty fancy name for the modest-looking bungalow fronting Pound Lane, but by all John's experience at the time it seemed to be a pretty fancy place to live. Built just a year or two before the war it was modern, solid, dry and draughtproof. Bathroom and lavatory, both inside, were snug and comfortable. At the back a narrow conservatory running the width of the bungalow caught afternoon and evening sun and opened on to a modest but neat and tidy garden maintained for them by Charlie. There was even a refrigerator. In terms of comfort and convenience it was everything that Harcourt was not.

'Hello, Johnny boy. Come on in.'

The usual generous welcome from his Uncle Bill greeted him. As the front door opened the house exuded comfort and an aura of smoked fish. A few pieces of furniture and some soft furnishings from the Stepney home had been taken to the relative security of their country retreat as soon as it was purchased. With them, in the depths of the upholstery, in the fabric of the curtains, and in the fibres of their clothes the hallmark of their trade had travelled. To

409

all the family who knew the background it was a friendly, comforting smell, and they sniffed at it with all the appreciation of the Bisto kids. 'Ah. That must be Em and Bill,' as Clara used to say.

Recollections of warmth, light, comfort, music, modern or old-time, piano or radio, and a sense of relative plenty in a world of shortages were what John remembered of those wartime weekends at La Retraite. The opportunities available to shopkeepers for the exchange of goods must have been difficult to resist, and the grey market of barter between traders was illegal but near universal. Fish, and in particular high-quality fish, commanded a premium that was reflected on Em's table. When it became a crime to bake white bread and the standard National Wholemeal loaf was the only eating, white bread still appeared with the winkles as it had in the past, but tasted twice as delicious. If butter wasn't available ad lib on the table, it was recognisably present on the cut slices, and not scraped on and off as was the general practice elsewhere. There was always a bottle or two on the sideboard, and a glass of something for visitors at a time when drink was hard to come by. Even after 26th July 1942, that day of infamy for the nation's children when sweets were finally rationed, chocolate was available at Bill's more frequently than might have been expected.

At rare intervals, and in modest quantities, many of John's pre-war favourites still made an appearance at meal times. Scallops, breadcrumbed and lightly fried, sweet-cured herrings, sprats, Bill's own smoked haddock: he enjoyed them all once again without any feelings of guilt, but was not inclined to brag of the indulgence when he got home. Now and again Bill sent him off with a couple of packets to deliver, one to his gran and one to home. That helped to ease any stirrings of conscience.

In fact during a La Retraite weekend the only noticeable deprivation was of tranquillity, stillness and silence. In their Stepney home throughout the day, and for most of the night, they lived their lives in a restless hubbub of sound. Along Commercial Road trams, carts and motor traffic rolled within a few feet of the shop. Pedestrians thronged the pavement, and at the junction station across the road trains sounded their arrival and departure into the small hours. It was never still. When the noise ceased they felt uneasy and their sleep was restless.

'It's like being at sea again. After a few days you no longer hear the regular beat of the engine. It's only when it stops you feel that the life has gone out of the ship.'

That was how Bill described their feelings. As soon as they arrived from London the wireless was switched on, and it stayed on throughout the day unless Em herself was at the piano. Comedy programmes, the big bands and the popular singers were what they enjoyed, but anything was better than silence.

The friends that occasionally came with them for a day or two away from the desolation of bomb-shattered London brought with them some of the life and flavour of the lost East End: Joe and Maggie, two Londoners as cockney as Bow Bells, with a constant stream of reminiscences of Limehouse life between the wars, and Lou or Len, an ex-boxer whose battered nose sniffed its way through the weekend as if he was constantly on the receiving end of a string of short-arm jabs.

Throughout every Saturday evening John was there with his cousin listening to their chat until Charlie called, and everyone left for a stroll down the lane for an hour or so at the Harrows Inn. Except for the winter months or the worst of weather the walk was a regular feature, taken as much for the pleasure of the country air as for any delights that the Harrows might have to offer. Even there, although he was only a Saturday patron, Bill seemed to have an entry. The little something that he carried down with him and passed over the counter meant that if there was anything special under it, Bill would have his share.

In summer, if the aunts happened to be home for the weekend, they might join them on the walk. Leslie and John tagged on behind, enjoyed a drink of their own and then moved off to the tank traps and pillboxes nearby until it was time to return home. In the warm twilight of a summer evening there could be six or seven of them laughing and talking as they sauntered back between the elms and hedgerows. The night air was benign, the countryside untroubled, and for a while they were able to forget the reality of war unless the drone of aircraft passing unseen overhead stilled their voices for a moment.

'Some of ours by the sound of it,' one of them murmured.

The others hardly needed telling. There had been no alert, and by then there were few who could not readily recognise the distinctive engine notes of 'theirs' and 'ours' as they crossed high above, hidden by cloud or in the darkness. Indeed there were many who could accurately identify not only friend or foe, but the class of aircraft by sound alone, and there was still plenty of opportunity for practice. As the noise of the engines died away, the talk and laughter resumed.

Towards the end of the walk Aunt Tot's old home came into view, dark and still in the gloaming. With it came recollections of happy times spent there, and the aunts drifted off into nostalgic memories of pre-war visits from Poplar, day trips to the Leigh cockle sheds, walks on the pier, country excursions in the horse and trap with Tot at the reins, and afternoon tea in her elegant front room. 'Good old days despite everything,' they concluded and resolved to mark them the following day by a visit to Tot's grave with flowers from the garden. A short way beyond Tot's they parted for home by ones and twos, until only Charlie was left for a final lonely walk in the gathering dark.

On Sunday mornings, while Bill, Em and any morning visitors settled down to an ITMA repeat and a few beers before lunch, the two boys were left to their own devices. The loss of The Anchorage wood and the pond, but most of all the loss of their majestic swing, had been a bitter blow. For a few weeks while the house stood empty they continued to enjoy it, but then, before they thought to climb and recover the rope, boy-less strangers moved in and it was lost to them.

The original source of supply remained, but they were no longer the only ones plundering the resource. It would be almost another year before the threat of invasion was formally declared to be at an end, but despite the absence of any official announcement or approval many farmers had evidently decided for themselves that the risk of airborne landings was long past. Not only were supplies of rope diminishing as they helped themselves, but here and there even the poles were being plucked out to ease the farming oper-ations. Although they had no clear notion of how they intended to use the rope, the boys did not want to lose it, and for two or three early summer Sundays they scoured the fields and carried off all that they could.

Surprisingly it was Mrs Arrowsmith who gave them refuge. Despite her outwardly formal and frosty image she proved to be astonishingly tolerant of boys and their activities and offered no objection as little by little they assumed occupation of part of a garden that was large even by plotland standards. Much of it was neatly cultivated and well maintained by her husband and a local farm worker looking for a little extra cash, but at the furthest point from the house it fell away into informality and wildness, before merging into the scrub of the neighbouring undeveloped plot, through which the boys could enter and leave unnoticed.

In that remote and untended patch they found a new base for their activities. In one corner a shallow, weedy pond overhung by a solitary willow was a nagging reminder of the wide, clear water they had lost. Close to the pond in a broad area of rough grass and shrubs there were seven or eight promising trees. None had the mature grandeur of The Anchorage elms, but they were high, wide-spreading and open, with reliable boughs that a climber could trust. A chicken shed sagging against the hedge and long unused pro-vided a wet-weather refuge and a store for the bits and pieces they collected.

From war films and newsreels they saw that commando training was the one activity where rope had a major role to play. Apart from energy and enthusiasm it was also the one resource they had in plenty, and they set about deploying it wherever and however they could. By the middle of the summer holiday much of their collection was in place. From the trunks and branches of the little grove of trees intersecting lines of thick, well-weathered War Department rope hung vertically, horizontally and obliquely in a tangled, interconnecting network. Its construction had been a testing process of trial and error, with rope burns, bruises, broken nails, and grazed and raw knuckles, knees and shins the price they paid for their frequent failures. Despite the obvious attractions of rope ladders and clambering nets their intentions were not matched by their ability and the difficulties of construction defeated them. After a few bone-shaking falls the attempts were abandoned, but in other respects they were satisfied with their primitive assault course.

The willow tree, although it had neither the height nor the overhang for a swing across the width of the pond, became the essential water hazard. All branches trailing over the pond were cut away and a rope dropped from the highest bough. With good acceleration and a vigorous launch it was possible to sweep around the tree in a wide semi-circle over the water and drop again on to the bank. The prudent or nervous held the rope high enough to

413

ensure their feet stayed well clear of the surface. Chuzzy, who was reckless and fleet of foot, held it low, took off like a swallow and swept wider, lower and faster than any others dared.

The assault course was the arena that Billy chose for his next confrontation with the malign fates that seemed to dog his heels and with the ox of a father who brought retribution. The boys had just moved on to the water hazard when Billy arrived. Chuzzy was giving one of his more extravagant displays at the end of the rope as the rest of them stood by desperately hoping for the mistake he never made. As he completed one elegant sweep after another Billy stood watching him in undisguised admiration.

He was an uncomplicated, artless country boy not given to self-analysis and was never able or willing to explain to them just what drove him to his acts of madness on that fine summer day. When the rope next hung idle he stepped forward, took it in his hands and, holding it hopelessly low, walked back from the tree and prepared himself for flight. There was a sublime, almost tragic, inevitability to the events that were to follow.

They watched his lumbering approach with keen anticipation and an absolute conviction as to the outcome. At the brink of the pond, but a step too far to arrest his progress, the same awful certainty dawned on Billy. Clutching desperately at the rope he threw himself out and over the water with a cry born more of anguish than excitement. He remained airborne until mid-pond where the toe of one foot traced a delicate curve through the surface duckweed until the drag of the water took hold. Subsiding gently, almost gracefully, into the shallows, he lay at length in the mudded water, fringed by duckweed, and still grasping the fag end of the rope.

Utterly unsympathetic, they celebrated his performance with jeers and laughter as he dragged himself from the pond. Surprisingly unresentful of their mockery, as he always was, Billy's intention was to stay with them for a while in the hope that in time, sunshine and activity would dry his clothes and allow him to shake off the clinging weed before he went home. Any prospect of this was frustrated by the sound of his mother calling for him across the intervening gardens.

While they were building their modest assault course, and later when they were at play, Mr Arrowsmith would often come out with a book and sit to read on the garden bench in front of the house. If they glanced his way the book might be open on his lap, but invariably he would be watching them. He never went closer and immediately returned to the house if they moved towards him. As Billy's little tragicomedy was played out he had been sitting there observing, but unmoving. When Mrs Abrey's call sounded across the gardens he walked back into the house, but as Billy shuffled his way miserably past the back door, reappeared, held out a towel and stood looking on as Billy took what remedial action he could. Nothing was said on either side. As Billy moved on he took back the towel and returned to the house. Despite his obvious interest in their activities that was the only occasion on which there was any interaction between them. For the rest of the time he was a distant figure silently observing them and a continuing mystery to John.

They didn't see Billy again until early afternoon. In one respect at least luck had been with him. Only his mother had been in the house when he returned. She was used to the excesses of the father, not only against Billy but also, as everyone knew, against her, and had said nothing of the morning's events when the father came home.

When Billy returned to them he had left his parents preparing themselves for an outing. Billy was already bright and shiny from the wash house, and dressed in his best visiting clothes. He only had a few minutes, he said, before they all set off on a family visit. While he waited for the call to rejoin his parents he sat oscillating gently on the seat of a swing in the grove of trees, enduring with apparent indifference their constant reminders of the morning's entertainment. To add bite to their comments they returned to the water hazard where Chuzzy obliged with a couple of exhibition numbers accomplished with his customary panache and grace.

When Billy left his swing to join them he lolled against the willow and watched as one by one they performed their routines and continued their taunts. When eventually he put his hand to the rope they had no serious expectation of any further diversions. He was being more than cautious. With the rope grasped at a sensible height he completed a standard circuit, smiled with relief and stepped off again for his return.

In mid-pond, above the deepest water, and for only a fraction of a second, he relaxed his grip. He gave no cry as he dropped, nor did he speak as he stood gripped ankle-deep in the stinking ooze and lapped waist-high by the muddied water. They couldn't believe their luck. It was a display of ineptitude beyond all reasonable expectation even from Billy, but as they celebrated hysterically they heard his father calling.

'Billy. Home!'

Home was not what Billy wanted. Given the choice the waters of the pond seemed infinitely preferable. The call came again, this time more insistent. By now the boys too were silent and looking at Billy. Still he stood unmoving.

'I'm not going to call you again.' This time there was anger in the voice.

Billy at last threw off his paralysis and howled a reply. 'Coming.'

He dragged himself from the mud and, with his face already smeared with tears, stumbled off towards home and retribution. They followed him as far as the gate where they stopped and crouched behind the hedge, anxious not to be seen, but eager in their mean little hearts to hear what went on. How that foul beast of a man must have beaten him! Before they crept away they heard more than enough to silence their giggles. But it wasn't their fault, was it? He didn't have to swing. They didn't make him do it. Their consciences were clear. Half an hour later they watched from Chuzzy's garden as the three of them passed: the mother flushed and flustered, Billy head down, red-eyed, disconsolate, and half dragged by his scowling brute of a father.

Billy was a big lad who was going to be a big man, and perhaps even then he had dreams of giving more than tit for tat as the years caught up with his father. On this occasion his revenge, if childishly crude, was inventive. In his father's absence from home Billy arrived with a pair of his working boots. Solemnly at Billy's request they pissed in them in turn and swilled their contribution around before emptying it out. The boots were left in the sun to dry for a few hours before being replaced under the bed. For all they got to know it may have been no more than a symbolic gesture of revolt, but it gave immense satisfaction and whatever the outcome it was never traced to Billy.

31

The Geese Are Getting Fat

On the day the war turned the corner temporally speaking the daily papers were carrying a mixed bag of news. Two more German spies had been hanged at Wandsworth. In the West End the theatres were once again thriving, lifting the spirits of the public in general and troops on leave in particular. At the St James's *Blithe Spirit* continued its record breaking run. At the Windmill Theatre, always open and in business during the darkest, most dangerous evenings of the Blitz, *Revudeville* was into its 155th edition, titillating its audience with a show liberally laced, as ever, with artfully choreographed tableaux vivants of nudes. Frozen in smile, attitude and, in wintertime, body, they always remained tantalisingly within the bounds of a decency imposed by the censors of the Lord Chamberlain's office. On the plains around the Don savage tank battles were being fought out as the Germans advanced in their heaviest offensive of the year with Stalingrad as their ultimate objective. For the consumer an expensive summer coat from Gorringes cost 7½ guineas, petrol stood at 2s 1d a gallon, potatoes at 2¾d a pound, Booth's Gin, if you could get it cost 17s, and a low-mileage 1936 Rolls Royce was a bargain at £975. For the first time American bombers had been in operation joining the RAF in a strike against German airfields in Holland, and in the desert, at the end of a critical couple of weeks following the fall of Tobruk, fierce artillery duels were being fought out along the El Alamein line.

With the outcome of the war still hanging in the balance on all fronts and domestic difficulties on the increase, Jack and his family would have had little reason for optimism as they settled into Harcourt, but as they moved through the second half of 1942 battles were to be fought and won on three distant fronts that would mark a major and decisive shift in the balance of power

417

between the Allied and the Axis forces. There would have been few, if any, at the time who saw it that way, but with hindsight that is how it was. In June American naval and air forces savaged the Japanese in the great battle for the Island of Midway. In August their land forces seized the initiative for the first time with their invasion and eventual occupation of Guadalcanal. Those two operations were to mark a turning point in the Pacific War. In mid-November the doors to church turrets were at last unlocked, the spiders and the bats disturbed, and bells rang out across the country to celebrate the recapture of Tobruk and victory in the battle of El Alamein. From then on Rommel and his panzer divisions were to be in retreat westwards across North Africa. At about the same time on the Eastern Front the Russians launched their great counter-offensive against the Germans at Stalingrad. Within a few days the whole of the German 6th Army and other divisions were encircled, and their wholesale destruction began. It would continue until the end of January when Von Paulus offered the surrender of his forces and the surviving remnants of what had been more than a quarter of a million men.

Living beside the lane brought a few practical improvements to family life, but added little to its variety. In the early hours of the morning the commuters' bus now woke them with blasts on the horn as it sounded a warning to dilatory regulars. The weekly buses to Pitsea and Wickford stopped almost on their doorstep, and Phoebe saw Clara a little more often when she dropped in on her way home with a few items of Poplar gossip, but incidents of war apart, those events summed up the excitement of an average day.

Private motor traffic was virtually non-existent. Apart from an occasional delivery lorry or a military convoy passing between the two main roads nothing much moved on the lane. The girls could play hopscotch, and the boys kick a ball around with little prospect of disturbance. Of the street life and activities that added variety and interest to the day in Poplar there was precious little, but even plotland shoddy was flecked with a few colourful threads.

If Pound Lane Lizzie had a surname it was not in common use, which is more than could be said for Lizzie herself. She lived with her mother close to the post office in one of the few semi-detached houses to be found in a world of bungalows. That apart, there was nothing in particular to distinguish the dwelling from its neighbours, yet the path through the grass and over the narrow bridge

418

to the front door was more than usually well trodden, for Lizzie offered comforts to the troops. The age and appearance of the mother in her infrequent excursions from the house were such as to confirm the general consensus of opinion that her activities were strictly limited to domestic support.

It says much of the quality of Lizzie's services that her reputation was more than parochial. From Vange, Pitsea, Tarpots and perhaps further afield squaddies on leave and at a loose end found their way to The Gun Inn on the Southend Road, where in a corner of the saloon bar Lizzie held her discreet soirees before strolling back home with her escorts. On the whole it seems to have been 'other ranks' only who sought her favours.

More than usually tall, with loose, rangy limbs, she was also affectionately known as Long Liz, but if her height distinguished her there was nothing at all meretricious or obvious about Liz or her profession. A little surreptitious observation of their own was enough for the boys to squash the one know-all in their ranks who had it on authority from his older brother that 'they' always wore a gold chain round an ankle. Lizzie's elegant ankles were patently unbound. Her dress was unremarkable apart from the frugality of cloth employed in the cut of her skirts, where support for the national campaign of economy and restraint happily coincided with an opportunity to display to the limit of decency, and a touch beyond, a fine pair of legs.

Legs were Lizzie's star attraction in a presentation which in other respects offered unexceptional supporting features. When she strode the lane on her way to hold court at The Gun she drew the pubescent oiks sniggering after her, but always at a prudent distance. One or two, feeling their oats, had tried an exchange of courtesies with Liz, but came away with their tails between their legs and a healthy respect for the edge to her tongue. No others tried.

The origins of the plotlands and the flood of wartime refugees from London had created a community that was essentially urban rather than rural in its outlook. As far as Lizzie's services were concerned most people were broad-minded and easy-going in their attitude. There was no reason to believe that she made them available to any local husbands or, if she did, it was done with remarkable discretion and went undetected. In general Lizzie was seen by a few who were generous and cosmopolitan in outlook as playing a useful role in the war effort and by most of the rest as an interesting source of gossip. Direct or hostile criticism was rare.

If the aunts' weekend leave happened to bring them home together they tried to let a friend or two from London know in advance, and when they gathered together in Bayhurst's garden on a summer Sunday afternoon the bustle and chat made it sound almost like old times. There was little talk about the progress of the war. It was the practical difficulties of day-to-day life, family news, reminiscences and inevitably gossip that occupied them, and as they gossiped John listened.

There was nothing mealy-mouthed about the family when they talked in front of children, and Charlie, who occasionally had a beer at The Gun, had been entertaining them with a description of one of Lizzie's evening receptions when Florrie arrived. Florrie, a cousin on Aunt Tot's side, had been seduced from church to chapel and was one of the few who were particularly hot and strong against Lizzie, all like her, and their followers. One attempt to close her down, a failure for lack of hard evidence, had left them seething, and when Lizzie's name recurred in the conversation Florrie started to say her piece.

She had a free run for a while. Kath and Clara were too polite to interrupt. Charlie sat smiling and waiting for Elsie finally to lose patience. 'Whore' and 'fornicators' passed unchallenged. The terms, when all was said, were no more than strictly accurate in the circumstances. Then Florrie turned to Lizzie's character, and Elsie had her say.

'Oh no, Flo, that won't do. You don't know anything about the girl except the one thing that gets up your nose so much. What else do you know? I knew girls like her when I was younger, and some of them were the salt of the earth. She keeps herself to herself . . .'

That raised a laugh.

'Well you know what I mean. She's no bother to any of us, and I don't hear any of the boys complaining. Why don't you just let the girl get on with it and find something better to do yourself?'

Florrie wasn't going to let things stand at that, but Lou had had enough and said so. Clara chipped in to play peacemaker and they turned to other things. But Elsie had put the general view about Lizzie in a nutshell, and 'get on with it' she did, right to the end of hostilities.

During the months at The Anchorage Henry the milkman had

been a shadowy figure. The condition of the steeper section of Clarence Road in winter, and of Henry's venerable old nag at all times, meant that his deliveries terminated at the crossroads. The two jugs for The Anchorage were left at Bayhurst to be filled there and collected later. Now at Harcourt they could at last put a face to the name.

For nearly thirty years, on every day of the year including Christmas Day, Henry had operated a milk round from the family farm at the bottom of the lane. Once morning milking was over the horse was harnessed, backed up into the shafts of an old farm cart, and led round to the milking shed. A nosebag of feed was hung inside the cart; four full churns of milk were loaded; the dog leapt in the back; and Henry was ready to set off. For almost twenty of those years Captain his horse had been between the shafts and was quite as secure and reliable as Henry in following their same unvarying rural round. In addition to milk, Henry brought with him a regular supply of gossip and local news.

Harcourt was at the very limit of Henry's round. Beyond Clarence Road allegiance was owed to Hawkes Dairies where old ways had given place to new. From Hawkes the milk was delivered in cardboard-capped bottles from custom-built milk floats, still horse-drawn, but very fancy with four small wheels and hard rubber tyres. They had an easy time of it on the surfaced roads of the newer developments towards the top of the lane, but would have stuck fast on the green lanes and tracks where Captain drew the cart with ease.

Despite Henry's old-fashioned style, there were few of his customers who would have chosen to move to Hawkes and their modern distribution system. Old ways still lingered on in the countryside, and it was not unusual for milk to arrive in churns and be ladled out into the customers' jugs in quart, pint or half-pint measures. The inconvenience was considered a small price to pay for the quality and flavour of unpasteurised milk fresh from the cow. The children had experience of both worlds. At school the milk sucked through a straw from their little bottles came pasteurised, thin and insipid. On Henry's milk, if it stood a short while, a soft crust of cream formed, and sips stolen from the rim of a brimming jug clung to the lips, slid over the tongue and slipped down the throat fresh, rich and delicious.

It did not, it is true, take kindly to hot, thundery weather. Few houses had any form of refrigeration, and without it by the end of the day milk could be turning and curdling. If it did, the thickened and congealed mess was turned out into a fine piece of muslin, tied, hung to drip, and overnight metamorphosed into cottage cheese. Lightly salted and blended with finely chopped chives it was a summer lunchtime delight.

By the locals in the lane who had grown up with him he was known as Young Henry, but he must have been as old as or older than Jack. Back on the farm Old Henry, his wife and a bachelor brother looked after things while Henry did his rounds. Henry, too, had remained unmarried, which most of those who met him found surprising.

He was well-built, good-looking for his age, but calculated in most respects to frustrate the expectations of anyone looking for a conventional country yokel. For a man out in all weathers he was unusually particular about his appearance. Despite his early-morning start and the local farming tradition of one shave a week, Henry arrived freshly shaven every day. His dress was practical, but always neat, clean and cared for. Boots, gaiters, dark trousers, striped shirt but no tie, waistcoat and jacket – the outfit remained unchanged over the years, but was supplemented by a topcoat and hat in winter and rough weather. Unusually for a countryman from old country stock he held views which sounded very much like socialism and gave him enough in common with Jack for them to sit over a cup of tea from time to time when Henry had made his last delivery.

Some milkmen making their rounds in the old style simply signalled their arrival and waited for their customers to come out with their jugs and cans to collect their milk. Others, like Henry, arrived at the door with the milk in a two or three-gallon can which was topped up as necessary from a churn in the cart. Leaving Captain snuffling choosily for choice titbits in the verge-side grasses, and the dog stretched out between the churns to deter any pilferers, Henry walked on ahead delivering to his customers until his container was nearly empty. At his call and whistle Captain dragged a last mouthful from the verge and moved forward to be in position when Henry reappeared. Henry devoted as much attention to his horse as he did to himself, but despite the feeding and grooming Captain was showing his years. Opaque in the eyes, grizzled round muzzle and nostrils, and lean in body and limb, he already looked to be knacker's meat when John first met him, but plodded on into the post-war years to enjoy a short retirement put out to grass when Henry at last surrendered his round to the competition.

Henry only deviated from his usual high standard of timekeeping in the last few days before Christmas when his service became increasingly erratic and tardy. Despite wartime shortages there were few of his customers who had not got a little drop of something on hand, and the closer he got to Christmas Day the more frequent and pressing the offers.

'Come on, Henry. Just a quick one for Christmas before you move on.'

But even quick ones couldn't be rushed, and at the limit of the round his timing slipped first by a few minutes, then by half an hour or so, and finally by an hour or more. On Christmas Day Henry left Harcourt until last, and it was mid-afternoon before he arrived, 'well oiled and in fine form', as Lou later described him. Asked to come in, he put down his can, invited Phoebe to help herself, took the chair offered and beamed at them.

'OK, Jack?'

'Fine, Henry. You?'

'Pretty fair, pretty fair you know.'

'One for the road as it's Christmas?'

'My pleasure, my pleasure, Jack. It's been a good day.'

He sniffed appreciatively at a tot of Black Label. His day was to get a little better before he left. That year, 1942, was the Gilmore Christmas. Not only their best Christmas of the war, but better than many that came after it. Of the supplies that Gilmore had crammed into his taxi much had been set aside for the occasion. After a beer and a sandwich cut from a tinned ham opened on Christmas Eve, Henry sat chatting and puffing an export Woodbine. Outside daylight was fading. Jack held up the bottle and looked at Henry.

'Well, just one for the gutter then, Jack, if it's all right with you.'

He pulled on and buttoned his topcoat. Taking the glass he wished them the best, swallowed his whisky, and turned away up the lane where Captain and the cart were waiting in the side road. When the cart came into view a few minutes later Henry was sitting on the boards in the back wedged between the churns with the dog on his lap. Head on chest and hat pulled down he could already have been asleep, but raised one hand in a parting salute as he passed. Captain, steady but sure in the thickening fog, plodded away towards home and stable.

Throughout that year their daily experience of war changed little. Occasionally, high overhead, there were dogfights and fighter attacks on passing bombers, but they were generally resolved far out of sight. Alerts and incursions continued, most frequently at night, and invariably passing beyond them to some distant target, but always bringing with them heavy ack-ack fire and a danger from falling shrapnel. But no bombs dropped on or near them, and there was just one significant local incident during the summer holiday of which they soon heard.

On a farm towards the bottom of the lane two cows had been found dead, apparently killed by cannon or machine-gun fire. There had been no alert, but gunfire had been heard in the early hours of the morning just before the discovery. Local opinion was that they must have been hit by an RAF fighter in pursuit of a raider flying at low level. Early victims of blue on blue it seemed, although the term was not used then.

John ran to the scene with the same ghoulish interest as the rest of the boys. The farmer was reluctant to do anything at all until instruction or approval had been received from the ministry, and the two beasts still lay where they had been felled, their wounds gaping surprisingly large and ragged. Scavenging crows were already at work pulling at the exposed flesh or pecking at the eyes, quite undisturbed by the couple of men standing a little way off. The boys lingered until a decision was taken and one of the heavy horses was led out in harness. A rope was tied around the hind legs, and one after the other the two carcasses were dragged from the field.

When school resumed after the summer holidays John found himself in the scholarship class, much to his surprise and the relief of his parents. In the small room at the back of the stage a chosen few of ten or eleven endured material shortages and primitive facilities, but enjoyed a teacher–pupil ratio that modern schools can only dream of.

Beyond the stage, in the main body of the school, thirty or more children with a year of their junior education still ahead of them were already marked down for the secondary school and denied even the opportunity to sit the scholarship examination. Tucked away in their cramped but quiet quarters behind the stage, the scholarship set were a privileged and favoured few. As a system of selection, or rather preselection, it was iniquitous, indefensible and not unique to St Margaret's, but if prevailing circumstances provided for nothing else, then Madam and her assistant teachers were probably in the best position to make the cut.

Those in the scholarship class were the special responsibility of Madam for most of the time, but received occasional lessons from other teachers when her duties as headmistress took her elsewhere. Crammed into their little room they were drilled and coaxed towards that special event some eight months away which would make or break them. They found that their elevation cut no ice with their contemporaries, however, and even if they welcomed the distinction it was something best celebrated quietly and away from school. For the successful few who went on to higher education in Brentwood the selection could be the thin end of a wedge that slowly severed the common bonds and interests they had with the friends of their childhood. The sensible and usual practice was to dismiss it as an honour neither sought nor relished.

In October the scholarship class was briefly merged again into the main school when their room was occupied by the doctor for the annual medical inspection; girls first, then boys. The stage curtains were drawn, and behind them in groups of twenty or so the boys stripped to the waist and, in braces and short trousers, stood in line waiting to be called. It took little time, but was presumably adequate to identify anything potentially serious. Chests were thumped and sounded with a stethoscope, ears were probed, tongues inspected, eyes peered into and a cursory examination made of the feet before they were passed out for the second stage of the event – nit hunting.

Gaunt, angular, glacial in demeanour and wrapped in an odour of disinfectant the nit-nurse personified all that might be anticipated in one whose working days were wasted away in a never-ending search for head lice. At least the doctor entertained his young visitors with a little patter and gave them some privacy. The nurse was contemptuous in her brevity and indifferent to any embarrassment she might cause during her examination in front of the others on stage.

'Name?'

Her list was ticked, and with a fine-tooth comb dripping with Lysol she scratched and scraped her way across the scalp.

'Next.'

That was the all-clear: no fellow travellers.

A positive sighting occasioned a string of sighs and clucks and could have been no more clearly announced if she had stood on her chair and shouted 'lousy'. It was a public humiliation that some faced out defiantly, but others were reduced to tears. The few identified as infested would be sent home at the end of the day with a note for their parents.

As summer moved towards autumn the boys watched the last of another harvest being brought in as they made their way to and from school at the start of the new term. On the farms much of the work was now done by the land girls, with troops occasionally being brought in at times of heavy pressure. With the horse teams, on the hay mowers and sweeps, managing the complicated thresher-reapers, spreading the muck, and behind the plough the land girls matched the men task for task. There were three regulars in the area and over a year or more the boys got to know them well. Not much older than their own sisters, they were a long way from home, hard worked, poorly paid, and more than ready to break off for a few minutes when the boys passed by.

Chuzzy was a particular favourite with them.

'I've got a brother just like you back at home, Chuzzy.'

'What time are you picking me up tonight then, Chuzzy?'

'You're going to be a real heartbreaker when you get older, aren't you, Chuzz?'

Self-confident and cheeky, he soaked up their flattery and practised on them the chat and banter that would earn him the reputation he enjoyed with the girls just a few years later.

Along with others from the community the land girls joined the school for the Harvest Festival procession and the service at St Margaret's church. Out of their working overalls and head-squares they looked quite different from the scruffy field workers the boys met each day. Hair trimmed, faces rouged, powdered and lipsticked from their precious supplies of make-up, and on display in their uniformed best, they were soon swept up by a few local lads home on leave who joined in at the festival.

In the autumn of 1942 a trip was made towards Southend for

the first time in more than two years. At the height of the invasion scare the town had been a restricted area, and in the period up to the fall of Dunkirk and the months that followed the focus of furious construction work. The Kursaal pleasure ground closed its gates; its cinema became a factory; the ballroom fell silent; and step by step the Londoners' seaside playground was transformed into a heavily fortified and strongly defended fortress. The pier joined the navy as HMS *Leigh*. The pier head became a convoy control centre, and of the handsome paddle steamers that called there, the *Crested Eagle* lay rotting on the beach at Dunkirk, lost with the three hundred men she was trying to save. Restrictions were easing, however, and the aunts, back at Bayhurst for a rare weekend together after a long, unbroken stint of work away from home, intended having a day out, and Phoebe and John were to join them.

On a mild, dry autumn day they followed the same route they had taken in that last golden summer of 1939. It was an unhurried progress: the aunts were tired and were going to make their first real break in more than a year a leisurely affair. Hazy sunshine caught at the broken walls of Hadleigh Castle on the distant meadows, and from the trees in the gardens on the Parade the breeze drifted a few leaves around their heads. The tide was on the flood, pushing its way up the many channels that cut into the flats, stirring the boats once again and lifting them from the mud. Beyond the shallows and the shipping on the river the coast of Kent shimmered in the distance. Below them, alongside the main creek, the roofs and buildings of Old Leigh were unchanged, and apart from distant barrage balloons it looked as serene and peaceful a scene as ever. The prospect that just one of the cockle sheds might possibly be open was tempting and brought back memories of happier times, but it would have meant dropping down the hill only to climb back up again, and Elsie was not in favour.

For a mile or so they kept to the roads running along the top of the cliffs before turning down a gentle gradient towards the seafront. Then, as they made their way east, the anti-invasion fortifications became increasingly obvious. Roads were either completely closed off by substantial barriers of concrete and steel, or pockmarked with holes and sockets into which steel bars, posts or other obstructions could be dropped. Where there were open spaces between the houses deep anti-tank ditches had been excavated or

427

further obstacles constructed, anything that could frustrate and tie down armour attempting to move inland from the beaches. Along the promenade, stretching away towards the pier, the front-line defences ran in an unbroken chain of concrete blocks. Taller than a man, and almost as wide as they were high, they seemed impenetrable and immovable. Draped around, between and behind them, hung tangled skeins of barbed wire, a snare not for armour but for infantry.

What they saw that day was only one small part of extensive, deep and interlocking fortifications running for more than three miles along the seafront, and then inland to form a defensive square that might entangle and contain invading armour from breaking out on to the flatlands beyond the town, where two roads and railway lines ran to the heart of London little more than forty miles away.

Turning from the sea they moved on to Westcliff Parade where a line of solid, brick-built, nineteenth-century houses stretched towards the east. Substantial, bow-fronted, with elegant verandas, balconies and conservatories commanding views of the cliffs and the sea beyond, they would just a few years earlier have continued to reflect all the affluence, confidence and self-satisfaction of their first Victorian owners. Now they stood dejected, their view one of concrete barriers, pillboxes, machine-gun posts and long coils of barbed wire. Gardens were neglected, some houses were shuttered and empty, others appeared to be occupied by troops.

From the Parade they turned inland on a visit to a family friend. Ada Lewis was unmarried and lived with her mother in modest accommodation further back from the cliffs. She and Elsie had met during their suffragette days, and she knew them all well from her pre-war visits to Poplar and Bayhurst. As rationing made unexpected visitors an embarrassing problem, they carried with them twists of tea and sugar, a pot of paste and some biscuits Phoebe had made from Gilmore's resources.

Of the many maiden and honorary aunts who indulged John and his cousins in their childhood Ada was another whose distinctive voice he most clearly remembered, and like Clara Dent her speech carried no trace of cockney. Softly spoken, with a voice modulated and musical, she had, like the actress Joan Greenwood, a slight catch or hesitancy in her delivery that was compelling and seductive. Early photographs showed an attractive young lady and yet like so many of them she remained unmarried.

There had been no meetings since the beginning of the Blitz, and there was more to talk about than the reminiscing that had occupied them when last he had seen them together. Southend had been the target of many air raids, and Ada's life had been altogether more hectic than the aunts. So for an hour or more, while they worked their way through a meagre meal of tea, paste sandwiches and biscuits, it was their war experiences they talked of.

It had been their intention to move on into the centre for a walk along Royal Terrace and Pier Hill, but having heard Ada's description of the war works and restrictions in the area Elsie had lost her appetite for yet more examples of the changes war had brought, and when eventually they said goodbye to Ada they turned for home.

At Harcourt the fowl they had taken with them from The Anchorage continued to flourish. All the hens were laying well enough, and Iris the wonder-bird continued to produce her daily egg with a clockwork regularity none of the others could match. There was a brief spell when she drew wind and Jack described her as 'broody', and then she was back at it as hard as ever. Lottie and Freddie insinuated themselves even further into their affections as pets. With no crops yet growing in the garden they were given free range until darkness fell and like the geese of Rome they acted as watchdogs of hearth and home. During the night it took no more than the sound of a footstep on the path around the house to set them honking in their night quarters. In the day the click of the latch on the front gate was enough to alert them in the furthest reaches of the garden. Necks stretched out like ramrods, wings beating wildly, and whooping out a war cry they swooped to defend the household. Freddie travelled like a missile straight and unerring. Lottie, whose name reflected a pronounced limp, still managed to move at speed, but with an eccentric trajectory like a light aircraft caught in a crosswind. Terrifying for strangers, and full of sound and fury, it was all show. The attack was never pressed home. If they knew the visitor well they would stay like dogs for a pat or tickle and then return to their grazing. Strangers they escorted to the back door before moving away again into the garden.

429

Everyone liked them, called them by name for their mash and petted them, but John was the only one stupid enough to bond with them. In the fine days of late summer he sat with them drawing out the lush sweet centres of the long grasses for them to bite at. He brought them any titbits he could scrounge from his mother or gran and broke open clods of earth to find them worms. They nibbled gently at his fingers, preened his hair and gabbled softly to him when he sat with them.

They were all betraying them, John most of all. The autumn moved remorselessly into the early weeks of winter and on towards Christmas. He had known their intended fate well enough from the day they were brought home, but knowing and comprehending were two quite different things. At Loosley Row in Clare's kitchen he had seen fowl plucked, drawn and prepared for the oven: few creatures seemed more completely and utterly dead, and as he watched the two of them in the early December mist thrusting and poking along the hedgerow for something tasty to supplement their daily rations he found it impossible to believe that was what they intended for them. As the days moved on he spoilt them, talked to them, cried with them and felt even more guilty and miserable.

He wasn't alone in having pangs of conscience, but the others bore up well under the strain. 'Being sensible,' they called it. John was the only one to try for a reprieve. The facts of life and death were gently explained to him by his father. That was the way things had to be. All the meat and fish they ate came to them in the same way. They had been given a good life, and they would have a quick death. It was a return for the time, effort and money that had been put into them, and they could not afford to keep them indefinitely as pets. In most things he found his father's explanations satisfactory. Not this time, but he knew as he listened to him that he had to accept their sentence as inevitable.

Despite his insistence on their fate, Jack had no intention of taking any part himself. He neither had the heart nor the competence to play the role of butcher. That would be undertaken by Mann & Son, their designated executioners, who would also for a small payment pluck and dress the carcass. They were not to be alone. In the days before Christmas there were many who made the journey to the butcher for the same reason and with the same heavy heart.

Transport was their first problem. The geese were heavy and restless when handled or held for too long, and they had nothing that they could wheel them in. Finally three days before Christmas they set out for the butcher's carrying the birds between them. Wisely, although he knew how things would be, Jack had not refused John's request to go along. The solution to their problem had been neither elegant nor altogether satisfactory. With some difficulty for Jack, many noisy protests from the geese, and floods of tears from John, Lottie and Freddie had each been consigned to the inside of a sack which restricted their wings and was tied loosely around their necks. Each sack was then dropped into a capacious shopping bag. Jack walked in the centre holding a handle of each bag. Phoebe was on one side holding Freddie. John was on the other with Lottie. Three abreast they proceeded slowly up the lane towards the butcher's with the upper neck and head of each goose protruding from the bags.

'You're all right there for Christmas, Jack.'

'Hello, Phoebe. Got one of those to spare for me?'

He cursed and hated everyone who passed them with a joke or comment.

Once they were under way the geese settled into a contented observation of the changing scene as they moved along, and John thought he was comfortably in control and doing well until Lottie started gently nibbling his fingers and babbling to him. He walked the rest of the way crying quietly. His tears were noticed, but nothing was said. It was better for him that way.

At the butcher's it was all over very quickly. They took them into a shed to the side of the shop. The sacks were untied, and John watched through a haze of tears as they were released into a small pen. He had no stomach for goodbyes. Running from the shed he turned towards the field alongside and hung sobbing over the fence.

'We'll be walking back slowly. Catch us up when you're ready.'

He heard the call from his father, and looked around as they walked off. It was a dismal December morning totally in keeping with his mood. Nobody else moved on the road and he was unobserved.

He waited a long time before he finally turned to follow them. The doors of the butcher's shed were closed, and all was silent as he passed. Sprinting the length of the lane as fast as he could, he was panting and gasping for breath when he caught them at the gate. His mother scruffled his hair.

'OK?'

He nodded.

'Why don't you go up and see what Chuzzy's doing?'

That seemed a good idea.

Only Freddie came home for Christmas. The mortal remains of Lottie were kept in the butcher's cold room for a family meal at New Year when Kath would be with them.

It was the best of Christmases. It was the worst of Christmases. Best because Gilmore's largesse had provided them with more than they could possibly have hoped for. Worse than any other year because of the centrepiece of their Christmas feast – and that year it did seem like a feast. Phoebe went out of her way to respect their feelings, and poor Freddie's cold and pallid carcass was kept from their sight until he arrived at the table on Christmas Day. Golden, crisp, steaming slightly from the oven heat, and bringing with him the rich aroma of stuffing, there seemed to be a complete disjunction between the food John saw before him and the feathered friend who had kept him company during the summer days.

'Right. Let's make a start.'

Jack carved, and as Lou and Clara had joined them for the meal Freddie was substantially diminished by the time they started to eat. They had beer with the meal, a full glass for John as it was a special occasion.

'Absent friends,' said Lou, lifting her glass.

'Absent friends.'

They were thinking of Gilmore and Dan at sea with the North Atlantic convoys, but John couldn't suppress a guilty look at Freddie's remains cooling on the carving dish.

It is said that the first crime eases the commission of the second, and so it was with the geese. When Lottie returned home for the New Year John was able to join in Moira's teasing opening toast.

'To Lottie and Freddie, the founders of the feast.'

'To Lottie and Freddie.'

32

The Turn of the Tide

December 1942 and New Year's Eve on the Eastern Front outside Stalingrad. The battlefield dark and still, locked in a killing frost. Nothing moves. Nothing is heard. In the last few moments before midnight the camera focuses on a young gunnery officer, watch in hand, looking out across the snow towards the distant German defences hidden in the night. As the final second of the dying year ticks away his cry is the only sound that breaks the silence: 'Glückliches neues Jahr.'

Even as his last word is spoken the opening bombardment of a final, overwhelming assault carries the reality of the Soviet Union's New Year greeting to the remnants of the isolated German army. Salvo after salvo from ranks of heavy artillery pieces light up the dark clouds and flood the icy landscape with light. Brighter still, and thick as hail, a thousand rockets from the Katyusha launchers reinforce the message of the shells. There would be no respite until the end of that month when the tattered and frozen remnants of the German 6th Army finally surrendered.

It was a stirring and riveting production that Movietone news presented to the Broadway audience towards the end of January. The events depicted were real enough, but a little judicious cutting and editing gave the drama all the spectacle and excitement it demanded. Together with the news of another heavy RAF raid on Berlin, and the first major strike of the US Air Force into Germany, it sent the audience home from the Broadway with a welcome boost to morale just when it was needed following the resumption of heavy night raids on London after a long period of comparative calm.

The exigencies of war made for strange bedfellows, and those were the years of an early but ephemeral Anglo-Soviet détente as the two countries pursued one all-consuming common cause. The

433

time was not long past, however, when Churchill, speaking as Chancellor of the Exchequer, had been vociferous in his denunciation of the dark power of Moscow and of the band of cosmopolitan conspirators from the underworld of the great cities of Europe and America who sat in the Kremlin in despotic possession of the mighty empire of Russia.

But other days brought other ways. The Russian army had performed prodigious feats, said Churchill, and Premier Stalin (surely the arch-conspirator of them all) was a great warrior whose name would be one of those most honoured in the history of the Russian people. In February of 1943 that sentiment was taken up and echoed across the nation in celebrations to mark the twenty-fifth anniversary of the Red Army. There were special intercessions in the churches for Russia and its people. Cabinet ministers spoke at official celebrations in all the major cities, and on a Sunday afternoon at the end of the month the BBC broadcast part of the musical and dramatic tribute from a pageant at the Albert Hall. It was a sentiment that would barely outlive the ending of the war.

The shift in the balance of airpower during the previous year had been obvious to everyone. The massive, thousand-bomber raids on Cologne, Essen and Bremen had taken place against a regular pattern of attacks with formations of hundreds not thousands, but it did not need the headlines that the super-raids generated to inform those living in the south and east of the swing of the pendulum. For two years or more in the flatlands of the Eastern Counties, from Essex through to Lincolnshire and beyond, an immense civil-engineering programme had been transforming cornfields and grazing land into launching pads for the round-the-clock bombing that the year would bring.

In the south of Essex, along the fringes of the estuary, they saw little or nothing of the massed formations of bombers that streamed over Cologne in that first great raid. Even in the immediate vicinity of the runways, the hundred or so that took off from each airfield during the last hour before midnight would have been no more than shadows passing into the last faint glow of the long summer's day, and returning, if they were lucky, in the early light of morning.

Initially bases for the RAF, but increasingly from 1942 for the US Air Force, the new airfields brought the sight and sounds of total war to the bucolic woods and meadows of Suffolk, the bustle of a large and shifting population to the hamlets of Norfolk and

434

the twang of foreign accents to the 'spit and sawdusts' that dotted the Essex countryside. Lavenham, Ludford Manor, Oulton, Great Snoring and a hundred other villages stirred from their long rural slumbers and never quite went to sleep again.

Although a few GIs were spotted in and around the plotlands, there was no major American base nearby and they were never seen in great numbers. Nor were their bombers much in evidence during 1942, but by the summer of 1943 everyone was familiar with the distinctive shapes of the B-17 Flying Fortress, the B-24 Liberators and their Thunderbolt and Lightning escorts. They flew their missions by day and could be seen high in the sky to the north, climbing and assembling for their flight path over the North Sea.

For more than three years the fortunes of war had not brought John or his friends close to the enemy or his aircraft. At the height of the Battle of Britain they had from time to time seen aircraft shot down, but they had either crashed far away or disappeared into the waters of the estuary. Pilots from both sides had bailed out and landed nearby, but were either quickly rounded up and arrested, or carried away and fêted long before the boys had a chance to arrive at the scene.

During the Easter holidays of 1943, however, three of them came face to face with their first German. At the sound of an aircraft they turned from their games in the Arrowsmiths' garden and watched as a homing bomber approached trailing smoke and losing height. Two shapes tumbled from the fuselage, their falls checked as the canopy of their parachutes swelled open above them. The aircraft passed on out of sight to crash some way off, but they watched the two parachutes closely as they drifted on the wind. One was being carried away from them, but the other was seen to be dropping into the fields alongside Rushbottom Lane just over the top of the hill.

They set off along the field paths without a thought to what they might encounter, but fast as they were in reaching the spot, others were there before them. The airman was lying where he had landed, with one leg twisted awkwardly beneath him. A woman and three men, none of them known to the boys, stood around him. Neither Home Guard nor police had arrived, but one of the men held a shotgun and another a long-handled hedge-cutting tool. Others who came running also carried improvised weapons of one sort or another, but it was soon quite obvious that none was needed. The German needed help, not force or restraint. It seemed that his leg or ankle was broken, and he was unable to stand.

Although the men around him talked among themselves they made no attempt to communicate with the airman who lay on the ground looking uneasily from face to face without speaking a word himself. John could see nothing resembling the familiar caricature images of the enemy that he knew from his comics and newspaper cartoons. He was young, frightened and in pain, but good-looking and disconcertingly like John's older cousin, Billy, himself in the Air Force.

In the metropolitan centres that had suffered more from the attention of the Luftwaffe the German might have had a rough ride of it, but rural Essex had been touched comparatively lightly by air raids, and the men around him seemed more awkward and uncertain than hostile or aggressive. One of the late arrivals eventually crouched beside him and offered him a cigarette. He took it with a nod of thanks, and with a few unintelligible words and some sign language indicated that his leg was badly injured. Eventually the police arrived, and the three boys stayed watching as the airman was carried away to the nearby farm on a stretcher improvised from a door.

Exciting as the encounter was, the boys were bitterly disappointed that fast as they had hurried to the scene, the canopy of the parachute had disappeared before they arrived. The harness and the severed lines lay on the ground, but of the silk that formed the fabric of the canopy there was nothing to be seen. The chance that they might have been able to get their hands on it had been a remote one, but that had certainly been their objective. There was the keenest competition for parachute silk as a spoil of war, and they had heard stories, possibly enhanced in the telling, of boys enriched by pounds when they had been the first to make off with the canopy from an abandoned parachute. There was nothing to choose between those of friend or foe. The canopies from either were voluminous, and in skilled hands the fine silk was made up into panties, slips, blouses, shirts and a variety of items unobtainable by any other means. It was the one prize in all their collecting that was to elude them to the end.

Despite its illegality there can have been few boys in the country for whom trophy collecting was not an obsession, and in the refurbished chicken shed at the end of Chuzzy's garden they kept

436

the pooled results of many hours of scouring the roads and countryside with their eyes to the ground. Shrapnel and anti-radar foil was relatively easy to come by, spent cartridges or cannon shells accumulated more slowly, and they had one choice item, a weathered and muddy parachute harness that Mickey had stumbled across on the marshes. Of one highly prized collectable, aircraft fragments, they had nothing. Of another, live ammunition, much sought after and with great trading value, they had an interesting collection that they kept well hidden.

At school they had been lectured and warned against any form of collecting, with graphic descriptions in particular of the dangers of Butterfly Bombs and live ammunition. Fortunately Butterfly Bombs were never encountered, but over more than three years of war live, as well as spent, ammunition had fallen from the skies into the countryside, and ignoring the lectures and advice, they built up their collection piece by piece. Much of it derived from the Battle of Britain and the early days of the Blitz when the skies were crowded and the combat intense, but it only came to light over the months and years that followed as they wandered the lanes and fields following the farming operations. Ploughing and harrowing, harvesting, haymaking and raking were all good times for collectors.

Why live as well as spent ammunition fell to earth they never understood, but they welcomed all that came their way. Possibly guns misfired, but there were also occasional reports of crews on crippled Allied bombers jettisoning everything detachable including ammunition and weapons in a desperate bid to find a little more lift to limp the last few miles to a home landing strip. Somewhere other souvenir hunters may have been treasuring battered guns as well as ammunition, but nothing so exciting ever fell on the boys' doorstep.

Just two types of ammunition came their way: machine-gun rounds and cannon shells. The cartridge case of the machine-gun round, about a finger thick and less than three inches long, appeared to be of brass. The cannon case was a silvery alloy, much thicker and an inch or so longer. They had the sense not to meddle with the caps on either type of round, but someone, somewhere in the brotherhood of souvenir-hungry boys had eased a cartridge out of its case and found stick cordite inside. The news of the discovery, and the use to which cordite could be put, spread quickly, but the information that came with it was imprecise. The boys had two types of round, but no idea whether both or just one contained the cordite.

If they were foolish in their meddling, they were not reckless. Chuzzy's simple reasoning was that as long as they stood behind the cartridge, and the case was securely held, there would be no risk: that sounded convincing. Just outside the house in his garden shed Mr Arrowsmith had a vice and a basic set of tools. They made a start there, with a cannon case clamped between the wooden jaws of the vice, and pointing away from the house, just in case. Working with pliers and a wrench they loosened and eventually withdrew the cartridge. Beneath a pad of wadding there was only powder – gunpowder to them, but almost certainly something much more sophisticated. Experiments with a few pinches produced some very satisfying flashes, but with only three more hard-won cannon rounds available they preferred to keep them intact.

The machine-gun round was dealt with in the same way, and there inside the case, beneath the wadding, they saw their sticks of cordite closely packed like strands of spaghetti, each about the same length as the cartridge case. A little tapping and manipulation loosened the strands and they eased them out. When all the rounds had been dealt with, they had what seemed a more than adequate pile of cordite sticks to work with, but a couple of days were quite long enough to see it all gone.

An overambitious attempt to use the sticks as a propellant in a piece of narrow piping was both extravagant in its consumption of cordite and a disappointing failure. The extended burst of flame had little entertainment value, and neither the boys nor the pipe were moved by the event. They enjoyed some brief but brilliant displays of fireworks after dark, all gross breaches of the blackout regulations, but in their hearts it was the big bang that they were after. With the explosives, a few empty containers from the shelves in the shed, and a fire at the end of the garden they conducted their experiments. Perhaps fortunately, they never achieved complete success, but after a couple of disappointing 'pops' when lids blew off with no more than a puff of flame, they got what they considered to be a more than gratifying result with a small Andrew's Liver Salts tin.

A generous mix of the remaining cannon powder and broken

cordite sticks was placed inside. The lid was hammered shut and closely wired down, and the tin dropped into the heart of the fire. At a distance, tucked behind the protective trunks of trees, they waited. Inevitably it was Chuzzy who lost patience after only a few moments and stepped out towards the fire just as the tin erupted. Dust, ash and glowing embers rose in a cloud from the fire and fell in a shower around him. A few fragments dropped with a satisfying hiss into the pond. Flights of birds exploded from the bushes, and the sound was enough to bring Mr Arrowsmith to the door of the house. He looked down the garden for a few seconds, but satisfied that they were all still on their feet turned back into the house and left them to it. Chuzzy emerged from his adventure ash-strewn and slightly singed from burning embers, but triumphant that he had been the only one who had witnessed the concluding event of their ordnance operations in all its glory.

During 1943 came a sequence of decisive moments in the war that by the end of the year left few people in any doubt that victory, if still a long way off, was assured. By the end of March, Bomber Command was engaged in massive and relentless operations in the Ruhr which would later extend to Germany at large. From the beginning of May, Gilmore had been able to embark on his transatlantic crossings secure in the knowledge that the U-boats had at last been swept from the seas. At the same time a quarter of a million prisoners were taken when the Axis forces in North Africa surrendered. As if to mark the occasion the ban on the ringing of church bells was relaxed, and signposts began to reappear in the Essex countryside. There was no longer any thought of invasion. On the other side of the Atlantic and in the highest secrecy the Manhattan Project opened at Los Alamos. Had people been aware of its existence and significance in what could possibly have been a race to outrun Germany to an atomic bomb it might have done something to moderate the growing sense of optimism.

In the second half of the year Sicily was invaded and taken in a mere thirty-eight days. In the Pacific the Americans launched their assaults on the Solomon and Gilbert islands – the first stepping stones in the battle towards Japan itself. In September they learned of the Italian surrender and one day later of the Allied invasion landings at Salerno. By the end of the month Smolensk, the keystone in the German defensive front in the east, was retaken by the Russians. On Christmas Eve Berlin was bombed, and on Boxing Day the battleship *Scharnhorst* was sunk by the navy.

Against the backdrop of such momentous military events they played out their domestic comedies, tragedies and triumphs. At home John followed the progress of the war in the *Daily Worker*, which Jack had started to take again when it resumed publication after being proscribed for more than eighteen months because of the initial opposition of the Communist Party to the war. He cut and dissected its pages for the maps, charts and pictures that analysed and recorded events, and stuck them together as a wartime diary in obsolete record books that Clara brought him from the laundry.

The pages that remained were tagged together in quarter sheets and hung for use in the lavatory: not a reflection on its political content of course. Any newspaper that came into the house was pressed into the same service. So it was that in those idle moments as he sat waiting for a sluggish constitution to perform its natural function he exercised his reading skills on fragmentary reports and articles in the hanging quarter sheets and took his first hesitant steps into the world of politics. In retrospect he considered that it had been an appropriate place to begin.

For light relief and a little innocent titillation he walked up to his gran's where the *Daily Mirror* was taken and he could indulge a fledgling pubescent interest in the activities of Jane in the strip cartoon. Apart from a few decorous corset and underwear advertisements in the women's magazines, or the occasional pin-up torn from a copy of *Men Only* and surreptitiously passed around at school, the publications of the forties offered precious little to tickle a young boy's fancy, but the trials and tribulations of Jane were guaranteed to find her enduring the passage of the war years undressed or half-dressed, but seldom fully clothed. Tall, willowy, curvaceous, teasingly veiled in a diaphanous negligee, or clad in the briefest of lacy underwear, she offered her followers a tantalising glimpse of shapely, slender legs, discreetly cheeky buttocks and confident, but not overassertive young breasts. She, or her like, must have been many a squaddy's home thought from abroad, and she presented the boys of the lane with a dream-like alternative to the vision of Long Lizzie.

In spring John called for one of his assignations with Jane to find his gran red-eyed from crying.

440

'Oh hallo, love. Poor old Mick's passed on. When Clara got up this morning she found him dead in the bottom of the cage.'

He looked to the cage where, for as long as he could remember, Mick had held court from his perch or swing. It was empty.

'He's in the scullery.'

He walked through to see where Clara had put him before she left for work.

'He's turned up his toes.'

The words were unspoken, but despite the tragic circumstances that was his immediate thought as he looked at him, and the euphemism was never more appropriate. With his feet in the air and his head resting to one side, Mick lay peacefully on his back in the tissue-lined bottom of a garden trug. When John reached in to pick him up his head fell back loosely, and as he held him limp and cold in his hands he sensed for the first time something of the awful difference between the living and the dead.

'Poor old Mick. He used to love it when Pappy had him out and tickled his poll.'

For his gran it was yet another severed link with the early years in Poplar, and they had a little cry together.

Mick had to be given a proper send-off and burial. During the day, alongside the path that ran round the bungalow, John dug a neat, deep grave in the clay. Later that evening, together with the toys from his cage, and cushioned with tissue paper, Mick was coffined in an old Jacob's biscuit tin. Overlooked from the windows by Phoebe, Lou and Clara, and followed by Valerie and Janice, another younger cousin, John carried Mick to the grave where he was placed, covered and marked with a wooden cross.

Moira had agreed to say a few last words and gave them a selection of three verses from *The Burial of Sir John Moore at Corruna* modified as appropriate for the occasion. Chosen presumably for its dramatic qualities which showed her voice to advantage, it was perhaps a little overripe for a parrot, but she performed it in style with a fine valedictory ring to the final line: 'And we left him alone in his glory.' He's still there: eighteen inches down and about six feet to the west of the foundations of the new house erected on the site of Bayhurst soon after Clara died, the last of John's Three Graces.

Through all the chances of war, when deaths and disasters were random and common affairs, the family had been lucky in avoiding the worst that it could bring. Carters Terrace had been abandoned, but the contents saved. Doll and Charlie had lost their home and most of their belongings, but no one had died or been seriously injured. Apart from that first encounter during Black Saturday the business of war had been conducted at a distance and, unlike many, John had never had to confront its reality face to face.

In the early summer of 1943 that was to change. Despite the sounding of an alert, Saturday breakfast had been taken as usual and the table cleared. It was a fine, bright morning and Jack had already set off slowly down the lane on the walk that he took every day in the hope that the exercise and fresh air would help his chest. Phoebe was busy about the house prior to going to the market when an aircraft was heard passing close overhead. There had been no firing, and they saw and heard nothing unusual until the noise of the engines was cut by the sound of an explosion followed by silence.

They walked to the front of the house and looked towards the direction of the blast. The air in the garden was heavy with the scent of lilac. Apart from the distant sound of a cuckoo and the trickle of water in the ditch, it was still and peaceful again, but in the distance above the hedges and trees a plume of dark, oily smoke began to cloud the sky. After looking for a few moments Phoebe and Moira went back to the house, but one or two people were already moving up the lane to investigate. Grabbing his jacket John ran to follow them.

There were a few Home Guard members in most communities, and two of the locals were already at the site when he arrived. They were able to keep the gathering crowd from the immediate area of the crash, but not far enough back to prevent them seeing more than some might have wanted. The plane had been a Junkers 88, but the spotting skills in which John took pride were useless to him that morning. Nothing remained that was recognisable as an aircraft, little that was obviously a part of one.

The wreckage lay at the edge of the field close to a thick hawthorn hedge. The impact had been at an acute angle and great speed. Two pits hacked into the earth marked the points where the engines had buried themselves deeply as they were sheared from the wings. In a shallower crater between them, where the bulk of the fuselage had struck, some of the remains were still burning and smouldering. The wheels and twisted undercarriage attached to them were the only clearly distinguishable parts.

Spread more widely around the site, torn and twisted fragments of metal skinning, jagged pieces of airframe and shattered blades lay in confusion among greasy clods of clay thrown up as propellers buckled and the engines chewed their way into the soft ground. Splinters of perspex glinted where they caught the sun. Of the crew there nothing to be seen, and one look at the tangled litter of metal to which the aircraft had been reduced made it clear that little identifiable would be left of them. Mingling with the sour, dank smell of the clay thrown up from the crater there was a heavier, sickening stench of oil, aviation fuel and the fumes that drifted from the still smouldering tangle of metal, rubber, leather, clothing and flesh.

Most of the crowd and all of the children remained until an ambulance arrived. Then, at last, it occurred to someone that children should be kept from the scene, and they were ushered off to a distance. As those remaining looked on, the ambulance men moved into the centre crater, and then further out around the site. Some body parts were found, wrapped and carried to the ambulance, but the business was soon over, and with a few words to the Home Guards the ambulance men left.

It was standard practice throughout the war for all downed aircraft to be examined by experts for any information that might be of use, or for evidence of innovations in equipment. Crash sites should have been protected, and souvenir gathering was illegal, but those who had gathered to gape at the site knew nothing of that, and neither it seemed did the Home Guard. Although they stayed on the site, they no longer made any attempt to stop those who wished to do so from moving in to look at the remains more closely, and when they left most took away with them some small part of the wreckage as a souvenir.

For the rest of the day, and in the days that followed, people were drawn to the site by a morbid fascination with the near total-effacement of four individuals and the fragmentary remains that the ambulance men had failed to clear. It was impossible to be unaware that among the debris, within the fractured metal, and even in the hawthorn hedge alongside the crash, traces of the crew remained. The same morbid curiosity saw the boys scouring the

443

wreckage and hedgerow to gawk at sights that both fascinated and repelled. While they were there they shared the hushed and sombre mood that caught at old and young alike, but when they turned for home with their trophies from the Junkers they were jubilant.

In all of their collecting whether it was rope, ammunition, parachute harness or aircraft parts they unwittingly broke the law. The Defence Regulations required anyone finding an article which 'he had reasonable cause to believe was used by HM Forces' to hand it in to the police or to the military, and the same regulations prohibited the collection of fragments from crashed enemy aircraft. Unwary souvenir hunters had died, prosecutions were not unknown, and in those areas that saw extensive enemy action there must have been few men or boys who came out of the war as honest citizens.

May was a month crowded with incident – the death of Mick, the Junkers crash and towards the end of the month John's scholarship examination – but before that came Phoebe's brief encounter with the world of war work. From the early days of the war young unmarried women had been conscripted either into the women's forces or to work in factories, on the railways, on the land, or in any occupation where the work was essential and the need great. Eventually all women under fifty, including married women, were required to register for such work.

There was an exemption for mothers like Phoebe with children under the age of fourteen, but the pay was unusually attractive. In the factories the average weekly wage for women was £3 10s with much more for the longer shifts that many had to work. This compared very favourably with the £2 8s a week earned by the aunts. Phoebe was tempted and volunteered.

On the Monday morning they were all up earlier than usual to see her off on the walk to the top of the lane for the workers' bus to the factory in Grays. She had already snatched some breakfast, and John and Moira were just finishing theirs when she came in from the bedroom.

'And I don't want any cheek from either of you.'

They looked up at her unusual morning greeting. This was their mother as they had never seen her before: trousered in clean, blue overalls; hair put up into a mesh hat with a broad peak; and a bag over her shoulder with Thermos flask and sandwiches. They walked

444

with her to the front gate, waved her off and returned for the morning news on the wireless.

It was a long shift and a long day. With travelling time it was early evening, and more than twelve hours after her morning departure, before she returned home. Work-stained, scruffy and exhausted she dropped into a chair.

'Well, that's the end of that. I jacked it in and asked for my cards when I left.'

As Jack put the kettle on the stove to make tea she had a little more to say about her workplace. It was hot, dusty, grimy and gritty. It stank of oil and grease. The only redeeming aspect of the deafening noise of machines and presses was that they drowned out the sound of the music droning on all day. It was impossible to talk. The toilets were filthy, the few work breaks too short and the foreman too lippy. In brief the game wasn't worth the candle.

It became clear after the war that working conditions as bad and worse than she described were not unusual, and even during the wartime emergency they led to strikes, so perhaps Phoebe had not been laying it on thick as they suspected at the time. Their domestic routine resumed its customary pattern, and that was the end of the factory adventure.

John heard no further discussion of the matter, and for him it was a one-day wonder and no more. Only after Phoebe's death more than forty years later did a remark from Moira make him realise that things may have looked very different to those old enough to see them from a different perspective. Her view, one that would have escaped John as a youngster, was that the money their mother could have earned might have done much to lift them from the hand-to-mouth existence to which reliance on the National Assistance Board condemned them. Nothing had been said at the time, and in fact it may not have been as clear-cut as Moira supposed even if their mother had stuck it out. The poverty trap has been around for a long time. 'The State giveth and the State taketh away' was probably as true of National Assistance Allowances then, as it is of many Social Security Benefits now, and even if Phoebe had stuck it out they may not have been much better off at the end of it all.

Little was made of John's impending scholarship examination as it approached, and no great expectations expressed. Nothing was said that might imply any pressure to succeed, and when the day arrived he had no undue apprehensions. Nor did he have any real understanding, as did his parents, of the implications for the rest of his life that the day might hold. Perhaps that was as well.

'Do your best.'

That was his father's only comment as he saw him off from the gate.

At school Madam had a few words for her fledglings before they set off.

'Take your time. Read the question carefully. Think before you write. Be neat and tidy. Make us all proud of you.'

He couldn't see Mickey, Chuzzy or Billy taking particular pride in anything he might achieve that day, but understood what she meant.

After a short bus ride with Madam, they joined other little groups of hopefuls each clustered around their own head teacher in the hall at Pitsea school. Then they moved into the room where seats, desks and papers were set out and waiting for them, and under the unsettling gaze of strange invigilators their testing time began.

John could recall only two papers; one in maths the other in English. When they were over his feelings about them were neutral. By the time he got home they were almost forgotten. There were better things to do on a summer evening than chew them over.

'How did it go?' from his father.

'All right I think.'

'Good!'

And he was on his way to Chuzzy's.

33

The Fruits of Victory

Just before the end of the summer term the results of the scholarship examination arrived. A year's pushing and shoving from Madam, a stimulating and lively family background, and a modest allocation of native wit and cunning had triumphed over innate laziness and lack of interest: John had passed.

Congratulations from his father: and a warning not to leave it quite so late in taking his fences in the future. Congratulations from his mother, who immediately began to worry how she would find and afford the new outfit that would be needed. From Moira, just to put his achievement in perspective and ensure that he kept a proper sense of proportion: 'Good God! They must have been throwing them away this year.' His gran gave him a kiss and a half-sovereign from the modest hoard she kept for such special occasions, and in due course he was rewarded by his aunts.

The last day at St Margaret's came and went with a special ceremony of farewell for those who were leaving, a few words from Madam, and an invitation to return to see them and report on progress at the new school. After the end-of-term service and a brief homily from Revd Bryers they were released and on their way home for the summer holidays.

The many changes taking place around them provided further evidence, if any was needed, that there was no longer any remote threat of invasion. In Leigh and Westcliff many of the restricted areas were no longer off-limits. Strong points and entries formerly manned and guarded now stood empty. Around the plotlands anti-glider defences had disappeared from most of the fields, and the army posts at the arterial road junction were unmanned. Scrub and tangled brambles grew high around the pillboxes, a few weeds and grasses had found a foothold on the roofs, and long fingers of ivy searched to extend their first tentative grip on the walls. Within a year or two they would be hidden by a more effective camouflage than the roughly daubed paint already fading from the concrete. More than sixty years after their construction many still remain, absorbed into the countryside and quite invisible to the casual passer-by.

As the days grew hotter the boys returned to their summer watering holes in the tank traps. In some fields cattle moving to and from the traps had trampled the edges and turned them into shallow, muddy morasses. Elsewhere three years' growth of weeds and grasses hid the scars of construction and provided welcoming, green banks down to the water's edge. The still, confined stretches of water warmed up quickly in the sun, attracting insects, birds and boys from the countryside around.

For sea bathing and the chlorine-laden swimming pools convention demanded costumes, but for the boys the simple pleasure of skinny-dipping, unconfined as nature intended, in local lakes·or ponds was infinitely superior. To those pleasures the soft, silky waters of the tank traps added a uniquely sensual experience.

The attractions of the traps were not obvious. They lacked the movement and sparkling invitation of the sea. Opaque and dull even after long days lying calm and still, they were an unenticing swirl of muddy, khaki yellows from the moment their waters were disturbed. But as the boys slipped into them and drifted idly on their backs; as they cruised them with lazy dog-paddles or rolled and twisted in the embrace of their summer warmth the waters swathed their bodies like folds of liquid silk and drifting clouds of infinitesimal motes of clay soothed and caressed their flesh. At the trap's edge, half-in, half-out of the tepid water, they stretched in the sun and wallowed in the soothing clay. They squeezed it, moulded it between their fingers and toes, scooped it up and spread it like butter over their bodies. They baked, they swam, they soaked then baked again in mud baths that might have rivalled the spas of Europe.

They started as tranquil, idyllic times, but water and mud were too tempting a combination. The soft clay was easily moulded into soggy cannon balls, and all too soon each was manoeuvring for the tactical advantage of a first strike. A general exchange of mud, water and insults followed, and it was all good fun unless, as sometimes happened, someone took a face full of clay, when tears or a fight brought the enjoyment to an end.

448

For a week in August all the old joys of Bayhurst were revived. Elsie and Kath were home on leave. Clara Dent and Eva were being squeezed in for an overnight visit, and Ada was joining them from Leigh. On the day they all met, Clara called in at Harcourt on her way home from work and made a point of asking them to join the party at Bayhurst in half an hour or so. They had intended doing that any way, but as she also sent John off to ask Doll, Charlie and Valerie to do the same and seemed particularly pleased with herself they suspected that she had something special in mind.

In the early evening of a fine summer's day they walked up the path to Bayhurst with the sun still high in the sky behind them and warm on their backs. Across the undeveloped plots at the bottom of the road a footpath running through scrub and bushes of maturing blackberries provided a short cut to the lane for those agile enough to jump the ditch at one end. From the bushes at the far end of the path Valerie was just appearing, and as they paused for her to join them Doll and Charlie turned into the road behind them.

When they arrived deckchairs and a light table were already set out in the garden. More chairs were brought from the house, and together with the garden bench there were seats for everyone. Some of them were meeting for the first time since the start of the Blitz, and there was a lot of ground to be covered. Wandering away by themselves Valerie and John squeezed together on to the seat of the swing and swayed gently, listening to the distant murmur of the conversation. Clara left the group for a moment and then came out from the bungalow carrying her shopping bag.

'Blimey, Clara! Where did you get those?'

It was Elsie who spoke.

Clara placed two bottles of wine on the table and asked Charlie to bring out some glasses.

'Algerian,' she said, 'One of my customers told me he could get his hands on some and I couldn't resist it. Eight bob a bottle though, so it shouldn't be too bad.'

'That would be one of your special customers would it, Clara?'

'Any more cheek from you and you'll get none.'

Clara's mature admirers had been a matter of interest and enjoyment to the family for years. She was still quite pretty and lively enough to make one of them happy if she had chosen to do so, but the relationships always remained at arm's length and eventually withered away.

Charlie returned with the glasses, and John moved in towards the table, anxious not to be forgotten. The corks were drawn, and the glasses filled and sparkling in the sun before Clara held up the bottle and looked towards him.

'All right, Jack?'

'I suppose so as it's a special occasion.'

Not just a splash in the bottom but almost three-quarters full, the glass was passed to him.

The wine, the first fruit of the Allied victory in North Africa, had reached British shops only a few weeks earlier and Clara's was the first to be seen. Her two bottles at eight bob each had been a pricey indulgence indeed.

John took a mouthful: warm, sweet and sticky, but a distinct improvement on Sanatogen. He was a greedy drinker and had emptied his glass while the others were still sipping and chatting. Rejoining his cousin he stretched out at length in the long grass with the heady fumes of the wine still in his mouth and nose. With a faint groan of protest at each change of direction the swing idled forwards and back. Valerie hummed softly to herself as she pulled on its ropes. Evening sunlight danced and flickered through the hedge, and from across the garden he could hear his ladies laughing and talking. It had to be at least sixpence from each of them when they left, he reckoned.

The war years gradually fell away. On Sunday evening they would set off for home once again with their bunches of flowers cut from the garden. Up the lane, down to Pitsea and over the hill to catch the train back to Poplar. It would be good to be back with Terry and Mick again. What would be on at The Gaiety he wondered, and what would Popjaw have been up to.

'John! John! Come on, old love, Ada's ready to leave.'

He woke with a start at his gran's call from the house. The sun was almost down, the garden empty, and from high in the sky to the north there came the sound of bombers.

The weeks of the summer holiday following his departure from St Margaret's passed away relatively peacefully. There were few German air incursions, and the sound of their own bombers passing was now so familiar that it scarcely provoked a comment. As September approached the thought of starting at a new school began to disturb his nights. From seniority at little St Margaret's, with a hundred or so pupils, to a very junior inferiority at Brentwood, where there were more than seven hundred, was not a thought that he was easy with.

There had been a brief preliminary visit with his mother for a meeting with Higgs the deputy headmaster, but this had only increased his apprehensions and quite dispelled the vague and naive dreams he had of a warm and welcoming cross between the anarchy of Will Hay's Academy of St Michael's and the cloistered attractions of Bunter's Greyfriars. The maze of buildings was complex and confusing, Higgs dry and academically severe. To learn also at that late stage that the school worked a six-day week was the final shattering blow. It was a long while before Chuzzy, Mickey and the rest ceased to get amusement from the fact that on Saturday mornings he was at his lessons while they were on the loose to do as they pleased.

At Brentwood the autumn term started a little later than at the other schools, and for two or three days he fretted and moped by himself until the morning arrived for his first journey on the school bus. Had he been a year earlier he would have had Moira for company, but her time at school was over.

Roused early by his father, and supervised more than usually closely in his ablutions by his mother, he was given a final critical inspection after breakfast before being sent on his way. With a little juggling of clothing coupons, and some financial help from his gran and the aunts, he had been kitted out to Phoebe's satisfaction, but to his own utter discomfort. Black shoes, grey jacket and short trousers, the school badge on his breast pocket, the school cap on his head and a gleaming new satchel slung over his shoulder: that was his outfit, all far too clean, neat and tidy. He couldn't have been more conspicuously distinguished as public school if he had walked the lane carrying a banner to that effect. The cap at least he could shove into his satchel until later; the rest he was stuck with.

He was relieved to find three or four others making the journey for the first time. They clustered together quietly as they waited for the school bus, overawed by the easy, confident manner of the old hands swapping stories of their holiday activities, and envious of their evident familiarity with the pattern of the term to come. They boarded last and were left in no doubt as to their standing in the pecking order: juniors at the front close to the driver, seniors at the back.

The bus, unlike the schools, was co-educational with a broad and basic curriculum. There was a primary lesson on hierarchical structures (a thick ear if you sat in the wrong place), and progression through a range of useful disciplines to conclude with sex education, a topic studiously avoided in the schools. A brief theoretical introduction from sebaceous but knowing seniors was supplemented by extensive practical work in the back seats of the bus, well out of the line of vision in the driver's rear-view mirror. The girls followed a slightly different but parallel syllabus up to the concluding practical classes when they joined forces, so to speak, with the boys. They were by any standards near innocent, almost decorous affairs, confined, more or less, to the fondling of incipient breasts, and the gentle explorations of soft, downy and virginal inner thighs. With most girls it was less, with a few a little more, and at the right time, in the right mood there were one or two of a more giving disposition.

The journey ended at the girls' high school below the old Mill Pond on the common. From there the boys walked towards town, entering school either by the main entrance or at the back gate by the Mitre Inn, a lunch-time refuge for one or two of the masters. As the high school worked only a five-day week, a smaller coach was used to take the boys on Saturday mornings, but for reasons never made clear they were abandoned at the end of the day to make their way home as best they could on public transport.

Brentwood was a minor public school. In the best of traditions, its foundation was of Tudor origin, having been established by Sir Anthony Browne in the dying days of Bloody Mary's reign. Outside the old school buildings the railed-off remains of an ancient elm stood monument to the predilections of her time. On the spot, just two years before the school was established, William Hunter, a young Protestant lad, had been burned to death for refusing to attend Mass. 'Pursued to death by Justice Browne for the Gospels sake,' said Foxe in his *Book of Martyrs*. Once a year to commemorate the founder, the same man, the whole school processed to St Peter's church at South Weald where Sir Anthony was buried.

Following a period marked by vicissitudes that brought its closure for a few years, the school revived, flourished and was extended and transformed over a period of thirty-one years from

1914 under headmaster James F. Hough, whose retirement came only after he had seen the school through a second world war under his stewardship.

A prospectus at the time would have shown swimming pool, squash courts, gymnasium, covered rifle range, fives court, workshops, tuck shop and seventy acres of playing fields. There was a fine oak-lined memorial hall, a well-stocked memorial library, a handsome chapel, seven boarding houses and a sanatorium, in addition to new blocks containing laboratories and an art room. In the late twenties the school had even boasted its own nine-hole golf course. There was corporal punishment by caning administered not only by masters but also by prefects. There was a preparatory department, an Officers Training Corps with its own in-house sergeant NCO, and a begowned teaching staff of between thirty and forty who, following the school motto and the wishes of the founder, were to imbue their charges with 'Virtue, Learning, Manners'.

In short, the school had most of the hallmarks that from a working-class East End perspective marked it out as a bastion of reaction and the Establishment, and for the first few weeks it seemed confusing, hostile and alien to everything that John knew and understood. Had he been capable of resolving and formulating the swirling impressions that he carried home with him during the early days he would have said that it reeked of privilege, and that the values it sought to inculcate were those of Church, King, Country, Empire and Tory Party. In most respects those early impressions of its values would have been justified, but when in later years adolescent revolt led him to a pointless assertion of his atheism, the school proved to be quite tolerant in its response. Dissenters were no longer burned at the stake, and so during prayers at the morning assembly he waited outside the Memorial Hall doors with the Jews and a few other ranks. Nor was he ever aware of any active discrimination or distinction between scholarship boys and those from the very different backgrounds that formed the core of the school's intake. Belatedly in his time at the school he came to have a better understanding of its values without being influenced by them and to recognise the privileges he enjoyed by being there.

For newcomers the start of that first day in the new school year was a hopeless, confusing free-for-all as they struggled and pushed

453

their way through a milling, heaving crush of boys in search of their classroom and a meeting with their form master. From then on a pattern emerged that would be followed over the years, as class by class they processed to the hall for the opening assembly of term. It began with a brief service.

> *Lord, behold us with thy blessing,*
> *Once again assembled here . . .*

At least that was one of the traditional aspects of public school life that fiction and film had made familiar, as was the formal academic dress the masters wore for the occasion: fur trimmed and colourful as opposed to the plain black teaching gown worn at other times. But there was apparently no school song, an omission which bred a niggling sense of disappointment that sat uneasily with John's feeling that he should in fact despise such things. Was he already being subverted?

Prayers and school notices concluded the assembly, and then the rest of the school departed while the new boys settled cross-legged on the floor to hear from the headmaster James Hough, MA. Jimmy – it would be several weeks before they had the confidence to call him that even amongst themselves – was a Mr Chipps made flesh: a pattern for a public-school headmaster in any *Boy's Own* yarn. On formal occasions, in addition to his gown, he still affected the mortar board which he removed as he delivered his short address of welcome. Lightly built, slightly stooped, with thinning hair, greying moustache and half-rimmed glasses he seemed benign, almost insignificant, yet under Jimmy the school had flourished as never before, and it was he who had the prescience to purchase the bulk of the acres that formed the school's playing fields.

All the enthusiasm and energy that must have driven him over those years was still there in his voice as he told them succinctly what they could expect, what was expected of them and concluded with a brief account of the foundation and origin of the school before sending them back to their class.

What there was of historical interest in the establishment was embedded in an old and much altered range of buildings linked to the main school by a covered arcade behind which were very basic changing rooms and lavatories. Beyond the arcade was the Victorian chapel and what was left of the Tudor origins of the school after the many alterations and additions. Dimly lit corridors led to the headmaster's chambers and other rooms used by housemasters, by smaller specialist classes for senior boys and as a prefects' common room. A summons to a junior to attend at a room beyond the chapel was not generally to be welcomed.

In the pre-war years stability and continuity of teaching staff was the norm for most schools, so that although by 1943 Jimmy was left with a complement that necessarily excluded the young and the fit, who were all in the Forces, there remained a solid core of older, experienced masters of whom more than a few had served in, and returned from, the First World War.

The quality of masters available as replacements for those who were absent on active service must at best have been mixed and uncertain, drawn as it was from a mature reserve of those who had never quite satisfied wherever they were, and others with little or no experience or entering teaching for the first time. The difference was immediately spotted and exploited by the boys. Discipline was invariably the problem. Any selection process would have established soon enough that a new master knew his subject, but it took day after day in front of unforgiving classes probing and testing for any weakness to sort out the saddest failures.

Paddy Dundon was one of them. A gentle, melancholic Irishman he was utterly at a loss when faced with a class on the rampage. He loved his literature, but unfortunately, perhaps understandably, he also loved his liquor. The Mitre on the edge of the common was his lunchtime refuge from the morning torments endured in the classroom, and from The Mitre each afternoon he returned bathed in the aura of the taproom, but refreshed and braced for the ordeal yet to come. In those days of shortages he must have had a very special relationship with the landlord, for he carried the smell of whisky as well as beer on his breath. Eventually he gave up any attempt at formal teaching and engaged his classes in just two forms of activity where past experience showed that he could command some attention: essay writing, or reading aloud selections from his favourite authors.

There was little that was orthodox about Paddy. He had a freewheeling, exploratory approach to essay writing in marked contrast to any of his colleagues. Taking as his subject a topic thrown up by discussion with the class, he encouraged them to explore its possibilities with him. Often they did little essay writing, but by the end of the lesson his blackboard and their notebooks would be covered with interrelated themes and ideas, and the essay completed when next they met.

Even more unconventional was his choice of reading matter, all of it calculated to get and hold a boy's attention, and much of it distinctly off the beaten academic track. Tastings of Robert Service, Kipling, Hardy and Housman were trailed past them. They heard a little Jack London, a few short stories, and excerpts from Dickens. Finally, when Paddy was a little more fired up than usual following his liquid lunch at The Mitre, he turned to Joyce, and on three or four occasions entertained the class with selections from *A Portrait of the Artist as a Young Man.*

With Joyce in his hand Paddy was a man transformed, and after some initial puzzlement and uncertainty his audience listened goggle-eyed. His Irish brogue, almost completely suppressed at other times, was given full rein, and he amused himself as much as the boys with the characters he played before them. At heart Paddy was a frustrated actor, and his readings were dramatic performances which had his class groaning with disappointment when the period bell signalled the end of the entertainment.

When, after only a few sessions, the readings from Joyce stopped, and Paddy moved to something else, there was a general request that he return to them. No amount of 'Please, Sir, please' could persuade him, which was strange. Paddy was usually a soft touch if they kept at him long enough. Only much later did one of the boys let slip that he had told his parents about the readings. His father had called at the school and complained to Jimmy that the material was unsuitable. Jimmy must have agreed, and it was their loss and misfortune that the intervention deprived them of Joyce's hellfire sermon with Paddy in full flow.

He didn't last much longer than the end of the war. As the other masters started to return from military service he left. With the weak disciplinarians John was as unforgiving as the rest of the boys, but he had a soft spot for Paddy and his father heard about him with amusement. A natural subversive he called him.

With Brentwood came the curse of homework. Evening after evening it stretched before him winding its way into the uncertain future. The fancy satchel was not just for show and sandwiches, and almost at once he was lugging home his evening's allotment of work. Nor was it to be his curse alone. As his homework problems arose he took them, or attempted to take them, to his father. Finding a way of making contact was the difficulty. Jack's capacity for self-absorption grew worse as he got older.

The autumn evenings settled into a regular routine. The meal was finished, the table cleared, and then there was no wireless until homework was done. Jack sat one side of the table, John the other. Jack settled to his reading or perhaps writing, and John to his homework until the first difficulty arose, and he turned to his father. It could be a tedious, drawn-out affair before he arrived at an answer.

'Dad.' He used the irritating two-tone opening, turning the word into a diphthong.

No response.

'Dad.' Short and sharp this time.

Nothing.

'Dad.' Louder and attenuated.

At last his father lifted his head and gazed at him.

It was invariably maths that created John's dilemmas, and having at last got some attention he turned to his textbook, read out the problem and looked up expectantly for the reply. Either his father's head would be down again or more frustratingly he would gaze at his son vacantly for a moment or two, smile and turn again to his book without a word.

'Jack!'

John's difficulty was one that his mother herself experienced and she was more likely to get a positive response.

'What?'

'Didn't you hear him?'

Between them they got his attention. John started again, and at last they made some progress.

Those early maths problems had an unnatural obsession with transport and trains approaching and departing each other at speeds beyond the wildest hopes of anyone who travelled on wartime railways. Those problems were the bane of John's life. For the fourth or fifth time, hopelessly lost in a maze of calculations, he took his speeding trains to his father who listened, shook his head and looked at him despairingly.

'Can't you see it's the same bloody problem each time? The principle's the same.'

It was his father's misfortune as much as his own that it was to be some while before John took hold of that idea as being of general application.

As the opening term progressed the rules and rituals of the new establishment became familiar, as did the faces and characters of the masters and mistresses. At Brentwood, apart from classes in laboratories or workshops, it was the master who moved to the class, not the class to the master. The classroom for the new boys was in the main block just a few steps away from the masters' common room. Throughout the day they watched their comings and goings, and at break times the scent of their pipe tobaccos drifted in to the boys through the swing doors.

There were perhaps two or three unhappy incompetents like Paddy, but most of the rest were efficient if unremarkable in any other way. If there was none that quite matched the eccentricity of manner that cinema and comics had led John to expect, there were those whose characters, idiosyncrasies and nicknames were permanently etched into the memories of the boys they taught, including a few of the old brigade marked physically or psychologically by their experiences in the First World War.

'Basher' Ashbee, the Classics master, hobbled painfully from room to room with the help of a pair of sticks and, once seated, stayed at his desk until the class was over. Latin, he told them, was a dead language, and despite his best efforts during their time together, dead it remained to many of them. With only a few years to serve before retirement, Basher drew on a depth of experience which despite his disability gave him an authority that no class sought to challenge.

H. J. Deane, inevitably 'Dixie' to his classes, specialised in maths and a robust coarseness of expression that earned him a place in their vulgar little hearts where scatological humour and crude sexual innuendo passed as wit. They had unstinted admiration for one boy who could belch and at the same time articulate with clarity 'The Archbishop of Canterbury'. They envied another small and otherwise inconspicuous lad who could fart like a cannon on request and had a golden future as a petomane. Of Gentry, whose sly and silent farts, mephitic and all-pervasive, brought tears to the eyes, they went in awe.

A Dixie/Gentry double act occurred once only. In a hot and stuffy classroom Dixie was at the blackboard, his back to the class.

On the front row Gentry eased himself on his seat. Behind and beside him, like deer in the wild, heads lifted and nostrils flared, straining for the hostile scent. The scratch of chalk ceased as Dixie turned to the class, assumed an air of unmitigated disgust and homed unerringly in to the front row.

'Gentry. Put your tail down, there's a draught.'

For several days Dixie's 'latest' did the rounds, enhancing his reputation still further, while Gentry, quite unabashed, revelled in the notoriety. His discharge was immortalised as a 'Gentry particular', a description that passed into general use for similar near-toxic offences.

Bill Barron, Falstaffian in size and appetites, had a love for all the good things in life and a waistline that despite the ravages of wartime austerity remained a testament to his indulgences during the interwar years. He blew through their lives like a gale and in later years conducted a running guerrilla campaign against the wife of Jimmy's successor, who, almost on arrival, instituted and hosted The Candlesticks Club, a chichi, after-school gathering devoted to the arts and belles-lettres, conducted by the light of candles and directed at the senior boys. It was attended by those who fancied themselves as literati, but were also more than happy to do something that might keep them in sweet with the old man himself. The project, which was misconceived from the start, was viewed by Bill as an attempt to usurp his position as senior literary authority in the school. It failed soon enough, but its prospects were not helped by the mocking extracts from the fictitious proceedings of The Fiddlesticks Club, conducted of course to the sound of fiddles, with which Bill entertained the sixth form. It was about as close to open warfare as it could be.

And there was Joe Hodgson who had much to answer for. He seemed the nonpareil of teachers to his classes, and many an unsuspecting young innocent followed him into the profession in the mistaken belief that teaching would be for him as relaxed and satisfying an occupation as it seemed to be for Joe.

Middle-aged, but ruggedly attractive, he looked younger than his years. His dark hair, untouched by grey and with the trace of a widow's peak, was side-parted and held in waves with just a touch of Brylcreem. Bold eyebrows, bright eyes, an assertive nose and a generous mouth, always clamped around a smoking pipe when not in class or on the sports field, completed the picture. He was casual

459

in clothes as he was in manner: highly polished Oxford shoes, grey flannels, white shirt, college tie and sports jacket – leather-patched at the elbows.

Joe made it all seem so easy. Relaxed and assured he kept discipline without effort and entertained his classes with the simplest of devices. He heard out the silliest of answers with an earnest face and gave it serious consideration before offering his comment.

'You make me laugh, dear' – a lengthy pause – 'But not much.'

His classes soon learned to judge the pause. A little longer than usual and they looked to Joe for a nod before chanting his punchline.

He taught history up to the fifth form and the outbreak of the First World War. At that point history ended for Joe as it did in *1066 and All That*, a book from which he entertained his classes with selected end-of-term readings.

Of the legendary homosexuality of public schools John was ignorant, but he saw and heard nothing that suggested its presence, and in the most basic sense the boys seemed to keep themselves to themselves. Perhaps in the secret places of the boarding houses they had communion, but if they did they didn't talk about it. It was certainly not for any homosexual reason that boys standing or moving in close proximity might be seen to have one, or perhaps both, of their hands pressed closely over their privates.

Zip fasteners were not in general use on children's clothes even before the war. During the war they became unobtainable, and so the flies on boys' trousers consisted of buttons and buttonholes. With constant use the holes slackened, the connection weakened, and thus at Brentwood, for the duration of the war or until the return of the zip, the sport of ripping was born.

The key to success lay in the opening gambit: an innocent, casual approach to within range when a lightning strike with hooked fingers would lay open the front of the victim's trousers, and allow the aggressor time for an immediate retreat before retaliation. For new boys that first encounter with a hostile hand plunging towards their balls could be a traumatic and intimidating experience, but they soon became proficient at the counter-strategy. Whatever the masters thought as they looked from their common room window at a playground of boys moving in the approved defensive posture wasn't known, and surprisingly a formal interdiction on the sport was never issued.

460

One extreme countermeasure, presumably undertaken by the boys themselves and not by their mothers, entailed tightening the buttonholes with cobblers' thread to make them more resistant in the event of attack. Carried to extremes this was a defensive tactic that could be overeffective, and the clashing of rutting stags locked in combat was as nothing compared to the twisting, tugging and heaving when chance brought two such well-defended boys together.

It was not until the closing months of the war that ripping as a fine art reached its logical conclusion. There was an enormity about the thought that terrified them, but somehow, initially as a joke, they speculated whether it might be possible, accidentally of course, to rip a master and survive unscathed. Most were contemptuously dismissive of the idea. Two or three thought it might just be possible, but only Danny Fields pressed his argument to the point where they dared him to make an attempt and as encouragement put some modest sums of money where their mouths were. Danny's character, a dangerous mix of Chuzzy's recklessness and the worldly naivety of Billy Abrey, was such that he was tempted and accepted. There could only be one possible target: Podo.

Podo, another of the wartime stand-in masters, was quite as ineffective as Paddy, but entirely lacking any of Paddy's charms. Pale, fleshy and mean-mouthed he lumbered around his laboratory where he bored in science for two lessons a week in classes that were in constant turmoil and entirely lacking in discipline.

They listened to Danny's tactics and considered them elegant and well-conceived. As the class surged around the benches in its customary chaos Danny would be with them carrying a book from which a ruler would protrude. In the moving crush he would brush close to Podo, flick the book and ruler, and the job would be done. Throughout two science classes Danny wandered around glassy-eyed and book in hand. He hovered close to Podo, approached him, moved off and then back again, but did nothing. Halfway through the third class, white-faced, nervous and stung by the constant taunts, he struck.

He told his friends afterwards that from then on everything seemed to happen in slow motion. It didn't look that way to them as they watched. Much faster than they thought the shambling Podo could move, an arm shot out and grabbed Danny by a lapel. The ensuing sequence was in the best bar-room brawl tradition

461

from one of their favourite Westerns, and they looked on half in awe, half in admiration. Held firmly at arm's length, Danny received the first blow with a gasp and a look of surprise. Released but still standing, the second blow carried him back to the wall. There he sagged, and subsided slowly to the floor, where he sat vacant-faced as a dribble of blood ran from his nose.

In a rare moment for Podo the class was utterly still and silent. He stood there flushed and breathing heavily before turning to them.

'Get on with your work.'

They did, but with little idea what they were supposed to be doing, and at the same time they watched out the final act in their little drama. Podo walked over to Danny, picked him up, and held him at arm's length. For a moment they thought, perhaps even hoped, that he was going to paste him again.

'Are you all right?'

Danny merely nodded.

'Wash your face under a tap then and dry it on this.'

He threw him a lab towel. Nothing more was said.

They never did establish whether Podo's flies were violated or not, but considered that Danny had earned the small amounts of money they had pledged him. They said nothing to their parents, nor Danny to his. There was no suspension and no disciplinary proceedings. They understood well enough that Danny's action was an outrage, and Podo evidently saw his response in the same light. Sleeping dogs were left to lie, and that was the end of the affair.

Of the school's six-day week, the afternoons of Wednesday and Saturday were devoted not to academic work but to sport: in winter soccer, with rugby as a later introduction, and in summer cricket and swimming. By some means the limited household resources and clothing coupons were stretched or extended by family contributions to buy John shorts, shirt and soccer boots. He also needed new swimming trunks to replace an old and ragged pair. They might well have been affordable, but Phoebe, always on the lookout for an economical solution, chose instead to rely on her skill with wool and her knitting needles.

They looked fine when she had finished them: dark blue, closely stitched and a good, snug fit. He saw no others wearing knitted trunks when he stepped out in them, but he had no apprehensions.

He was a good swimmer and had complete faith in his mother's handiwork.

In line with the public-school ethos that what was harsh, austere and unpleasant bred strength of character, the pool was in the open air and invariably numbingly cold in early summer. Any form of immersion by stages was a torment, and for competent swimmers there was only one form of entry: a plunging dive at the deep end. John drew breath and took off.

The difference between the coefficients of drag for wool and naked skin had clearly never exercised the mind of the designer of the pattern to which Phoebe had turned her hand. The practical implications of that difference John was to discover.

It was a neat, clean dive: fingers pointed, arms and body straight as an arrow as he entered the pool, but he was puzzled by a sudden heaviness around his waist, and the hands that seemed to drag at his costume. He twisted, kicked out at something impeding his legs, struck out with two or three vigorous strokes and was free of the weight and clutching hands: he was also free of his costume.

While he swanned around disconsolately the costume was recovered from the depths of the pool by one of the other swimmers and passed to the supervising master. He held it up, stretched and distended by the weight of water it had absorbed.

'You can't possibly put this back on. Come out and get dressed.'

It wasn't the jeers and laughter at his nakedness that bothered him, but the thought that the trunks had been exposed for what they were: penny-pinching and home-made.

It was such minor incidents and not any form of active discrimination that singled out just a few of the scholarship boys from those enjoying more prosperous backgrounds. They ate their sandwiches together in the tuck shop at lunchtime because they could not afford the cost of lunches at the school canteen. They played cricket not in whites, but in their ordinary grey flannels and school shirt. Optional and after-school activities were closed to them because they meant additional costs, either on the activities themselves or on public transport home after the school bus had left.

More significantly, unlike those who had come up from the prep school, they lacked the preliminary groundwork that should have been laid for parts of the syllabus. Efficient as Madam had been in preparing them for the scholarship examination, many of the highways, let alone byways, of grammar and syntax had been beyond her brief. From the prep school, however, they arrived with a working understanding of declensions and tenses that languages demanded and teachers assumed. For the unlucky few who arrived untutored in such mysteries, the intractable demands of dative, ablative or vocative, and the intricacies of conditional, past perfect or future perfect, would prove a step too far. Latin for them would remain as dead as the dodo.

The days at Brentwood were troubled little by any action from the continuing war. A few daytime alerts interrupted routine, but otherwise it continued unchanged. Then in 1945 when the school reassembled after the Christmas break one of the senior boys brought back the news that the school was advertising for a new headmaster: £1,250 a year and all found for himself and his family, he reported. It was the general opinion that that was a pretty good screw. At the end of the summer term in the closing days of the war against Japan, and after more than thirty years at the school, Jimmy left them for his years of retirement. Under his successor, old traditions, customs and attitudes were taken down from the shelves, dusted off and examined. Some were replaced, others amended or discarded. Allison and his wife may have ruffled a few feathers in the common room, but the underlying ethos was undisturbed and the ship sailed on into the post-war years.

464

34

Endgame

As the world moved though the fifth winter of the war, the austerity, the deprivation, the unremitting endless grind of just ordinary day-to-day existence seemed finally to be gnawing away at the physical resilience and spirit of the older members of the family who had once seemed so indestructible to the youngsters.

After more than four years, war had permeated the very fabric of existence in ways that went far beyond the immediate risk to life and limb from bombing and the impact of blackout, shortages, rationing and travel restrictions. War had embedded itself into the minutiae of living and the most trivial of activities. It governed the style of men's suits, the length of ladies' skirts, the height of their heels and the depth of water in their baths. It deprived them of their silk stockings and substituted Silktona, a liquid paint-on concoction. It banned them from throwing confetti at weddings or hanging their washing out at night. It gave them *The Radio Doctor*, cookery classes from Potato Pete, baa-baa turnovers ('Take one sheep's head. . . .') and rook pie ('Skin and draw six young rooks . . .'). From 1942, in increasing numbers, it gave them the GIs, and in time there were mixed feelings about that.

War personified confronted the people at every twist and turn of their daily lives. It warned and exhorted them: *Careless Talk Costs Lives, Remember Your Gas Mask, Hitler Hopes You'll Be Late Tomorrow, Lend a Hand on the Land, Don't Be a Squander-bug, Dig for Victory, Save Fuel for Battle, Work Overtime – Clock on for Victory*. There were hundreds more. Where exhortations and warnings failed, it prosecuted them for failing to obey the salvage laws, for being persistently late for work without reasonable excuse, or for spreading alarm and despondency. It opened and read their letters and sent its spies out into their shops and markets to check what they were saying and doing.

It found its way into their most intimate and private places as part of a national determination to mock, deride or diminish the Hitler pack by all means including the crudest: Goebbels' face adorned the bottom of bedroom jerries, and 'Shitler's Toilet Roll – A Unique Bum Paper Guaranteed Non-Irritant' was a popular novelty item.

War invaded the children's comics and books: *William Did His Bit*; in *The Champion* Rockfist Rogan of the RAF hounded the Hun; in *The Beano* Pansy Potter built air-raid shelters, and Lord Snooty's gang harried the Wehrmacht. Rogan had his counterpart for the girls in *Worrals of the WAAF*, Snooty his in the characters of *Girls' Crystal*; and for the toddlers there was *Blossom: The Brave Balloon* and *Nursery Rhymes from Potato Pete*. War featured in their jigsaws, their card games, their paint and storybooks, and on novelty dartboards Hitler bent double and offered his arse as the bullseye.

They sang of it: 'Coming in on a Wing and a Prayer'; 'Yes, We Have No Bananas'; and 'Meet me in the Black-out, Sweetheart'. And they sang of the way it would be when it was all over: 'When They Sound the Last All-clear' and 'I'm Gonna Get Lit up When the Lights Go on in London.' And on pay days war featured in endless appeals for their money for Spitfire Funds, Stalingrad Weeks, Air Raid Distress Funds, War Weapons Weeks, Wings for Victory Weeks, A Penny a Week Fund, Help China Appeals, Aid to Russia Flag Days. There was never a shortage of worthy causes.

Like countless millions the world over Lou and her family had had enough, they wanted it over, and they wanted it over now. Yet despite the many signs during 1943 that the war was slowly being won, there were to be times during 1944 when it seemed as though it was all starting again, and at the turn of the year their own domestic troubles arrived to add to the general sense of war weariness.

At the end of 1943 the weather mirrored the mood of the time: bleak, overcast and shrouded in fog. Shortages were at their height. Gilmore had not been seen for months, and on his last flying visit from a northern port had been able to bring little more than a few cigarettes for Jack. Nor would there be any seasonal relief from the government. 'I'm not Father Christmas,' said Lord Woolton on leaving the Ministry of Food with the parting message that there would be no increase in rations for the festive season. Festive? His use made a mockery of the word. The half-promise that there would be one Christmas egg for everyone remained unfulfilled, but they lived in hope that they would at least get the one pound of oranges per ration book promised for the New Year.

The promise of oranges could not have been better timed. At the end of 1943 audiences at the Broadway had queued to see *Millions Like Us*, one of the better docudramas dealing with life in war-torn Britain. In a brief nostalgic introduction to the film the narrator lingers over the delights of those golden pre-war days. When he refers in passing to oranges the screen is illuminated with an explanatory text: 'The orange is a spherical, pulpish fruit of reddish yellow colour.' It got the intended laugh, of course, but it was a measure of the nation's deprivation and longing that the humble orange had been transmuted to a visionary object of desire.

At Harcourt money as always was tight. Some of the old decorations survived, but presents were thin on the ground and of the 'make do and mend' variety. Phoebe was recycling old knitware into basic scarves and gloves, or knitting dolls and clowns for the younger children of the family. Cards were home-made, both decorations and verse. Their Christmas meals may have been better than many enjoyed, but they were short commons indeed compared with the indulgences of the previous year. A couple of slim cockerels were taken for slaughter without the heart searching that had attended the final rites of Lottie and Freddie: somehow it was difficult to build up the same degree of rapport with chickens. They were lucky in having their own modest supply of fresh eggs from the hens, but despite the scrimping and saving in the run-up to Christmas reserves of butter, dried fruit and sugar were almost non-existent.

Good cooks fled screaming from the nation's kitchens at the atrocities committed on inoffensive, traditional recipes for cakes and puddings, where grated carrots, grated apple and diced beetroot struggled hopelessly as substitutes for sugar and dried fruit, and a sickly mix of condensed milk thinned and manipulated with cornflour deputised for cream. It would have been an affront to the pleasures of Christmases past to have flattered those ersatz concoctions with the season's name: carrot cake (not remotely like the modern confection) and carrot pudding was what they were and what they remained despite Phoebe's best efforts. The Algerian wine, long since just a happy memory, was replaced by

VP Rich Ruby, where the name may accurately have described the colour, but certainly not the flavour. One of Clara's regulars had put her on to a bottle of Booth's Gin. Add a few brown and pale ales and the remains of a bottle of Sanatogen, and that was the measure of the liquid spirits.

When Lou fell ill and was confined to bed four or five days before Christmas it was clear that it wouldn't be one of the best. At seventy-six years of age she couldn't be left alone. Someone would have to keep an eye on her during the day, but Clara was working up to and including Christmas Eve, and Elsie and Kath were not expected home before then. The bedroom at Bayhurst was a cold and cheerless place to spend a day alone beside an open grate that could not be trusted with a fire, so Lou was moved for the festive season. Chairs and a sofa were taken from the living room and replaced by a bed. The cast-iron range, which she had tended and polished as lovingly as the one in Poplar, could safely be left burning without constant attention, and from Harcourt there was always someone to pop up during the day to see how things were.

A couple of days before Christmas Nora Heard called on Phoebe with a cloth-wrapped parcel. She had heard that Lou was ill and, as it was Christmas, thought that she might like to try something a little different with her dinner. She unwrapped her offering, and Phoebe looked doubtfully at the two misshapen, lumpy and distended sausages on the kitchen table. Pallid, oleaginous and blotched, it was a measure of the depths to which austerity had reduced the nation that they could possibly be offered as a gift or considered as fit for human consumption.

In hushed tones, aware of the underlying illegality of her proceedings, Nora explained the origins of her offering, which Phoebe had already guessed at. In defiance of the Ministry of Food, the pig-stickers of the local mafiosi had once again been at work. Nora, as an active contributor, had received her cut. On this occasion it had included the blood, which was always in great demand. Her product, she explained, was a cross between a haggis and a black pudding. Ingredients: pig's blood, chopped fatty pork, liver and lights, suet, oatmeal, onion, herbs etc. It was not a pretty or inviting sight, but she was proud of it and pleased to have the chance to repay the occasional help she had received from Lou and the aunts before the war. Phoebe kept one of the offerings;

468

the other was taken up to Clara when she returned home from work. She looked at it sniffed it, and shook her head.

'Well, I'm not even showing that to Ma, and if we cook it in the house it'll turn her stomach over.'

In fact by Christmas Lou was eating little more than slops and insisted that Clara, Kath and Elsie join them for dinner at Harcourt. The fire in the range was made up; Lou was tucked cosily into bed; the wireless was turned on, and she was left to herself for a few hours. Elsie arrived with a bottle of Whiteways British sherry and, when the glasses had been filled, went to join Phoebe in the kitchen, which she invariably did when she wasn't doing the cooking herself. Years of working experience, she was convinced, put her in a position to offer a little helpful advice. It was a habit that did not endear her to her sisters.

Shortly before the chicken was due out of the oven, Phoebe produced and sliced the sausage as Elsie looked on suspiciously. The assorted ingredients in their blood-dark matrix looked even worse than the fleshy intestines containing them.

'What on earth's that, Phoebe?'

Phoebe told her the story as she dropped the slices into a frying pan. Elsie bent to inspect more closely and sniffed cautiously. As the slices spat and sizzled thin curls of smoke carried the first flush of their aroma to her nose, through the kitchen and into the living room. It carried the fragrance of old times and another world. It was pork and crackling; it was sage-and-onion stuffing; it was thyme and rosemary; it was bacon, black pudding and dry-cured beef; it was all they had been missing for so long. Tangy and piquant, Nora's herby haggis was a triumph, an island of old-fashioned flavour in a sea of undistinguished blandness. Carrot pudding and mock cream seemed a derisory sequel, but they contained hardly acquired ingredients and nothing went to waste.

Before it was dark the fire was damped down, and they all walked up to Bayhurst where, in the fading light, Lou was half-dozing, half-listening to Christmas music on the wireless. The curtains were drawn, the gas lit and a fire set in the front room, where a little later Doll, Charlie and Valerie joined them. With Lou laid up in bed in the next room it was a subdued affair until they heard a call:

'For Christ's sake, Elsie, pour me a drink of something, give us a tune, and stop the whispering. It's Christmas, not a bloody wake.'

'You're not supposed to have any, Ma. It's not good for your ulcer.'

'I'll look after my ulcer, you look after my drink.'

She sat up, sipping at half a glass of wine as they all pressed in from the front room to have a word.

'And it's no good looking at me like that. If I can't have a glass at Christmas, when can I? It'll probably be my last so I'll enjoy it.'

That was the first of the many occasions when Lou got her way with that argument: she was in fact to enjoy many more Christmases before she got to her parting glass.

Time and neglect had continued to lay siege to the piano: keys out of order and strings out of tune made it a dubious aid to any singer but Elsie did her best. Young Valerie, who had inherited the family voice, gave her gran a carol, but after that it was, as always, the nostalgic old favourites that they turned to with nodding acknowledgement to a few wartime songs in the same sentimental vein: 'When the Lights go on again all over the World', 'Who's Taking You Home Tonight' and 'The White Cliffs of Dover.' But their hearts weren't really in it, and well before midnight they were groping their way home through a thickening fog.

Lou remained out of action for several weeks, and New Year's Eve came and went virtually uncelebrated. She was just out of bed and recovering when night-time sirens, silent for so long, were heard again. Once more the sky was flooded with searchlights, and the crack of ack-ack fire followed the drone of bombers passing on their way to London. The raids continued intermittently into April, but in the darkness, uproar and confusion there were now effective night fighters harrying and taking their toll of the raiders. Clara returned from work with news of yet more widespread destruction and fires, of hundreds killed, and thousands made homeless around the Surrey Docks and in Battersea. The sequence of raids was subsequently called the Little Blitz. Little or not, it brought the same death and destruction as in the dark nights of 1940 and 1941, but even as the German raids on London continued with ninety or one hundred bombers, the Allies were launching attacks on Berlin, Hamburg, Leipzig and Stuttgart with seven, eight or nine hundred aircraft.

By the end of March the raids of the Little Blitz were over, the nights were quiet again and Phoebe returned triumphant from the market. Spanish onions, the promised oranges and even lemons

470

from Sicily were once again in limited supply. She produced two of each from her shopping bag like a conjurer from a hat. They held them, squeezed them and sniffed them and then by way of celebration quartered not an orange but a lemon, and sprinkled with just a touch of precious sugar they sucked and chewed their way through to the rind which was set aside for grating and flavouring.

Fine, warm weather arrived early in April, together with a gift from Jack's old friend Jimmy Bellamy that was to transform John's days. At Pitsea station, about one hour too early in his anxiety not to be late, he waited impatiently in the morning sunshine for the train that would deliver his bicycle from Barking, where Jimmy was consigning it to the guard's van. As the train steamed away he looked at his prize. It was old, it was a little battered, but it was his, and he was not a novice when it came to cycling. Chuzzy and one or two others had bikes on which he had learned to ride, but generally he was the passenger on someone else's crossbar. Now he would be giving the lifts.

In a world dominated at every turn by motor traffic, the freedom and sheer delight that was cycling in wartime, rural Essex is an experience as far beyond recapture as the life and community of the old East End. The major roads carried little motor traffic: buses, a few goods or business vehicles, the occasional army convoy, but very few cars. On minor roads there was even less to be seen. Country lanes and byways were virtually deserted. On Saturday mornings the high streets in the market towns of Wickford, Billericay and Pitsea were busy, but with people not traffic.

For young boys the bicycle was the key that opened the door to a wide new world that they could travel, explore and enjoy at little or no more risk than playing at home. There was no need of restriction to garden, park or play street. Safety helmets were unheard of, and a downhill run on a country road was an exhilaration of speed and wind, in a silence broken only by the rustic sounds from the fields around them, the hum of the tyres and their own shouts of delight. The Bowers Gifford marshes were minutes away, Benfleet Creek and the slopes of Hadleigh Castle just a short ride, and an hour or so took them to the waters and mud flats of the River Crouch or Leigh-on-Sea.

For the boys the world was a paradise waiting to be explored, but one into which reality increasingly intruded as the days of April and May grew hotter. For more than four years the arterial

471

road had stood silent and almost deserted apart from the occasional military convoy. Now not only did that traffic come more frequently, it stopped, and it stayed. Gradually by the side of the road colonies of troops built up, camping on the grass verges. In one carriageway lorries, armoured personnel carriers, heavy transporters, half-tracks, jeeps and other mobile military equipment stretched away towards London in one direction, towards Southend in the other. On the other carriageway service traffic buzzed backwards and forwards night and day. Local opinion was united in the view that this marked preparations for the invasion of Europe and the Second Front, long awaited and expected.

As far as the neighbourhood boys were concerned it was not the invasion of Europe that concerned them, but the invasion of the local tank traps when temperatures climbed higher and higher towards the end of May and their watering holes were discovered by the troops camping at the end of the road. When the boys arrived for their swim to find the traps heaving with those great hairy monsters, most of them behaving like overgrown schoolboys themselves, they thought it a bloody cheek and sulked at a distance until some shouts from the road had the troops out of the water and pulling on their gear at the double.

Within less than two weeks the colonies of troops and equipment had dispersed to their embarkation ports at Grays and Tilbury. Stillness and silence returned to the arterial road and the tank traps. Hot, sultry weather continued to the end of May when temperatures were in the mid-eighties and higher. At the end of the month Clara returned from London with stories of storms and hailstones the size of marbles, and then shortly before the Normandy landings the weather broke. A few days later those overgrown schoolboys from the tank traps were fighting their way through the waters of the Channel and on to the beaches of Normandy, many of them not to return

Shortly after the landings *Casablanca* returned to The Broadway cinema. On its earlier visit John's attempts to find a 'bona fide guardian' to take him in had been unsuccessful. This time he was lucky, and in between an undistinguished supporting picture and the main feature he saw early film of the invasion. The wireless and the papers had been occupied by little else for more than a week after it took place, but by the middle of June people in the south-east were diverted by events much closer to home.

472

The first guided missile to be fired in anger fell on England on 13th June 1944: within days hundreds were being launched. 'Doodlebug' was always much too ambiguous and almost affectionate a nickname for a weapon that delivered death and destruction as randomly and extensively as the V-1. The Germans, as usual, had more precise terminology available: *Vergeltungswaffe* or 'reprisal weapon'. Fortunately for the south-east of England, and London in particular, they failed to bring to it quite the same efficiency that had marked their terror campaigns in Europe and Russia, but it was devastating enough.

Interceptions and guidance failures meant that some three-quarters of the weapons launched failed to reach their intended target in London, but with the final point of impact to some degree a matter of chance and uncertainty, it made the V-1 more of a potential threat to the remote corner of the plotlands than the earlier raiders had been. Previously when bombers had been heard approaching, it had generally been safe to assume that they would be overflying on their way to strategic targets, or to London and the docks. That assumption could not be made with the V-1s.

The appearance of the first over the lane defied all local plane-spotting expertise. It came lower than any bomber and it was fast: an ugly, cigar-shaped device with stubby wings and an engine that looked as though it had been tacked on as an afterthought – the first jet engine as they were to learn. Bursts of ack-ack fire sought to track it, but did not disturb its flight. Soon out of sight and sound, it passed across the fields on its way towards London. Within hours others were seen, and at the peak of the offensive more than two hundred were crossing the coast in a day. Those that passed in the dark brought the added spectacle of the long yellow-orange flame of jet exhaust that followed the sound of the flying bomb as it made its passage across the night sky. Within hours the wildest conjectures and rumours were rife, and for a while the talk was of nothing else, but it would be almost a week before any official explanation was offered to Londoners baffled and demoralised by the arrival of a new and terrifying weapon within days of the Normandy invasions when it seemed that the struggle was so close to being won.

The home secretary referred unhelpfully to pilotless aircraft and missiles, which was no more than everyone had inferred. There was speculation that the craft were in some way radio-controlled, and then the first references to rocket or jet propulsion. Finally at the end of a week came the first definitive information: range, speed, construction, guidance system and an explosive power of about one ton, together with the news that they had been known about and their sites under air attack for many months.

On a Saturday morning not long after the first V-1 struck, Pitsea market was busy with the usual bustle and noise from shoppers and traders. Phoebe and Lou were poking around for anything that might be off-ration, and John was at a distance looking through a selection of second-hand comics when the distant sound of a siren was heard. An initial flurry of movement stopped, and the market fell silent as the distinctive rasping sound of a jet engine was heard followed by the crack of desultory ack-ack fire and the appearance of a V-1 from clouds above the crest of the hill to the east. As it approached the market along the line of the main road, Phoebe called out to John to join her, but apart from a few other shouts and the quick scurrying of children to their mothers all was still as their heads turned to watch the bomb as it came on towards them. It would have been prudent to seek some shelter from falling shrapnel if nothing else, but the approaching missile had everyone transfixed. All eyes and ears were alert as they watched its approach, straining to detect any deviation in its trajectory or change in the note of the engine.

It would have been less than half a minute before it was passing overhead with its engine still sounding reassuringly robust and noisy. It seemed to be for much longer that the market stood hushed and waiting. The relieved sighs and the low murmur of resuming conversation died away to an even deeper silence when abruptly the roar of the engine stopped. Although the missile had passed on into cloud all eyes turned again to the sky as they waited and listened for what had to follow. It seemed for a while as though there would be nothing: it was taking far too long. When at last the sound reached them it was not the intense explosion they expected, but a heavy, dull and muffled blast. Even before they left the market it was known that the bomb had exploded harmlessly in farmland.

Of the many that were seen in the plotlands before their launch sites were finally overrun by the invading Allied forces, most passed overhead and on to their intended targets in and around London, or fell harmlessly into farmland. Just once, when Phoebe

474

was on her way back from the butcher's, the danger came closer to home. The missile was approaching from the east, but was still some way off and hidden by low cloud when the sound of the engine ceased. When that happened it was always sudden and unexpected with no preliminary hesitation or spluttering: one second a robust, reassuring roar the next a silence that seemed even more deafening. In the time that was available only the deep drainage ditch alongside the lane, happily near dry in the late summer, offered any form of shelter. Phoebe hesitated only briefly before scrambling in through nettles and brambles and crouching with her head in her hands and her feet in several inches of water. It seemed an interminable length of time before she heard a distant blast, much further away than she expected, and in farmland where no harm was done. She arrived home wet-footed, scratched, stinging and dishevelled, but otherwise unhurt. In London, however, the missiles brought such destruction, injury and death that a new wave of refugees left the city, many to remain away until the last V-2 had fallen more than eight months later.

The V1 onslaught lasted for a little under three months during which more than eight thousand were launched, killing over six thousand and injuring thousands more. On 7th September 1944 when the last of the launch sites had been overrun by the Allied invasion forces, and with timing even more unfortunate than Chamberlain's before Dunkirk, Duncan Sandys, the chairman of the Flying-Bomb Counter Measures committee, announced 'Except possibly for a few last shots the battle of London is over.'

On the following day the first V-2 rocket dropped into the leafy suburbs of Chiswick, just a stone's throw from the Mortlake bend on the Thames. Supersonic, and therefore silent and unexpected until they struck, the V-2's were a devastatingly destructive weapon against which there was no possibility of interception, no defence and no advance warning. The explosion and the blast arrived from nowhere. Lagging behind too late to give any warning came the roar of the rocket itself, followed by a sonic boom that was heard for miles. For those who survived in the vicinity of the early strikes or heard the sonic booms their experiences would remain inexplicable for more than two months. Not until 11th November, and only after reports in the newspapers that propaganda broadcasts in Germany were making much of the devastating effects of their V-2 missile, was any official explanation offered when Churchill made the disclosure that attacks by rocket bombs had been taking place for many weeks. For many in London and the suburbs, who had already endured so much, it was one unnerving threat too far. There was another minor exodus, which this time included Clara and Eva Dent who had sat it out through all that had gone before. They came to stay briefly with Lou at Bayhurst, but later moved on to relatives near Chelmsford. An unfortunate choice as Chelmsford itself was hit shortly after they went there, but fortunately not close to them. In total more than a thousand V-2 rocket missiles were to fall on southern England, but mainly on London, until just four weeks before the war in Europe ended.

On a fine Sunday morning a couple of weeks after the V-2 attacks began, Jimmy Bellamy and Kate arrived unexpectedly at the back door. Snappily dressed in shorts and cycling gear from the pre-war years they stood there hot and sweating after their long cycle ride from Poplar. Dusted off, oiled and serviced, Jim's tandem had been pressed back into use for the first time in many years and rested, shiny and gleaming as ever, against the garden hedge.

Apart from Jack none of them had seen Jimmy for almost two years, but neither the years of rationing and austerity nor the stress of his ARP work throughout the war had left a trace. Round, robust and lively as ever, it was, as Phoebe said, a tonic to see and hear him.

Jim brought the latest news of Poplar with him, and it was a sad catalogue of change, destruction and all too frequently death, with first-hand reports of the impact of the V-1s to add to the second-hand news they received from Clara. The names meant nothing to John; they were friends from Jack's early days, some of them killed in the bombing, a few dying from natural causes. Amid the growing wasteland the four houses in the terrace still stood virtually unscathed, but around them many buildings, sometimes whole streets, had disappeared, and none of the family friends and neighbours were left in the area. Jim had called at Carrie's a few weeks earlier, but the house was empty and locked and he had no news of her.

Poplar now meant less and less to John. He had little interest in what was left there, and no expectation or desire to return as once he had. Leaving Jim and Jack deep in conversation, he wandered out to look over the tandem with the eye of an experienced cyclist. After a while they came out and joined him.

'Fancy a spin, John, before we set off for home?'

Did he? He had hoped for nothing else since they arrived.

With a spanner from the saddlebag the rear seat was lowered a little, a few adjustments made to the handlebars and they were ready.

'Right, John. You know the area – a round trip, back in not more than half an hour.'

John liked that: being asked and being relied upon.

'Just remember. I steer, you don't.'

As they moved off down the lane he saw nothing of the road ahead. Jimmy's backside, back and shoulders, massive and broad, filled the horizon before him. His weight and the drive from two chunky legs kept the tandem rock solid and moved them on fast enough until John also found his touch on the pedals, and then they flew. He called out one or two of the landmarks, but talking was difficult and they sped on silently. On the arterial road a long, steady and gentle gradient took them up to Rayleigh Weir, and then across country to join the old Southend road back home. After a mile or so Jimmy could see the reason for John's choice of route. Ahead of them, down Bread and Cheese Hill, in the space of just a few hundred yards the road dropped the two hundred feet they had climbed so gradually when they set out. Jimmy stopped the tandem and turned to him: 'You've been up here on your bike, I suppose?' John nodded. It had been a favourite run in spring when the tender young shoots of the hawthorn leaves were their bread and cheese refreshments before they set off for the rush home down the hill.

Then they were off again, pedalling hard for the few level yards before the hill started to fall away in front of them when Jimmy eased off the pedals, bent low over the handlebars, and offered them up to gravity with a faith in his brakes or a benevolent providence that must have been absolute. Past cottages and tea rooms they accelerated. Past the one sedate lorry that lay in their path, and faster still until the hawthorn banks were a passing blur and John clung on half-dizzied with the motion. Ten minutes later, still breathless with the excitement of his hill run, he was back home, and almost immediately Jimmy and Kate were on their way back to Poplar, the wartime grind and the V-2s.

35

The Final Chapter

The month of Jimmy's visit marked the first sign of a thaw in the gripping frost of the home-front wartime existence. From 'Black-out', total and absolute, they moved to 'Dim-out'. No direct light could be shown from the house, and curtains still had to be drawn, but only if there was an alert would it be necessary to return to the ugly, thick blackout protection. By the end of the year even the few gaslamps of the lane were back in business, but they cast only a feeble glow at the best of times.

At Bayhurst, tucked away from general view, and with the softer, adjustable gas lighting, the regulations were stretched a little and for the first time in five years it was possible for Lou to light up and sit through dusk and early evening with the curtains and windows open to the night. In itself it was a little thing, but it was a welcome sign of a return to normality after five years of war, and it gave great delight to Lou and Clara and those who called in to see them just for the pleasure of that novel experience.

Gilmore's ship was once again in the London area and he made a brief sequence of visits. Following the defeat of the U-boats the Atlantic crossing had ceased to be a gamble against the odds, although there were still losses enough. The attitude of the customs had been modified accordingly. It was no longer possible to drive out of the docks with a taxi full of goods, but suitcases and bags were still given the nod: hence the three visits from a heavily laden Gilmore over as many days. He could not bring the profusion of that glorious earlier visit but they did pretty well. In particular he brought cigarettes by the hundreds, and for the first time the opportunity arose for John to help himself when that old desire to join the men gripped him. From the bulk packs lying open in Gilmore's bag he was able to steal away with two packs of twenty.

The children's hideouts in the thickets at the end of Bayhurst's garden were still there, and he used them from time to time when he wanted to conceal himself where he could see but not be seen. Later in the day, tucked away in one of the hides, with Chuzzy and Mickey as accomplices after the event, he pulled the loot from his pockets: one pack of Chesterfield and one of Camel, forty cigarettes in total. Their previous experiments had been limited to an occasional purloined fag furtively puffed and handed round between four or five of them. Little enough, but sufficient to introduce them to the gasping, choking experience of inhaling the smoke: the first step, they thought, on the road to being an adult. Forty was more than they could have dreamed of.

They looked at the treasure before them. The cigarettes, double wrapped 'to preserve the full, rich flavour' looked almost too good to open. Shiny cellophane sleeves enclosed crisp, decorated, inner packaging. Glossy and sophisticated in design, the packs looked and felt distinctive and exclusive: a complete contrast to the flimsy, cheap packaging of the wartime products they saw in the shops. They unwrapped both packs, and even in the open air the sweet, fruity aroma of the fresh tobacco scented their hideaway. They sniffed at the tobacco like old hands before making their choice. Mickey and Chuzzy were enticed by the dreaming spires and minarets on the Chesterfield pack, John by the sense of mystery in the Turkish blend of Camel.

The cigarettes were fat, pleasantly firm and seductive. They lay back against the bushes, lit up and cautiously inspired their first lungful of American carcinogens.

> *Five little fags in a dainty little packet,*
> *Five cigarettes that cost one dee,*
> *Five little whiffs underneath his jacket,*
> *Five wobbles in his little mary.*
> *Five little sniffs, and in five little jiffs,*
> *He'll be lying on the tramway lines*
> *Wishing he could touch the cable,*
> *Looking greener than the label*
> *On little Willy's Wild Woodbines.*

It was an old smoking song with a few arcane references. John's father used to sing it to him when he was a toddler, and it went some way towards describing their condition as they struggled to the butt ends of their cigarettes. None of them had been prepared to lose face and cry quits before another, and if they weren't green their heads were swimming. With sick head, stale mouth and an uneasy sense of nausea, John gazed out from a haze of smoke, through the screen of bushes, and across the garden, where beyond the trellis the soft, subdued light of his gran's gaslamp glowed in the gathering gloom and the curtains remained undrawn. Years of war were moving to their close; years of servitude to nicotine beginning.

In the months leading up to the last wartime Christmas a final victory was no longer in any doubt despite temporary reverses at Arnhem and in the Ardennes: it was just a matter of how soon it would come. At sea the *Tirpitz*, the last major German threat, had been sunk. In Europe British forces liberated Brussels in September, and in the same month the US Third Army reached the German border on the Moselle. In October the Red Army entered Germany in East Prussia, and the capture of Aachen by the US First Army was celebrated as the first German city to be occupied. In the Philippines the Americans had all but destroyed Japanese sea power, and the long struggle to liberate those islands was under way.

Against that background the bombardment by V-1s and V-2s continued in the run-up to what was to be as depressing and comfortless a festive season as the family would have for many years. In November the four cockerels they had been fattening up for themselves and others were lost to a fox that found its way in under the wire. It was a bloody business, noisy enough to alert them late at night, but by the time they got out to the chicken run it was too late. Only one of the birds had been taken, but two more had been killed and the third was so torn and savaged that Jack had to finish it off.

The hens were kept separately in a pen which fortunately had been secure. After more than three years of egg production Iris was still with them. Apart from time off for a couple of moults she produced almost as well as she did when in her prime. There was never any question of sacrificing a productive hen for meat, and so at Christmas time there was no bird on the table and it was back to pot-roast.

Almost up to Christmas the weather had been wet and mild, but hopes that they would be spared the rigours of earlier years were dashed on Christmas Eve when they were surprised by the arrival of an Arctic chill that was bitter and deep and brought a hoar frost that clung to the trees and hedgerows like snow. The cold lasted through to the end of the year and beyond, with days where the temperature stuck well below freezing, and by New Year's Eve there were skaters on the Hampstead ponds. Mid-January snowfalls added to the general misery as temperatures continued to plunge, and even Big Ben was briefly silenced when its striking hammers were frozen.

Strikes in the coal industry earlier in the year had seriously affected production, and for most of the year coal supplies had been restricted to 5cwt a month. Even with the stocks built up in summer and autumn, the severe weather meant that their coal reserves were disappearing like sand through a sieve. Once again apart from the living room the house was surrendered to the frost, and they were back to clustering around a fire lit late in the day, while frequent power cuts cast them into gloomy evenings passed in the light of a flickering candle or two. Winter remained quite unrelenting in keeping up the tradition it had established in the early years of the war.

The Ministry of Food, profligate as ever, announced extra Christmas allowances that were sufficient to tease, but not to satisfy: an additional 8d of meat, an extra half-pound of sugar, a little more fat and an extra 8oz of sweets for the children. Nothing was left from Gilmore's visits. Alcohol was virtually unobtainable except on the black market at prices most could not afford. Even Clara's admirers were unable to direct her to any supplies to lighten their darkness.

It was a small gathering at Bayhurst on that last Christmas night of the war. Neither aunt was at home, and Charlie and family now lived too far away for an evening visit. In the little living room a good fire glowed in Lou's gleaming range regardless of diminishing coal stocks, and from his portrait Pappy cast a quizzical glance over a sideboard groaning under the weight of the evening's refreshments: a few ersatz mince pies, a plate of ham sandwiches, a Christmas/carrot cake, a bottle of Whiteways ginger wine, some British sherry and a few of Mann's medicinal ales. It wasn't exactly Christmas at Dingley Dell, but at least the house looked festive: Clara, as she always did, had taken time to decorate the rooms with what was left of the Carters Terrace collection.

In Elsie's absence the piano stood silent, as much a blessing as a curse considering its condition, and the evening was spent chatting to the background noise of the wireless: *Christmas Night at Eight O'Clock*, a Command Performance and a Christmas cabaret just before everyone called it a night. There was a little talk of the war. Mainly it was reminiscing about Christmases past, and looking forward to the post-war years that were not far ahead. Although the old house still stood in the terrace, it was clear that there were no thoughts of any return to London, nor to the society or social conditions of the years that were spent there. For the first time since the outbreak of war there was once again talk of domestic politics. It had already been made clear by the Labour Party that there would be no question of continuing the long-running wartime coalition after the next election and that the party would go to the country with a full socialist programme. The family had no doubt where their votes would be going when post-war policies were at issue. New Year's Eve was no better provisioned than Christmas, but there was at last a genuine optimism and expectation in the toast to a peaceful New Year.

Some eighteen months earlier Moira had enjoyed a permanent release from her bondage at the high school. Her determination to try to make her way in the theatre was undiminished, but she gave a grudging acceptance to her father's argument that it would be sensible to have a second string to her bow and went straight from school to a full-time secretarial course. Following that, to get some practical experience behind her, she joined the Pound Lane regulars on the morning bus to the station and a secretarial job in the city.

Work in the city not only brought her the first money of her own, but at the end of the working day left her within easy reach of the London theatres where the Old Vic Company at the New Theatre was in the middle of a season that would enter theatrical history. Evening theatre-going, even from as far away as Pitsea, presented no problem, as the late theatre openings of the pre-war years had long been abandoned. Most now started at six-thirty, some as early as six, and it was relatively easy to take in an evening performance and catch a train back in time for a bus along the main road.

Late on an evening in the depths of the January frosts Moira returned from the New Theatre frozen, but utterly in thrall to

Olivier after seeing his Richard III in a performance that stamped its mark on the character in a way that was the stuff of theatrical legend and the fount of countless parodies. Such was her enthusiasm that she would not only be seeing it for a second time, but felt that it was the right stuff for her young brother's introduction to the world of the stage.

In mid-March, suitably scrubbed, buffed and polished, and having given an undertaking that he would demand no refreshments after a bite to eat in a Lyons Corner House, John climbed the steps in the New Theatre and squeezed himself into one of the few rows of seats in the balcony for the matinee performance. First impressions, especially in the theatre, can set prejudices or preferences that last for life, and Moira had chosen carefully.

'Well?' she said as they left the theatre and he had to acknowledge that although there were no laughs and he didn't understand it all, it was pretty impressive. That seemed to satisfy her.

It was during the last five or six interminable months of the war, as the family soldiered on to the distant sounds of continuing V-bomb attacks and news of increasingly bitter fighting as the perimeter defended by the German forces shrank towards Berlin, that John began to experience his own personal problems. His nights were once again being disturbed, not by bombers, but by pubescent visions of the mocking girl from the local dairy. Nothing was said at home as adolescence claimed him, but in his wanderings around his father's bookshelves he found that a couple of books had appeared that were perhaps intended for his information, education and possibly pleasure. Slipping from the house with the books, he sought out quiet places where he was indeed informed and educated as he read and absorbed the detail they contained, and sought to reconcile it with the wilder schoolboy legends on the same themes.

He found himself considering the older members of the family in a new and questioning way. Could they really have indulged in all this? With his gran, despite the positive evidence of his clutch of aunts and uncles, he might have found it impossible to look beyond her crabbed age to the passionate vigour of youth, had it not been for the enthusiasm with which she embraced *Forever Amber*. Gilmore had brought a copy back from the USA shortly after its publication there at the end of 1944, and well before it came out in England, but its reputation had preceded it, and once it got to Lou she wasn't parted from it until she had worked her way through every scandalous episode. She entered into her reading methodically and slowly, not from any deficiency in her ability, but for the pleasure of savouring its delights sentence by sentence as she sat slowly oscillating in her American-style rocking chair, clucking and tut-tutting with simulated disapproval but evident enjoyment.

His gran's performance as she read the book led John to seek it out during those quiet moments of the day when Clara was at work and Lou was having her afternoon lie-down. Tucked away behind the cushions on her rocking chair it didn't take much finding, nor did it take John much longer to find his way to the juicy sections. They certainly made a more stimulating, enlightening and entertaining read than his father's books.

Sensational and notorious in its day the UK market value of the book soared when it was banned and charged with obscenity in Massachusetts, burned in the streets and excoriated by the Hays Office. Such was the demand that advertisements appeared in the personal columns: 'For sale – nice clean [sic] copy of *Forever Amber*. What offers?' Subtitled *Forever Under* by the wags its flavour can best be judged by the clinical dissection of the contents made by the Massachusetts prosecutor who listed 70 references to sexual intercourse, 39 illegitimate pregnancies, 7 abortions, 10 descriptions of women dressing, undressing or bathing in the presence of gentlemen, 5 references to incest, 13 references ridiculing marriage and went on to conclude, 'The references to women's bosoms and other parts of their anatomy were so numerous I did not even attempt to count them.' How life, times and the ways of the world had changed since the trifling exploits of the naughty vicar of Stiffkey captured the imagination and attention of the nation.

In February came news of the devastating raids on Dresden. 650,000 incendiaries showered on the city and its centre ablaze, proclaimed the papers, and much was made of the strategic importance of the city in their reports. Some indication of the scale of destruction was given in immediate post-war descriptions of the 'catalogue of ruin and desolation in Dresden the glory of German baroque,' but it would be years before the horror of the firestorm was known and even longer before the accusations came that tactically and strategically it was superfluous to the outcome of the war.

Then from Easter onwards came the accelerating sequence of events that finally brought the long years of the European war to their conclusion.

On 23rd April all blackout restrictions were lifted.

On 25th troops from the Eastern and Western fronts linked arms and Berlin was surrounded. On 29th Mussolini was executed together with his mistress, and within days pictures of them hanging upside down in the Piazzale Loreto in Milan were appearing in the papers.

On 30th April Hitler committed suicide. Berlin surrendered on 2nd May, and Germany capitulated five days later.

Amidst general euphoria Victory in Europe Day was celebrated nationwide on 8th May. Had the family still been together at home in Poplar there would perhaps have been one of the old-time celebrations. There, bonfires were blazing on the bombed sites and in the streets. Sirens sounded from the ships on the river, and searchlight displays lit up the night sky. The King and Queen drove through the East End, and old neighbours who had endured it all from start to finish partied together in the bunting-hung streets.

Sadly, beyond the East End the old community spirit couldn't survive the wartime dispersal of its people into unfamiliar environments, and the rough tracks and scattered dwellings of the plotlands didn't lend themselves to street parties. By May of 1945 the family that had once been so close was far-flung, and their intimate circle of friends had gone their separate ways. Bill was in Stepney, apart from weekends, and Charlie too distant to visit easily. Elsie and Kath were working away and apart from Jack and his family, only Louisa and Clara was left. Moira, like so many of her age, joined up with friends and headed for the West End where buildings were floodlit, rejoicing was unconfined and crowds thronged the streets and squares until dawn.

At Bayhurst, where the few who were left met in the evening, Louisa and Jack, tired and war-weary like the rest of the world and thankful to have the killing over, were more phlegmatic in their response to the events. They had seen it all before: the same euphoria and celebrations after four years of the 'War to End All Wars'; the promises of a 'Land Fit for Heroes'; and then the

Depression, unemployment and little more than twenty years later the same old madness.

Although in Europe the guns had at last fallen silent, on the domestic Home Front little was to change. Within a fortnight further reductions in rations were announced: cooking fat was cut from two ounces to one a week, bacon from four to three, the fresh-meat allocation was reduced, and housewives forewarned that there would be no extra sugar for the following Christmas. It was a regime of rationing that was to get worse before it got better, and it would linger on for another nine years. On 2nd September Japan surrendered following the two atomic bombings. After six years the 'Hot War' was over; the Cold War was the coming attraction and would run for forty years. Korea, the Cuban Crisis and Vietnam were waiting in the wings. It was a good time for a young boy to be growing up.

Money Equivalents

In 1940 £1 had the equivalent purchasing power of £30 today

Old Currency	Written As	Decimal Penny Equivalent
Farthing	¼d	App ¹⁄₁₀p
Half-penny or Ha'penny	½d	App ⅕p
Penny	1d	Under ½p
Sixpence	6d	2½p
Shilling =12d	1/- or 1s	5p
Ten shilling Note	10/- or 10s	50p
One Pound = 20 shillings = 240 pence	£1	£1.00p
One Guinea = 21 shillings	-	£1.05p

Examples

Two pence and three farthings	2¾d
Sixpence halfpenny	6½d
Six shillings and two pence	6/2 or 6s 2d
One Pound nineteen shilling and eleven pence	£1 19s 11d or £1/19/11

Family and General Timeline 1932–1945

1932 *The family celebrates a birth.* Nazi Brown-Shirt reign of terror in Germany.

1933 Hitler appointed Chancellor. Takes dictatorial powers.

1934 Hitler assumes title of Führer. *The last unclouded times for the family.*

1935 Hitler begins open re-armament and conscription.
      May: *the family joins crowds at Home Fleet visit to Southend*
      June: Anglo-German Naval Agreement signed. German fleet now called 'War Navy'

1936 Oct: *Jack joins in opposition to fascist march through Jewish area of the East End.*

1937 April: German Luftwaffe terror bomb Guernica during the Spanish Civil War.
      Jack joins in Hyde Park rallies protesting against German intervention in Spain.
      Hitler and Nazis increasingly seen by many as a threat to peace in Europe.
      In Essex the family learn of mock air raids and searchlight practice along the Thames.

1938 March: German troops occupy Austria.
      Sept: Britain capitulates to Nazi territorial demands and signs Munich Agreement.
      Gas Masks issued. Ration Cards now ready in the event of war.
      John tries on his gas mask and sees trenches being dug in the local park.

1939 March: Hitler violates Munich Agreement and occupies Czechoslovakia.
      Louisa receives her 'Your Food in Wartime' leaflet. Barrage balloon and blackout trials in London.

September: Germany invades Poland. *The family children join in the great evacuation.*

War is declared but the anticipated terror bombing of London does not take place.

December: *the family children are brought back home.*

1940   May/June: German Blitzkrieg launched leading to Dunkirk evacuation.

July: *in Essex the family watch their first air battle.*

September 7th: Blitz starts. *John and Phoebe trapped in park shelter.* Heavy bombing and destruction in Poplar.

September 8th: *the family leave for Essex as a temporary shelter from the Blitz. They watch dogfights and hear the German bombers passing on their way to London.*

September 19th: *faced with the prospect of imminent invasion the women and children are sent to find shelter in Buckinghamshire.*

November: *news received of the destruction of a family home.*

December: *some family members return to Essex, and on 29th from the Chiltern Hills Jack and family see the glow of the great London firestorm.*

1941   June: Hitler invades Russia. *Jack and family return to Essex to occupy The Anchorage.*

December 7th: Japanese attack Pearl Harbor. America joins the war.

By early December Germans at the gates of Moscow. Leningrad surrounded (start of 900-day siege). Hong Kong falls to the Japanese.

1942   February: Singapore falls. Pressure on Moscow relieved, but by early autumn German troops enter Stalingrad. America suffers major reverses in the Pacific.

May/June: Britain launches three 1,000-bomber raids on Germany.

The second half of the year sees major Allied offensives at Midway, Guadalcanal, El Alamein and Stalingrad that will mark a decisive shift in the balance of power.

December: *the family hear church bells at Christmas for the first time in four years.*

1943   Jan: the Germans suffer a major defeat at Stalingrad.

May: Axis forces in North Africa surrender. *The family celebrates with Algerian wine.*

By early autumn Allied forces invade Italy which surrenders.

John encounters a live German and the reality of war at a crash site.

1944 Jan: *the family hear the bombers passing overhead as the 'Little Blitz' begins on London.* Siege of Leningrad lifted. America retakes Wake Island.

May: *John and his friends meet troops assembling nearby for the invasion of Europe.*

June 6th: D-Day. The Allies land in France.

June 13th: the first V1 flying bomb hits the UK to begin an eleven week bombardment.

Sept 7th: *Louisa celebrates the end of blackout – curtains open again into the night.*

Sept 8th: as the V1s cease the first V2 rocket hits London. They will continue until the month before the final victory.

In heavy fighting Allied advances and successes continue on all fronts.

1945 *Victory in sight: family discuss domestic politics for the first time in six years.*

On Eastern and Western Fronts Allied troops press on into the heart of Germany.

April 30th: Hitler commits suicide.

May 7th: Germany surrenders unconditionally.

May 8th: *Moira joins the crowds in London to celebrate VE-Day.*

In the Pacific the Americans continue their advances with bloody fighting.

August 6th and 9th: two atomic bombs dropped on Japan.

Sept 2nd: the Japanese sign the document of surrender.